God's World Science Series

God's World Science Series

God's Protected World

Grade 3

Teacher's Manual

Rod and Staff Publishers, Inc.
Hwy. 172, Crockett, Kentucky 41413
Telephone: (606) 522-4348

In Appreciation

To God who created the world and protects it, we give praise and thanks. To God who revealed Himself and the purpose of His creation in the Bible, we give praise and thanks. To God who has redeemed the church through the blood of Christ, we give praise and thanks. To God who has sustained the church and has given us children to love and nurture, we give praise and thanks. To God who gives us the freedom and resources to have Christian schools, we give praise and thanks. To God who enabled His servants to publish this science textbook, we give praise and thanks.

We are grateful that God enabled Sister Naomi Eicher Lapp to write the text for this book. Brother Lester Showalter served as editor. Brother Lester Miller made most of the drawings. Many reviewers gave helpful suggestions and corrections. We are grateful for all of their services.

This textbook is produced to acquaint the rising generation with the wonders and usefulness of God's protected world. May our children not only come to know the works of God but also set their hope in God and love and serve Him all their days. To Him be the glory. Amen.

Printed in U.S.A.

ISBN 978-07399-0609-5

Catalog no. 14391

10   11   12   13   —   20   19   18   17   16   15   14   13

CONTENTS

INTRODUCTION

"I have no greater joy than to hear that my children walk in truth" (3 John 4). *God's Protected World* is written with the sincere desire to help you teach your students God's truth. May you experience the joy of seeing obedience to truth in their lives.

Why Do We Teach Science to Third Graders?

1. *God's created world should be appreciated.* Who enjoys a breathtaking mountain view or an awesome sunrise and does not immediately wish to share it? Likewise, if you as a teacher are impressed with the marvelous world God created and has maintained, you will want to share your knowledge with your students.

Many times elementary teachers feel that they are very limited in scientific knowledge. That need not hinder the diligent teacher. First of all, you will want to learn along with your students. Even a little outside reading in an encyclopedia or a higher level science book can help to give a broader scope to the lesson and will help you to enrich your lesson presentation.

Furthermore, it is no disgrace to need to admit that you do not know the answer to a particular question. Actually, all man's knowledge is very small in comparison with God's limitless knowledge. To even some of the simplest questions, we must admit, "I do not know." There is no complete answer to "What is matter?" "What is gravity?" "What is light?" and "How do elements form compounds?" We honor the wisdom of God by freely admitting that we do not understand many things about His creation.

However, many times your lack of understanding should be an invitation to do further study. You will inspire your students to diligent study if they know you are also active in searching for new information and understanding.

2. *Children's natural curiosity must be respected.* God has given children a strong desire to understand the world about them. Their "Why?" and "What's that?" questions provide countless opportunities to guide their young minds into noble and God-conscious paths. Questions like "How does a bird fly?" and "What makes a tornado?" are opportunities for impromptu science classes.

Systematic science instruction will open up new vistas for the children. This will stimulate further inquiry. As their teacher, you can wisely direct this exploration. If you should neglect to provide the adult guidance that their curiosity needs, they will likely pursue unwholesome curiosity and seek their answers from their peers.

3. *Children must be taught to worship God, not His creation.* Imagine a car left in a remote area that is inhabited only by primitive, nomadic tribes. The nomads would happen upon the car, which, to them, is a strange, unheard-of contraption.

As the nomads curiously explore the car, one man discovers that the door will open! He is loudly praised for this accomplishment. Soon another man discovers that turning the key will start the engine. He is likewise applauded. The third man learns how to operate the windshield wipers. And so it goes, on and on. Each intelligent "pioneer of discovery" is honored.

But the nomads do not dream that a greater intelligence was needed to invent the car. Never once do they seek to know and honor its inventor.

How ignorant that would be! Yet, modern scientists are no better than these imaginary nomads. Do they seek the Creator of the universe? Do they not honor Henry Ford, an inventor of automobiles, above the God who created Ford's mind, the materials that he used, and the laws that govern a car's operation?

You have the privilege of relating the child's science experiences to God's revealed truth in His Word. You can warn him against theories that undermine or contradict the Bible.

4. *Science can help create student enthusiasm for school in general.* Science class is often scheduled for the afternoon when interest lags. Try to spark and maintain interest by using many concrete illustrations and demonstrations, such as those given in the "Extra Activities" section. Treat each science class as if it were your most important class of the day. Of what value are grandiose plans for a future unit if the present unit is taught in a flavorless and slipshod manner?

What Are the Objectives for Teaching Third Grade Science?

—To inspire children with the many aspects of God's greatness and wisdom.
—To acquaint children with God's creation and His plan to protect and sustain it.
—To show children the relationship between God's creation and His Word.
—To teach children a body of science facts and vocabulary that will prove useful in their later life.
—To encourage children to develop mutual respect and class harmony.
—To create in children a thirst for learning and a love for truth.

About the Symbol on the Cover

The simple drawing on the front and back covers symbolizes science. The white ash leaf is just one part of the great and beautiful world God created. It is this world that we investigate in science. The magnifying glass is one of the many tools that men use to study leaves and other parts of that world. The leaf was made by God; the magnifying glass was made by man. The leaf is a living thing; the magnifying glass is nonliving. Men can make useful tools from the materials God has placed on the earth, but they cannot produce life. Only God can give life. A true study of science should focus on the handiwork of God and not on the inventions of men. Even when we study about useful devices that men have made, the emphasis should be on the laws and materials of God that made the inventions possible and on the way we can use those pieces of equipment to the glory of God.

What Is the Theme of This Book?

The theme and title of this book is *God's Protected World*. The study of the Flood helps to unify this theme throughout the book. For example, studying the animals that entered the ark provides an opportunity to show God's continued protection of the animals today. The rainbow speaks of a loving, protective God who keeps His promises.

What Are Some Values of This Theme to Third Graders?

—Confidence in our caring, protective God
—Awe at God's marvelous plan for protection
—Respect for God's impartiality in protecting His created world
—Knowledge of their body and the earth in order to protect them and use them wisely as good stewards

What Plans Are Recommended for Teaching the Units?

Each lesson is divided into two parts: "Reading Together" and "Reading on Your Own." The first part can be used to introduce the lesson. It provides an opportunity for discussion and oral reading practice. The second part calls for individual reading comprehension. This second part can be assigned along with the "Test Your Reading" questions. In the following science class period, these questions can be checked and discussed.

In the answer key, the total possible points are included in each lesson for your convenience. You may want to accumulate the total points over two or three lessons before calculating a percentage grade.

A review lesson is provided at the end of each unit. Unit tests are available in a separate test booklet. These should be supplemented with occasional quizzes and reviews of past units.

The vocabulary words are very important. The students should be familiar with both their meanings and pronunciations. For a daily drill in pronunciation, you could first say all the New Words and then go around the room, each student in turn saying a word, or the students could sound out the words, using their phonetic skills. The more the words are repeated, the better they are remembered.

The quizzes are especially intended to drill the vocabulary word meanings. Give them as a challenge, not a dreaded ordeal. Your own attitude will greatly affect the classroom atmosphere.

Report card grades can be calculated by counting the average of daily lessons once, the review lessons once, and the unit test scores twice. You may also want to allow quizzes and extra projects to affect the grade.

This textbook contains 7 units with 4 to 8 lessons per unit plus a review lesson for each unit. There are a total of 39 lessons, 7 review lessons, and 7 tests. Covering a lesson each science class and using a period for each review and test, makes a total of 53 class periods of work. Having science class twice a week for 36 weeks of school makes 72 science classes per year. That would give about 20 extra periods for activities and year-end review and testing. If you plan instead for 3 science periods per week, that would allow for 2 class periods for all the lessons.

How Can I Enrich My Science Teaching?

An encyclopedia will provide you with additional information as you study topics related to the individual lessons. You may also enjoy studying a particular unit in the local library. Books in the children's nonfiction section of the library can provide helpful ideas and related information.

Demonstrations with actual materials are an important part of science teaching. They not only stimulate interest in the lesson, but they make the lesson more understandable. A student can read an explanation in the text and have trouble comprehending its abstract concepts. A simple concrete demonstration can clarify the principle and help it stick in the mind.

A demonstration is most effective on the day of the lesson. To be prepared, you will need to look ahead so you can have the needed materials on hand. A list of such materials is given after the description of each activity. Sometimes you may need to improvise or borrow special items from a patron. Others will need to be purchased from local stores or from a science supplier. Home Training Tools is a very economical source (800-860-6272; 546 S 18th St. W, Suite B, Billings, MT 59102).

It will be helpful for the future to begin a collection of common items that can be ready at hand for doing demonstrations. If you do not already have one, you may want to consider starting a science storage corner. A counter-level cabinet with a 2' x 4' Formica top would be a good beginning. With caster wheels, it could be easily moved to the front of the class when needed. Several drawers and shelves below could store the materials used in demonstrations.

The "Extra Activities", suggested in the student textbook, are an important part of science instruction. These can be used in a variety of ways:
—Teacher demonstrations during the class period
—Class discussions about the possible results of the activities
—Individual or group demonstrations
—Extra work for the faster students
—Extra credit projects for the slower students
—Homework activities to be reported orally or in written form
—Class projects, particularly the unit projects that extend over a period of several weeks

As much as possible, involve the students in doing these activities. Science deals with the real physical world, and it will be more meaningful and interesting if the students can get their hands on the things they are studying. Assign the work according to your judgment of their individual ability. Help them understand that God wants each one to develop his abilities for His glory. We should not promote the idea of being a scientist but of being the best servant of God that each can be.

May God richly bless you in your challenging "labour of love" in the classroom. "But the God of all grace, who hath called us unto his eternal glory by Christ Jesus, after that ye have suffered a while, make you perfect, stablish, strengthen, settle you. To him be glory and dominion for ever and ever. Amen" (1 Peter 5:10, 11).

Pupil's book

introduction

INTRODUCTION

At the very beginning of the Bible, we are told that God created the heaven and the earth. On the earth He placed living things. On the second day of creation He made plants. On the fifth and sixth days He made animals and man. When He was finished making the earth, God saw that it was good.

The earth is a good place for living things. In many ways God protects the world He created. God wants the living things He created to have a nice place to live. But when men became very wicked, God used a flood to punish the people. All of the people died in the Flood except Noah and his family. God protected Noah with a great boat called the ark. After the Flood God promised Noah that He would not destroy the earth with a flood again.

This science book will tell you about some of the ways God protects His world. The seven units of study are all related to Noah. Noah trusted God to take care of him. Noah obeyed God and built an ark just the way God told him. God protected Noah and a great number of animals in the ark. From the life of Noah, you can learn many things about God's protected world. You, too, can trust and obey God like faithful Noah.

How to Study for a Test

Do you know how to get ready for a test? If you follow these four steps carefully, you will know most or all of the answers on your test. Then you can get a good score!

1. *Theme:* Look at the table of contents on page 6. The unit title tells the main theme. See what the lesson titles say about the main theme. Remember these main ideas.
2. *New Words:* Be sure you know all the New Words and their meanings.
3. *Exercises:* Ask yourself the "Test Your Reading" questions from each lesson. If you can easily answer them, go on to the next lesson. If you do not know the answers, study that lesson carefully.
4. *Review lesson:* Study all of the review lesson, "Do You Remember What You Learned?" After it has been checked, see which questions you got wrong. Study especially the lessons that tell about those questions.

5

Unit One
God Gave Us Water

"In the days of Noah, . . . eight souls were saved by water" (1 Peter 3:20).

Unit One
God Gave Us Water

For Your Inspiration

Would you like to know how water is typified in the Bible? For the sake of brevity, the following selections of Scripture give only parts of the verses indicated by the references.

1. *Water in ceremonial cleansing: the Word of God*

   "They shall wash with water, that they die not" (Exodus 30:19–21).

   "He that is washed . . . is clean every whit" (John 13:1–17).

   "Now ye are clean through the word which I have spoken unto you" (John 15:3).

   "That he might sanctify and cleanse it with the washing of water by the word" (Ephesians 5:26).

2. *Refreshing, life-giving, flowing water: the Holy Spirit*

   "And thou shalt smite the rock, and there shall come water out of it, that the people may drink" (Exodus 17:6).

   "But the water that I shall give him shall be in him a well of water springing up into everlasting life" (John 4:14).

   "He that believeth on me, . . . out of his belly shall flow rivers of living water" (John 7:38).

3. *Turbulent seas: the nations*

   "The floods of ungodly men" (Psalm 18:4).

   "But the wicked are like the troubled sea" (Isaiah 57:20).

   "The waters which thou sawest . . . are peoples, and multitudes, and nations, and tongues" (Revelation 17:15).

4. *Water spilled on the ground: human helplessness*

   "And they . . . drew water, and poured it out

Welcome to the study of science! Science is not new to you. You have already enjoyed science many times. When you study God's world, you are studying science. Perhaps this past summer, your family saw bears and elephants at the zoo. Or you may have taken a walk in the field and found daisies and wild roses. Even the food you eat is part of science. Water is part of science. The first lesson in this book is about water.

This science book will also tell about Noah. Did you know that Noah learned science too? His "classroom" was outdoors. His teacher was God Himself. God taught him to build the ark. God taught him how to take care of the animals. Noah learned about water, wood, and many other things. He must have been happy to have the very best science teacher of all.

Water was very important to Noah. His ark floated on water. By using water, God saved Noah and his family from the destruction of a wicked world. Noah was very thankful for this.

We are thankful for water. It helps us in many ways. We need water to live. God uses it to protect His world. In Unit One, you will study about water. Enjoy your study about water, for it is a very special part of God's creation.

8

before the Lord . . . and said there, We have sinned" (1 Samuel 7:6).

   "For we must needs die, and are as water spilt on the ground" (2 Samuel 14:14).

   "I am poured out like water" (Psalm 22:14).

   "All knees shall be weak as water" (Ezekiel 7:17).

5. *Flood water: judgment*

   "I will cause it to rain upon the earth . . . ; and every living substance that I have made will I destroy" (Genesis 7:4).

   "I am come into deep waters, where the floods overflow me" (Psalm 69:2).

   "But let judgment run down as waters" (Amos 5:24).

6. *Bitter waters: death*

   "They could not drink of the waters of Marah, for they were bitter" (Exodus 15:23).

   "Many men died of the waters, because they were made bitter" (Revelation 8:11).

Water Is Important to Us

New Words

dissolve (di • zolv′), to make a material disappear into water.

property (prop′ ər • tē), what a material is like.

solution (sə • loo̅′ shən), a clear mixture of water and some
material.

Reading Together

What would you do without water? Pretend that tomorrow the water would be turned off. You could not wash yourself before breakfast. Your mother could not wash the breakfast dishes or your clothes. She could not water her plants.

At school, you might play hard, and your hands might get dirty. You might feel very warm and thirsty. You want water!

You can see how much we need water. Did you know that more than one-half of your body is water? Without water, you could not live more than a week. Your body needs about eight glasses (half a gallon) of water every day. If you live to be eighty years old, your body will need as much as four big tractor trailer trucks of water.

Does this mean that you drink all that water? No, you "eat" some of it. Your food is partly water. For example, more than half of an egg is water.

Your body will need four truckloads of water in eighty years.

A tomato and a watermelon also have much water in them. When you drink orange juice, milk, or tea, you are also drinking the water in them.

Every plant, animal, and person needs water. Without water, there would be no apples, roses, or pine trees. The cows and chickens would die. There would be no hamburgers

9

Lesson 1

CONCEPTS TO TEACH

- Living things must have water to live.
- Water is used for washing.
- Water is used to make many useful things.
- Water is used to make solutions.
- Water has properties that are helpful.
- Water is used to put out fires.
- God put much water on the earth for us in the sky, ground, streams, rivers, lakes, and oceans.

Note: For the vocabulary words, the students may have a problem understanding the difference between *dissolve* and *solution.* If so, you could say that *dissolve* is what a material does in water; *solution* is what it becomes. Give examples in sentence form like this: "Do we dissolve or solution salt? Do we make a dissolve or a solution of salt? Do we drink a dissolve or a solution? Does sugar dissolve or solution in water?"

HELPS FOR THE TEACHER

Introducing the Lesson

While introducing Lesson 1, you are also acquainting the students with the textbook as a whole. Have them find the Table of Contents. With it, lead them to discover what they will be studying this year. Ask, "How many big parts, or units, does this book have? What is the subject of each unit?" Notice how the lesson titles show that the lessons are all related to one idea. Ask, "What is the one big idea of the first unit? How does each lesson in the first unit tell about the idea of the unit?"

Next, you can have the students page through the book. Ask them to tell, by looking at the pictures, what they will be learning this year.

Now ask them to turn to Lesson 1. Discuss the pictures. See if they notice the many ways we use water. Ask for others, such as traveling by water or enjoying the beauty of a waterfall or the ocean.

Show them a globe. Ask whether the earth has

What uses of water are shown here?

or ice cream. Without water, there would be no "you"!

How good our God is! Are you thankful that He gave water for your home and school?

Reading on Your Own

Water is used for much more than washing and drinking. It is used to make many things. Maybe you have watched a builder mixing cement with water to make concrete. Sprays, paste, and some kinds of paint are made with water. The paper in this book was made from wood that was mashed and then mixed with water.

What happens when we mix white sugar with water? First, the water looks cloudy. Then slowly it becomes clear. The sugar and water make a *solution*. Sugar solutions are used to can peaches and other fruit. Sugar water and all other solutions are clear.

Where does the sugar go? We say that it *dissolves* in the water. We cannot see it anymore. But we know that the sugar is still there because the solution tastes sweet. Tea, salt, and many other things can also dissolve in water.

Water has many important properties. A *property* of a material tells what it is like. Water is clear. Water tastes good and feels wet when we touch it. These are properties of water.

Another good property of water is that it will not burn. Firemen are glad for this property. Have you ever watched firemen spraying water on a fire? *Hiss! Pop! Crack!* The fire seems strong, but the cold water is

more land or more water. Ask for guesses of how much more—two, three, or five times? Do not give them the correct answer, but ask them to find it in the lesson.

Materials needed:
• *globe*

Extra Information

Did you know—

. . . that one *drop* of water contains millions of water molecules?

. . . that to raise the wheat for one loaf of bread, it takes more than 100 gallons of water?

. . . that each minute under the shower takes five gallons of water?

. . . that the average person uses 70 gallons of water daily?

stronger. The firemen try to drown all the fire before much harm is done.

Our great God knew all about our need for water. He put many billions of gallons of water on the earth. In fact, the earth is covered with almost three times as much water as land.

We can see the water in streams, rivers, lakes, and oceans. Big cities often get their water from rivers and lakes. Although the ocean has much more water than rivers and lakes, only a few cities get their water from the ocean. Can you guess why? Ocean water is a solution of salt. Salt is dissolved in the ocean water. The people would die if they drank salty water. The cities that use ocean water must first take out the salt.

Some water is under the ground. If you live in a small town or in the country, probably your water is pumped from a well deep in the ground. Some people live near a spring where the water flows out by itself.

Some of the water is above the earth. It is waiting in the clouds. Someday it will fall to the ground as rain or snow.

Thank God for water. He put just enough water on the earth. He put it in the best places. He gave it the right properties. How wise God is!

Test Your Reading

Did you understand what you read? Find out by giving the answers. Number your paper from 1 to 10.

1. List three ways we use water. (Can you think of any ways not given in the lesson?)
2. How much water do we need every day?
3. Name three things that are made with water. (Again, try to think of things not given in the lesson.)
4. Name four properties of water.
5. Why do you think potatoes get wrinkled after a long while? (Think about what you learned today.)

Choose the best ending for each sentence. Write the letter on your paper.

6. The word *solution* means
   (a) water used for washing.
   (b) something dissolved in water.
   (c) the water in food.

Answers for "Test Your Reading"

1. (Any three) Drinking, washing, making useful things (such as concrete, sprays, and paste), making solutions, putting out fires, fishing, watering crops, traveling by boat, etc.   (3)
2. About eight glasses (one-half gallon)   (1)
3. (Any three) Concrete, paint, paper, sprays, paste, etc.   (3)
4. It is clear. It tastes good. It feels wet. It will not burn.   (4)
5. Potatoes get wrinkled because they lose water and dry out.   (1)
6. b

Unit Project

Make a little "water world" for a unit project. It can help to make the lessons about the water cycle and erosion more real and understandable. It is also rewarding for the class to work together on such a project.

If you use a box, first line it with the heavy sheet of plastic to make it watertight. Actually, a large, shallow box would be better than a small, deep aquarium.

The soil should be damp so that it can be packed, but it should not be so muddy that it cannot be graded easily. Put the soil into the water-tight box. Use the photo as your guide to form some hills and mountains. Form a bowl-shaped hole up in the hills for a lake. Form a winding ditch from the lake to the one end of the box which is the ocean.

Materials needed:

- *large aquarium or large flat box*
- *heavy plastic sheet (if you use a box)*
- *soil*
- *green sponge*
- *plastic food wrap*
- *bucket of fine topsoil*
- *moss*
- *toothpicks*
- *wooden blocks or cardboard folded to form houses*

Line the lake and the river with plastic food wrap. Allow the wrap to extend on all sides of the lake and river about an extra inch or two. Next, cover the sides of the lake and river with another half inch of soil. Make sure the land slopes toward the river. Pack the soil well and wet it down with a clothes sprinkler or by sprinkling water on it with your fingers.

Pour some water into the lake, and watch the water clean the river of any bits of loose soil as it flows into the ocean.

Cut or tear off small pieces of green sponge. Push toothpicks through them and stick them into

7. c
8. a
9. b
10. a   *(Total: 17 points)*

7. All solutions are
   (a) cold.
   (b) white.
   (c) clear.
8. An example of a solution is
   (a) sugar water.
   (b) muddy water.
   (c) milk and water.
9. The word *property* means
   (a) that water is cold and clear.
   (b) what something is like.
   (c) where water is stored.
10. The earth has
   (a) three times as much water as land.
   (b) as much water as land.
   (c) three times as much land as water.

Comments on "Extra Activities"

1. The liquids given in the pupil's text should be classified as follows. (Additional liquids are listed here.)

Solutions

vinegar*

rubbing alcohol*

hot Jell-O*

tea* (without milk)

cough syrup*

Kool-Aid*

tincture of iodine or Merthiolate

Extra Activities

Do these activities as your teacher directs.

1. Make a test about solutions. Get as many of these things as you can. Put them in little jars or bowls.
   - vinegar   • milk   • tea
   - orange juice   • muddy water   • cough syrup
   - rubbing alcohol   • hot Jell-O   • Kool-Aid

   Try to decide which are solutions. Remember, solutions are clear. They may be colored, but you can still see things through them. If you are not sure which are solutions, ask your teacher.

   You might also give the test to other people at school or at home. Ask them if they can tell you which are solutions. If they guess most of them right, give them a solution of iced tea or Kool-Aid to drink.

   Materials needed:
   - *liquids listed above*
   - *9 to 12 small jars (baby food jars work fine)*

the ground to make bushes and trees. Use the moss to cover the hills with grass. Put the grass, bushes, and trees on the hills but not on the fields. Try to make your water world look as real as you can.

Bulletin Board

Make a large bulletin board display on the same theme as the illustration on page 10 of the text. Cut out a large blue drop of water for the center. The title could be *The Importance of Water in Our Lives.* Have the students bring pictures to illustrate this theme. Choose some Bible verses that are suitable to accompany the pictures. Make this an add-to bulletin board. As more pictures are brought in, keep adding them to the board until the display is papered with illustrations. This will impress the students with the concept that water touches almost every phase of our lives.

2. Find out for yourself that food has water in it. Take slices of various foods, such as an apple, a banana, a tomato, a potato, and bread. Put them in a dish in a warm, sunny window. See how big they are now. Weigh them if your school has an accurate balance.

    Compare the size and weight in your next science class. Do the pieces get smaller? Do they change shape? Do they lose weight? Why?
    Materials needed:
    • *slices of the foods listed above*
    • *large, flat dish or several small dishes*

3. Make a study to find where the students in your room get their water at home. At the top of a chart, write "Where Do We Get Our Water?" Under it, write Well, Spring, Cistern, and City Pipeline.

    Write the name of each student below the word that tells where they get their water.

4. Make a solution of salt water that is as salty as ocean water. Measure out one cup of water. Add one teaspoon of salt. Stir until all of the salt is dissolved. Dip your finger into the salt solution and put a few drops on your tongue. This is how salty ocean water is. This water is too salty to drink. It would make you sick.
    Materials needed:
    • *measuring cup*
    • *measuring teaspoon*
    • *water (1 cup)*
    • *salt (1 teaspoon)*

Listerine
honey
bleach
varnish

Suspensions
orange juice*
milk*
muddy water*
India ink (dilute with water)
milk of magnesia
Pepto-Bismol (any medicine that says "Shake well before using")
paint

*liquids listed in the text

2. The slices will become smaller and drier because they lose water.

4. This activity would be especially appropriate to do during the science class, since it takes very little time.

QUIZ

Write the New Words on the chalkboard. Ask the students to say or write the word they think of when you give the phrases below.

1. Tells what something is like   (*property*)
2. Clear mixture   (*solution*)
3. To make a solution   (*dissolve*)

Now ask, "What New Word do you think of when I say . . ."

4. Sugar water   (*solution*)
5. Feels wet and tastes good   (*property*)
6. To mix something with water until it disappears   (*dissolve*)

Lesson 2

Water Has Three States

New Words

gas (gas), something like air that can change both its size and shape.

ice (īs), water that is solid.

liquid (lik′ • wid), something wet; it can change shape but not size.

solid (sol′ • id), something firm; it keeps its size and shape.

state (stāt), how something looks and acts in size and shape.

steam (stēm), water that is heated enough to be a gas.

Reading Together

How does water look? Do you think of "wavy" or "splashing" or "clear"? Let's think some more. Sometimes water is hard and whitish. And sometimes you cannot see it even if it is right in front of your nose! How can that be?

We are talking about three forms, or states, of water. The *state* of water is not always the same. It can look and act in three different ways.

When water is hard and whitish, we call it *ice*. Ice is in the *solid* state. If we take ice cubes from the ice cube tray and lay them in the kitchen sink, they keep their square shape. They are not bigger or smaller than before. Their size and shape do not change, because ice is a solid.

Ice is not the only solid. Anything that keeps its size and shape is a solid. Your pencil, scissors, and desk are solids. The school building is a solid.

The wet, splashy state of water is *liquid.* We can pour a liquid from one place to another. We can drink some liquids, such as water, milk, and grape juice. But of course we would not drink liquids like ink or glue!

Is liquid water round or square? Is it tall or short? What strange questions! The shape of liquid water will change. Put it in a bowl and it is round. Put it in a box and it is square. Its shape changes to fit the place where we put it.

Think of putting a cup of water into a bucket. Do we have more water than before? No, we still have just one cup of water. If we would pour the water back into the cup, it would

14

Lesson 2

CONCEPTS TO TEACH

• Ice is the solid state of water.

Note: Distinguish the scientific meaning of *state* from the political meaning, "a part of a country."

• A solid keeps both its size and shape.

• We drink liquid water.

• A liquid changes its shape but not its size.

• Steam is water in the form of a gas.

Note: In common usage, *steam* has various meanings: water as a gas, the cloud of condensation from water vapor or steam, condensation on a cold window, and water vapor (water mixed with air). You may need to clarify these different uses for the word *steam*, but avoid distracting from the basic concept of the three states of matter.

• A gas changes both its size and shape.

Note: Be sure that your students do not confuse *gas* with *gasoline*.

HELPS FOR THE TEACHER

Introducing the Lesson

Before class, make your students curious. Let them see you putting a teakettle of water on a hot plate to boil. When the water boils, explain the three states of water, using a glass of water, an ice cube, and the steam from the teakettle. Give examples of a solid, a liquid (the drink in their lunch box), and a gas (the air) in the room. Then turn to their lesson. Discuss the pictures, and ask why one of the jars on page 15 looks empty.

After you tell about the different sizes and shapes of the states of matter, you could quote Colossians 1:17, "And he is before all things, and by him all things consist." The word *consist* means "hold together." Explain that it is God's word alone that makes solids, liquids, and gases hold together. Each state consists in its own orderly way, just as God planned in the beginning.

The states of matter

all fit in. Changing the water's shape does not change its size or amount. All liquids change their shape but not their size.

Reading on Your Own

When liquid water is heated very hot on a stove, some of the water rises into the air. We call this kind of water *steam.* You have seen steam rising from a pan as Mother cooks food for your meals. When water is heated in a teakettle, steam comes out of the spout.

You know that this steam is not solid like ice. And it will not stay in the bottom of the pan like liquid water. Steam is water in a special state called a *gas.* A gas can change both its shape and size. When a gas is inside a teakettle, it has the shape of the teakettle. If the gas is inside a jar , it has the shape of the jar. In this way, a gas is like a liquid. Both a liquid and a gas can change their shapes.

But a gas is different from a liquid in a special way. A gas will spread out to fill whatever it is in.

Materials needed:
- *teakettle*
- *hot plate*
- *water glass*
- *water*
- *ice cube*

Extra Information

Did you know—

. . . that in a solid, the molecules shiver and vibrate, seemingly locked up in tiny, fenced-in pens? (The "pens" are the strong molecular attractions.)

. . . that in a liquid, the molecules move faster and slide over each other, as if breaking the fences? (Their speed increases the distance between them and thus lessens the molecular attraction.)

. . . that in a gas, the molecules collide swiftly and violently, causing them to scatter? They seem to have no boundaries (or very little attraction).

. . . that *plasma* is called the fourth state of matter? Most stars are made of plasma, which is a kind of electrically charged gas found only at extremely high temperatures.

Can you find the three states of water in this picture?

The steam in a teakettle will spread out to fill the teakettle. A gas can change its size to fill a teakettle. If we take off the lid, the steam will spread out into the room. After a while, some of the water will be everywhere in the air of the room.

Air itself is a gas. You know that air fills a room completely. Air does not go to the bottom of the room like liquid water.

Think of the smell of bread baking. The smell is caused by a gas. If the kitchen door and windows are closed, most of the smell will stay in the kitchen. But if we open the door, the smell will change its size. It will spread out to fill the house with a good smell. It changes easily from a small size to a larger size.

For another example, what happens if we put a cup of steam into a big jar? It will spread out and fill the whole jar. But a cup of solid ice or liquid water would not fill the jar. Solids and liquids do not change their size like gas does. All gases change both their size and shape.

Now look at the picture on this page. Can you find all three states of water? The water in the lake is liquid. The ice cubes in the glasses and pitcher are solid. The steam coming from the teakettle is a gas.

These three states of water are God's idea. They are very important to us. So do not forget about water, ice, and gases. You will meet them again in the coming lessons.

Unit Project

Work can continue on the "water world" project introduced in Lesson 1.

QUIZ

Solid, Liquid, or Gas?

Read the items and have the students write *S*, *L*, or *G*.

1. ice *(S)*
2. water *(L)*
3. steam *(G)*
4. orange juice *(L)*
5. wood *(S)*
6. air *(G)*
7. glass *(S)*
8. pancake syrup *(L)*
9. smell of a rose *(G)*
10. pudding *(S or L. Discuss this one.)*

Test Your Reading

A. In this picture, find two gases, five liquids, and at least six solids. Write them in lists under the headings Solid, Liquid, *and* Gas.

Just Before Supper

B. Fill the blanks with the correct New Word.

1. The way a material acts in size and shape is called its ——.
2. Solid water is called ——.
3. Both the size and shape of a —— do not change.
4. The water we drink is in the —— state.
5. The shape of a —— changes, but the size stays the same.
6. Water that is a gas is called ——.
7. Both the size and shape of a —— will change easily.

Answers for "Test Your Reading"

A.   *Solid*
            (Any six)

pans	bread
bowls	knives
floor	forks
wall	spoons
stove	paper
sink	carton
table	window
chair	ladder
plates	bucket

Liquid
(Any five)

water	paint
milk	glue
honey	gravy

Gas
(two)
air
steam

B. 1. state
    2. ice
    3. solid
    4. liquid
    5. liquid
    6. steam
    7. gas   *(Total: 20 points)*

Comments on "Extra Activities"

1. Frost, hail, snow, and sleet are other names of solid water.

2. *Steam:* dampening clothes while ironing, building up pressure in pressure cooker, helping to breathe, soothing throat and lungs.

   Water: washing, cooking, cleaning, drinking, making paste for wallpaper, mixing spray material.

   Ice: cooling drinking water, making ice cream, applying ice pack to severe bruises, keeping food cool for travel.

3. *Where to find the materials*

   Mercury can be obtained from broken thermometers, mercury switches, or mercury switch thermostats. (*CAUTION:* Avoid contact with the skin since mercury compounds are very poisonous.)

   Silly Putty may have various names, such as "bouncing putty," "playing putty," or "color putty." It is often sold in a plastic egg in the toy section of stores. This material is a silicone compound, in which the silicon forms long chains similar to carbon atoms in organic compounds.

The experiments

   Carbon dioxide: The match goes out as soon as it is lowered below the mouth of the jar, indicating that the jar is full of the gas. This illustrates the property of gases to fill the container they are in.

   Mercury: The mercury takes the shape of the flat bottom of the bottle. This illustrates the property of liquids to take the shape of the container they are in.

   Silly Putty: The Silly Putty holds its shape as a ball. No, liquids do not bounce. The "snowman" illustrates the property of solids to keep their shape. The Silly Putty demonstrates the fact that some materials do not have a distinct melting point like water. As they are warmed, they get softer and behave more like liquids than like solids. When they are cooled, they get stiffer and behave more like solids. Glass is another example of a material that does not have a distinct melting point.

Extra Activities

Do these activities as your teacher directs.

1. Ice is not the only name for solid water. Can you think of four other names for solid water that are made by the weather?

2. All three states of water are used in our homes. Write a paragraph about how steam, water, and ice are used in our homes. Your parents or an older brother or sister may help you find out about it.

3. To help you learn better about the properties of gases, liquids, and solids, experiment with three special materials.

   Carbon dioxide: Put 2 tablespoons of baking soda in a quart jar. Pour in 3 tablespoons of vinegar. Immediately lay a piece of cardboard over the mouth of the jar. Do you see the carbon dioxide gas being formed? After a half minute, lower a lighted match into the mouth of the jar. Carbon dioxide will put out fires. When does the match go out? How full is the jar with gas? What property of gases does this show?

   Mercury: Mercury is the only metal that can be a liquid at room temperature. Pour some mercury into a test tube. Notice how it fits the curved bottom. Make a paper cone. Pour the mercury into the cone and notice how it fits the cone. Pour it into a bottle with a flat bottom. Now what shape does it have? What does this tell you about liquids?

   Silly Putty: Roll Silly Putty into a ball. Place it on the table. Does it hold its shape? Bounce it on the floor. Could you bounce a liquid on the floor? Roll it into three small balls, and set them up like a snowman. What property of solids does this show? Surprise! Let your "snowman" stand overnight. Do you think Silly Putty is a solid or a liquid?

Materials needed:
- *measuring tablespoon*
- *quart jar*
- *baking soda (2 tablespoons)*
- *vinegar (3 tablespoons)*
- *cardboard: 3" x 3"*
- *matches*
- *mercury (CAUTION: Avoid contact with the skin, since mercury compounds are very poisonous.)*
- *test tube*
- *paper*
- *small bottle with a flat bottom*
- *Silly Putty*

The State of Water
Can Be Changed

New Words

boil (boil), to change a liquid into a gas by heating.

freeze (frēz), to change a liquid into a solid by cooling.

melt (melt), to change a solid into a liquid by heating.

Reading Together

You know that water has three different states. Can we change it from one state to another? Yes, it is easy.

We can pour water into a paper cup. If we put the cupful of water into the freezer, the water becomes very cold. Finally, it becomes very hard. We could turn the paper cup over, and the ice would not come out. It is solid now. The liquid water becomes solid water when we *freeze* it.

Now, let's take some ice cubes out of the freezer and put them in a pan on a warm stove. Soon the ice will not be little squares in the middle of the pan. It will become a liquid that spreads over the whole bottom of the pan. Solid water becomes liquid water when we *melt* it.

If we turn the burner on the stove higher, soon we will see the water in the pan move and bubble. If we heat it long enough, all the water will change to steam. The pan will be dry inside. Where did the water go? It

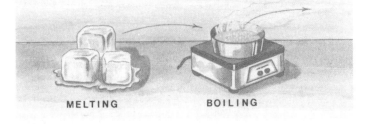

MELTING   BOILING

19

Lesson 3

CONCEPTS TO TEACH

- When water is made very cold, it turns into a solid called ice.
- Turning a liquid into a solid is called freezing.
- Turning a solid into a liquid is called melting.
- When water is made very hot, it turns into a gas called steam.
- Turning a liquid into a gas is called boiling.

HELPS FOR THE TEACHER

Introducing the Lesson

Today you may again have the water in the teakettle boiling and an ice cube. Review the New Words from the last lesson. Then ask the students whether they think the state of water stays the same or whether it can change. See if they notice any change (the ice cube melting, the water boiling).

Ask all the class to name a possession (not a food or a pet) for which they are thankful. Tell whether or not the state of each object was changed when it was made. (Except for wooden objects and some clothes made of wool or cotton, most things they own have been changed in state during their manufacture.) Emphasize the wisdom of God in providing for changes of state.

Materials needed:

- *teakettle*
- *water*
- *hot plate*
- *ice cube*

became a gas. It went into the air. A liquid becomes a gas when we *boil* it.

Freezing, melting, and boiling change the state of water. These same changes can happen to other solids, liquids, and gases. Why are these changes important?

Sometimes solids are melted in order to shape them. Glass is melted to shape it into bottles and dishes. Sometimes liquids are boiled to make things out of them. Oil from the ground is boiled to separate the fuel oil and gasoline. Freezing is very important to us too. Your mother freezes many kinds of food so that they will not spoil.

If things could not be melted, boiled, and frozen, your life would be very different. You could not have a pen, comb, or lunch box. You could not have a spoon, plate, or cup. There would be no cars or tractors to ride. You could not have glass windows or paved roads. In fact, you might choke on ice cream if the heat of your body could not melt it!

Reading on Your Own

We can boil water, milk, vinegar, and cooking oil on a kitchen stove. A kitchen stove is hot enough to boil liquids like these. But it is not hot enough to boil every material.

Iron is a solid. It could never melt on a kitchen stove like ice and butter. But it can melt in a large furnace. The iron is made very, very hot. When it is hot enough, it changes into a liquid. Liquid iron runs like water. Men pour it into molds to make parts for tractors, cars, and other machines.

The rocks we see are in the solid state. Can rocks become liquid? Yes, even rocks can melt. Deep inside the earth, it is much warmer than on the outside where we live. It is hot enough to melt rocks. This liquid rock usually stays inside the earth. But sometimes the liquid rock comes out through cracks in the earth.

Liquid rock runs in streams down the side of a volcano.

Ice, butter, iron, and rocks can all be melted. Most other solids will melt also. But some kinds of solids need to be made hotter than other kinds of solids before they will melt. Iron and rocks need to be much hotter to melt than ice or butter.

You know that liquid water changes to solid ice when we freeze it. Milk, oil, and other liquids also

Extra Information

Did you know—

. . . that some solids such as dry ice and iodine will not melt when heated? They skip the liquid state and *sublime* directly into gases.

. . . that today all gases can be liquefied and solidified?

. . . that clear, bluish liquid air, at least –312°F (about –190°C) will boil furiously when poured on ice?

QUIZ

Melting, Boiling, or Freezing?

Read the sentences and have the students write *M*, *B*, or *F*.

1. Ice becomes water. *(M)*
2. Water becomes steam. *(B)*
3. Water becomes ice. *(F)*
4. A liquid becomes a gas. *(B)*
5. A liquid becomes a solid. *(F)*
6. A solid becomes a liquid. *(M)*
7. You eat ice cream. *(M)*
8. Your mother makes hot tea. *(B)*
9. Salt is sprinkled on snowy roads. *(M)*
10. You make homemade ice cream. *(M and F. Discuss this one.)*

become solids by freezing them. Even liquid air can become solid.

Have you ever heard of liquid air? Air can be made very, very cold. It can be made so cold that it becomes a liquid like water. This liquid air can be poured just like any other liquid.

Liquid air can be made even colder. Then it is frozen, solid air! Its size and shape do not change, just like solid ice.

Water, milk, oil, and liquid air will all freeze with enough cooling. But solid air is far colder than solid ice. Why? Different kinds of liquids need different amounts of cooling before they freeze.

The state of anything can be changed. Solids can melt. Liquids can boil or freeze. Heating changes things from one state to another.

God decided how things would change from one state to another. Notice what the Bible says about melting ice. "He casteth forth his ice like morsels: who can stand before his cold? He sendeth out his word, and melteth them" (Psalm 147:17, 18).

God very wisely planned that different things would freeze or melt or boil at different temperatures. If He had not, all things would have the same state at the same temperature. Everything would be either a solid, a liquid, or a gas! We could not live in such a world. Aren't you glad for our world of solids, liquids, and gases?

─────────── **Test Your Reading** ───────────

Number your paper from 1 to 10. Are these sentences true? Write yes *if the sentence is true. Write* no *if it is not true.*

1. Water can change from one state to another.
2. Water becomes ice when we freeze it.
3. Water becomes steam when we melt it.
4. A solid becomes a liquid when we boil it.
5. Different solids melt with different amounts of heating.
6. All liquids freeze with the same amount of cooling.

Choose the best ending for each sentence. Write the letter on your paper.

7. Freezing is changing a
   (a) gas to a liquid.
   (b) solid to a liquid.
   (c) liquid to a solid.
8. Melting is changing a
   (a) gas to a liquid.
   (b) solid to a liquid.
   (c) liquid to a solid.
9. Boiling is changing a
   (a) liquid to a gas.
   (b) liquid to a solid.
   (c) solid to a liquid.
10. Water changes its state because of
    (a) solids or liquids dissolving.
    (b) heating or cooling.
    (c) making things with it.

Answers for "Test Your Reading"

1. yes
2. yes
3. no
4. no
5. yes
6. no
7. c
8. b
9. a
10. b   *(Total: 10 points)*

Comments on "Extra Activities"

1. Directions for making a simple alcohol burner are given on pages 174 and 175 of the teacher's manual for *Investigating God's Orderly World,* Book One.

   Boiling should take about seven times longer than melting. Melting requires 80 calories of heat per gram. Boiling requires 540 calories of heat per gram.

2. A beekeeper should be able to give you some beeswax. Candle wax can be used as a substitute.

   The order of melting with melting points:
   butter (32°C, 90°F)
   paraffin (about 55°C, 131°F)
   beeswax (about 63°C, 146°F)

3. The order of freezing (approximately): water, milk, vinegar, "ocean water," syrup, cooking oil. (The syrup and oil will not freeze solid.)

Extra Activities

Do these activities as your teacher directs.

1. Test how much heat is needed for melting ice and boiling water. Place an ice cube in a small pan, and begin heating it with an alcohol burner. Time how long it takes for all of the ice cube to melt. Time how long it takes for the water to begin to boil. Time how long it takes for all the water to boil away. Which takes more heat, melting ice or boiling water?

   Materials needed:
   - *small pan*
   - *ice cube*
   - *alcohol burner or hot plate*
   - *clock*

2. Which melts first, butter, beeswax, or paraffin? Test them and see. Put some cold water in a small pan. Put a small piece of butter, beeswax, and paraffin in the water. All three will float on the water and remain a solid because the water is cold. Slowly heat the water with a hot plate or alcohol burner. Which piece melts first? Continue to heat the water until the second piece melts. Which is it? How much longer must you heat the water until the third piece melts?

   Materials needed:
   - *small pan*
   - *water*
   - *butter (small piece)*
   - *beeswax (small piece)*
   - *alcohol burner or hot plate*
   - *paraffin (small piece)*

3. Which liquids will freeze the fastest? You can make a test. Write the name of each liquid listed below on a piece of masking tape. Tape the names to the different compartments of an ice tray. Then fill each compartment with the correct liquid, and place the ice tray into the freezer. Check it every 30 minutes. Use a toothpick to see when the liquids become solid. Write down the order in which the liquids freeze.

   Materials needed:
   - *masking tape*
   - *ice tray with separate compartments*
   - *freezer*
   - *toothpick*
   - *various liquids*
   - *water*
   - *milk*
   - *syrup*
   - *cooking oil*
   - *vinegar*
   - *"ocean water" from Lesson 1*

Rain Brings Us Water

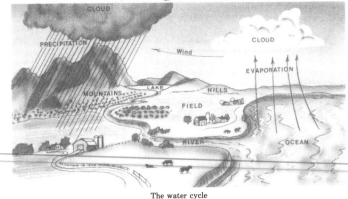

The water cycle

"He . . . gave us rain from heaven, and fruitful seasons" (Acts 14:17).

New Words

condensation (kon′ den • sā′ shən), the way water comes out of the air.

cycle (sī kəl), things happening in several steps that are repeated.

evaporation (i • vap′ ə • rā′ shən), the way water goes into the air.

Reading Together

Did you ever play in a stream? It is so much fun. The water bubbles. It feels smooth and clean. It splashes when you smack it. Can you stop it? No, it always slips through your hands. The stream seems in such a hurry to get to the river!

When the stream meets the river, does it stop? No, the river is hurrying to the ocean. At the ocean, the waterdrops will go on a trip high into the sky! Let's find out about their trip.

23

Lesson 4

CONCEPTS TO TEACH

- Rain is a blessing from God.
- Water goes into the air by evaporation.
- Heating causes evaporation.
- The more that water is heated, the faster it evaporates.
- Most water evaporates from the ocean.
- The air (wind) carries the water from the ocean to the land.
- Clouds form from the water in the air.
- Water comes out of the air by condensation.

Note: Explain that rain is only one result of the general principle of condensation. Otherwise, they might misunderstand the last paragraph. All condensation is water coming out of the air, but not all condensation is rain. The examples of condensation in the quiz for this lesson should help clarify this point.

- Cooling causes condensation.
- God makes the water go through a big cycle.
- The water cycle keeps the rivers flowing and supplies our fresh water.

The water in the river keeps flowing on and on and on. Where does all the water come from? It comes from the rain. When it rains, the water falls over all the land. The water wets the trees, the gardens, and the grass.

Some of the water you drink . . .

Some water soaks into the ground, but the rest runs off to the lowest places. First, the water runs into little streams. The streams run into rivers, and the rivers flow into the ocean. If we had no more rain to fill the rivers and streams, they would become empty.

The river water comes from the rain. But where does the rain come from? Does God make new water every time it rains? That would never work. If God would keep making new rainwater, soon the earth would be flooded. We would have too much water.

No, the rainwater is very old. It is much older than you are. Long ago when God made the earth, He made all the rainwater.

People are still using that same water. Some people probably use the same water that Noah used. Think of the water you drank this morning. Some of the drops may have been in the Red Sea when Moses crossed it.

Reading on Your Own

God does not make new rain. The same water falls again and again. After the rainwater falls to the earth, somehow it has to get back up into the sky for the next time. How does it happen?

. . . may have been in the Red Sea in Moses' time.

Do you still remember what happens when you boil liquid water? Heat will change the state of the water. Some of the boiling water will become a gas called steam.

Water can also become a gas without being boiled. This happens because liquid water always has

---

HELPS FOR THE TEACHER

Introducing the Lesson

Just before class, wet a small portion of the chalkboard. Also, fill a glass with ice cubes and water. Then ask where the water on the chalkboard is going. Explain that it goes into the air.

Next, take a washcloth and sprinkle it with water. Keep wetting it until it starts dripping. Explain that just as the cloth can hold only so much liquid water, the air can hold only so much evaporated water.

Last, show the ice water. Let the students guess where the moisture on the side of the glass comes from. Does it leak out from the inside? Does it soak through like the water in the washcloth? Explain that the air around the glass was cooled, and that water comes out of the air when it is cooled.

Talk about the rain during the Flood. Before this, it had never rained. Somehow God had watered the earth with mists and streams (Genesis 2:5, 6, 10). Describe how strange it must have seemed to see water falling from the sky. Describe the fearful reactions of those who had ridiculed Noah. This should help the students respect Noah even more for his faith and obedience.

Materials needed:
- *water*
- *drinking glass*
- *ice cubes*
- *washcloth*

some heat. The heat will make some of the water change into a gas. This is called *evaporation*. The evaporated water goes into the air.

The warmer the water is, the faster it evaporates. Cool water evaporates slowly. Warm water evaporates faster. Boiling water evaporates the fastest of all.

Now can you understand how the water gets back up into the sky? Yes, it evaporates into a gas. Water evaporates from the plants, fields, rivers, and lakes. But the most water evaporates from the oceans.

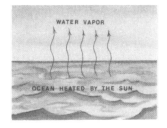

Evaporation

Remember the trip that the waterdrops take? When they reach the ocean, evaporation causes the water to go up into the sky. The evaporated waterdrops rise higher and higher above the ocean. Then the wind sweeps them along for many miles. They are carried back to the land, high above flat fields, big cities, and tall mountains.

By this time, the evaporated water has gathered into big, gray clouds. The air is much cooler than it was before. The cooled air cannot

Condensation

hold all the evaporated water. Some of it must become liquid water again. It falls to the earth as rain.

Condensation causes this trip down, down, down, and *splash!* Soon the waterdrops are hurrying from the stream to the river and on to the ocean again. And so it continues all the time.

Condensation is the opposite of evaporation. Evaporation is water going into the air by heating. Condensation is water coming out of the air by cooling. It is like a big circle. We call it a *cycle* because it happens again and again.

God planned this water cycle of evaporation and condensation. It

Extra Information
Did you know—
. . . that raindrops are round, not shaped like teardrops?
. . . that the heaviest rainfall recorded to date was 73 inches within 24 hours? It fell on the island of Réunion in the Indian Ocean.
. . . that the least rainfall ever recorded was 0.03 inch within 59 years in the country of Chile?
. . . that jet trails (caused by condensation of jet exhausts) are artificial cirrus clouds?

Note: Do you know why moist, warm air rises? Water vapor weighs less than air, and so "wet" air is lighter than "dry" air. Also, since the "warmer" molecules use more room to vibrate than "cooler" molecules, warm air is less dense than cool air. For these reasons, warm, moist air always rises, and cool, dry air always sinks in the water cycle.

A Science Poem
The students might enjoy this poem that includes concepts taught in the last few lessons. You could write the words *boiled, ocean, cold,* and *steam* on the chalkboard. Ask them to supply the missing word when you pause.

Funny Water

The teakettle's dry! The teakettle's dry!
  The water has (boiled) off in vapor.
Where has it gone? Oh, where has it gone?
  It's cutting a runaway caper.

The vapor has vanished! It floated away!
  I cannot think where it can be—
Oh, here on the windowpane, gathered in drops,
  The vapor has settled, I see.

Water, O Water, how funny you are!
  The heat makes you vanish in (steam),
The (cold) brings you back into millions of drops
  For teakettle, (ocean), and stream.

Used by permission.

keeps giving us a supply of fresh water. It keeps the streams and rivers flowing. "All the rivers run into the sea; yet the sea is not full; unto the place from whence the rivers come, thither they return again" (Ecclesiastes 1:7). This water cycle helps keep the plants and animals alive. It helps keep you alive too. If you must play inside because of condensation, do not grumble. Instead say, "Thank You, God, for the rain!"

Answers for "Test Your Reading"

1. ocean
2. God
3. ocean
4. wind (or air)
5. cycle
6. d
7. e
8. f
9. b
10. c
11. a   *(Total: 11 points)*

Comments on "Extra Activities"

1. The water in the uncovered jar evaporated. The water in the covered jar cannot evaporate very much, because it cannot get out and mix with the air.

——————— Test Your Reading ———————

Write the correct word to fill each blank.

1. Streams and rivers flow into the ——.
2. Rain is a gift from ——.
3. The greatest amount of water evaporates from the ——.
4. The —— carries the evaporated water from the ocean to the land.
5. The trip that the water takes from the ocean into the air, down as rain, and back to the ocean again is called the water ——.

Write the letter of the correct word for each blank.

6. Water going into the air is called ——.   a. clouds
7. Evaporation happens because of ——.   b. cooling
8. Something that happens again and again   c. condensation
   is a ——.   d. evaporation
9. Condensation happens because of ——.   e. heating
10. Water coming out of the air is called ——.   f. cycle
11. The water in the air forms ——.

Extra Activities

Do these activities as your teacher directs.

1. Find out about evaporation. Put one teaspoon of water into each of two baby food jars. Put the lid tightly on one jar. Now place both jars in a warm, sunny window. Check them the next day. Does the lid make a difference in the evaporation? Why?
   Materials needed:
   • *water*
   • *measuring teaspoon*
   • *2 baby food jars*
   • *baby food jar lid*

Unit Project

You can use the "water world" to illustrate the water cycle. Wet the ground in your model world. Put water in the lake and ocean. Cover the top of the aquarium or box with a piece of glass. Put a pie plate on the glass just above the land. Put some ice cubes and a little water in the pie plate. Let it stand for an hour. Take the pie plate away. Do you see water droplets hanging down from the "cloud"? What made the droplets form there? Where did the water come from? Do any of the droplets fall? How long would the water cycle in the water world continue if you kept the glass on tightly?

You may want to hold a steaming teakettle over the ocean and let the spout direct the steam against the underside of the pie plate filled with ice. Does it "rain" on your water world?

Materials needed:

• *water*   • *ice cubes*
• *glass to cover aquarium*   • *teakettle*
• *pie plate*   • *hot plate*

QUIZ

Evaporation or Condensation?

Ask the questions and have the students write *E* or *C*.

1. Why does a blackboard dry after you wash it? *(E)*
2. Why do concrete walls "sweat"? *(C)*
3. Why does your mother keep the bread in bags? *(E)*
4. Why does it rain? *(C)*
5. Why do clouds form? *(C)*
6. Why do wet clothes dry? *(E)*
7. Why does the mirror fog up when you take a bath? *(C)*

2. Find out about the speed of evaporation. Put one teaspoon of water in each of three baby food jars. Leave them uncovered. Put one jar in a cool place. Put the next jar in a warm, sunny window. Hang the third jar at least 12 inches above an alcohol burner. What difference does the amount of heat make on the evaporation? Explain why.

Materials needed:
- *3 baby food jars*
- *water*
- *measuring teaspoon*
- *alcohol burner*

3. Find out about condensation. Fill a shiny metal can with ice cubes. Add water to fill the spaces between the ice cubes. Let the can stand until it gets very cold. What do you see forming on the outside of the can? Where does it come from? Why is the ice necessary?

Materials needed:
- *shiny metal can*
- *ice cubes*
- *water*

4. Make a big poster of the water cycle for your classroom. You could make it like the picture at the beginning of this lesson. Draw clouds and raindrops on one side. Label them Condensation. Draw big arrows like this ↑↑↑ above the ocean. Label them Evaporation. Use crayons, markers, or poster paints to color your poster brightly. Label the poster "The Water Cycle" in big letters at the top.

Materials needed:
- *large sheet of poster board*
- *crayons, markers, or poster paints*

5. You can make a miniature water cycle. Put some water in a small pan and heat it on a hot plate. When you can see steam rising from your miniature "ocean," hold a metal mixing bowl above it with some water and ice in it. You will see condensation on the bowl and water dropping from your metal "cloud" back into the "ocean."

Materials needed:
- *small pan*
- *water*
- *hot plate*
- *metal mixing bowl*
- *ice cubes*

2. The water in the jar above the alcohol burner evaporates fastest because it is heated the most. The more the water is heated, the faster it evaporates.

3. Water droplets form on the outside of the can. The water comes out of the air around the can. The ice cools the can enough to make the air give up its water.

4. A bulletin board could be designed featuring the water cycle. Pictures of oceans, clouds, rain, mountains, fields, streams, and rivers could be placed in a circle with arrows connecting the various parts. Lettering could identify what happens in each part of the cycle. Ecclesiastes 1:7 would be an appropriate verse to use on either the poster or the bulletin board.

Lesson 5

Water Has Force

New Words

pressure (presh′ ər), the force of water pushing against something.
weight (wāt), how heavy something is.

Reading Together

Do you know how much you weigh? You may weigh fifty, sixty, or seventy pounds (twenty, twenty-five, or thirty kilograms). You may weigh more or less than others, but everyone weighs something.

Water also weighs something. Whether you have a cup, a bucket, or a bathtub full of water, the water has *weight*.

You have weight also. Anything that has weight will press downward. You already know about that. Has anyone ever stepped on your toe? Ouch! That person's weight pressed down, didn't it?

Water also has weight. When you put your hand under water, the weight of the water presses against your hand. The force of this pressing is called *pressure*. The pressure of water depends on how deep the water is. For example, two feet of water has more pressure than one foot of water. The deeper the water, the greater the pressure.

Now look at the pictures. Can you guess which shape has the most water pressure at the bottom?

The pressure depends only on how deep the water is. A foot of water in a bathtub has the same pressure at the bottom as a foot of water in a lake.

28

Lesson 5

CONCEPTS TO TEACH

- Water has weight.
- The force of water is called pressure.
- The greater the depth of the water, the greater the pressure.
- We use the pressure of water to push water where we need it.
- The pressure at the bottom of the ocean is so great that it would crush us.

HELPS FOR THE TEACHER

Introducing the Lesson

Begin class by reviewing some ways we use water. Ask where we get our water. (The pond? the river? a well?) Help the students see that the water that comes from the faucet does not come directly from natural sources, but it must be put under pressure. If you have time, you may follow the suggestion given in "Comments on 'Extra Activities' " for Activity 1.

You might also mention that long ago, pioneers carried their water and used much less water than we use today. Help them realize that running water is not "free." Remind them not to waste it at school or anywhere.

Reading on Your Own

Which water on the earth has the most pressure? Where is the very deepest water of all? If you guessed the ocean, you are right.

Some plants grow deep in the ocean. Some fish live deep in the ocean. They can live in great water pressure.

People swim in the water at the top of the ocean. And if they wear a special diving suit, they can go more than two hundred feet deep. Some people travel even deeper in special ships called submarines. But even submarines dare only go so far down into the ocean.

In the deepest part of the ocean, the water pressure is very, very great. Only a few plants and animals can live there. No people in submarines can go down there.

If you could go down six miles into the deepest ocean, the pressure would crush you. Every part of your body would feel like big trucks were on top of it. Do you see how strong water pressure can be?

We use water pressure to do work for us. Did you ever wonder how water comes up to a house on a hill? Or how water comes to an upstairs bathroom? You know that water will not run uphill by itself. It has to be pushed. Water pressure does the work of pushing.

Look at this picture. Have you ever seen a water tower like this in a city? This is one way to make water

Why do they make water towers so tall?

pressure do work. Do you see how tall the water tower is? The water pressure is very great at the bottom. It will force the water through big pipes. The pipes carry the water into the homes of people. When the people open a faucet, out rushes the water. The water tower uses the weight of water to make pressure.

Extra Information

Did you know—

. . . that some fish, accustomed to great water pressure, will explode if brought to the surface of the ocean?

. . . that Challenger Deep, the deepest spot in the ocean, is 36,198 feet deep and would cover 29,028-foot Mount Everest, the highest mountain in the world, with a mile to spare? The pressure at that depth is over eight tons per square inch.

. . . that generally, about 20 percent of a city's water is wasted through leakage?

. . . that the great water pressure at the base of dams is often used to produce electricity? For example, the Hoover Dam on the Colorado River is 725 feet (221 meters) high (higher than eight 90-foot silos stacked on top of each other), and the pressure at its base is 312 pounds per square inch.

Additional Activity

Help the students find out how much water is wasted by a leaking faucet. Place the measuring cup under a dripping faucet. Leave it there for one hour. Then show the students how we can use mathematics to calculate how much water is wasted in one day and then in one year.

_____ cups x 24 hours = _____ cups per day

_____ cups per day x 365 days ÷ 16 cups per gallon = _____ gallons per year

Materials needed:
• *clock*
• *measuring cup with graduations on the side*

Answers for "Test Your Reading"

1. d
2. e
3. e
4. a
5. c
6. b
7. c
8. b
9. b   *(Total: 9 points)*

Comments on "Extra Activities"

1. This activity could be profitably used to introduce the lesson. As the students see the water rushing out of the hole, ask, "What is making the water rush out of the hole? How could we make it shoot out farther?" (Make the water deeper or blow into the can.) "Which would make the water shoot farther, a wider can or a taller can?" Do not necessarily answer all their questions now, but stimulate their curiosity.

   The squirting length becomes shorter. As the water level falls, the pressure becomes less.

——— Test Your Reading ———

Choose the word that best finishes each sentence. Write the letter on your paper. You will use one letter twice.

1. Water, plants, and people have
2. The weight of water causes
3. The deeper the water, the greater the
4. People cannot live in the deep
5. Water pressure can push water
6. In some cities, water pressure comes from a

   a. ocean
   b. water tower
   c. uphill
   d. weight
   e. pressure

Choose the best ending for each sentence. Write the letter on your paper.

7. Your weight means
   (a) how big you are.
   (b) how strong you are.
   (c) how heavy you are.
8. Water pressure is greatest in the bottom of a full
   (a) pie plate.
   (b) bucket.
   (c) water glass.
9. A good water tower must be
   (a) strong and round.
   (b) strong and high.
   (c) round and wide.

Extra Activities

Do these activities as your teacher directs.

1. You can learn about water pressure for yourself. Punch a hole near the bottom of a gallon jug or can. Set the can on a low stool. Place a pan so that it will catch the water. Now fill the can with water. Measure how far the water squirts out of the hole. As the water keeps coming, keep measuring. Does the squirting length become longer, shorter, or stay the same? Why?
   Materials needed:
   • *gallon plastic jug or metal can*
   • *something to punch a hole (such as a hammer and nail or a compass point)*
   • *low stool*   • *pan*
   • *water*   • *ruler*
2. You might enjoy learning more about divers or submarines. Look up "Diving, Underwater" or "Submarine" in the *World Book Encyclopedia.* Give an oral report to the class.

QUIZ

Weight or Pressure?

Read the sentences and have the students write *W* or *P.*

1. You step on a scales to find it.   *(W)*
2. You feel it when you put your hands in water to wash them.   *(P)*
3. It is the force of water.   *(P)*
4. It is the downward force of anything.   *(W)*
5. The deeper the water, the greater it is.   *(P)*
6. It makes water rush out of a hole in a water pipe.   *(P)*
7. You feel it when you lift a bucket of water. *(W)*
8. You feel it when you put your thumb on the end of a garden hose.   *(P)*

Water Can Destroy

New Words

canyon (kan′ yən), a deep valley with steep, rocky sides.

contour plowing (kon′ tür plou′ ing), plowing around hills.

cover crop (kuv′ ər krop), a crop that covers the ground and holds soil well.

erosion (i • rō′ zhən), the wearing away of land by water.

flood (flud), much water over what was dry land.

gully (gul′ ē), a deep ditch dug by water erosion.

Reading Together

What happened in the picture above? Is the water helping people? You have learned how water helps us, but the same water can also destroy.

Too much water at once makes a *flood.* A flood ruins crops and good land. It can wreck a whole town. A flash flood can destroy a house in seconds. It can hurt many animals and people. Floods help us respect the power of water.

31

Lesson 6

CONCEPTS TO TEACH

- Floods destroy crops, animals, people, and buildings.
- One time God destroyed the world with a great flood because of man's sin.
- Erosion carries soil away.
- Erosion can form deep gullies, badlands, and canyons.
- Careless men can cause erosion by plowing too much land or by plowing up and down the hills.
- Good farmers practice contour plowing and plant cover crops to reduce erosion.

Note: Tell the students that man's greed has led him to use careless farming practices that have been responsible for much harmful erosion. Ask them whether they have seen a muddy river or stream. Explain that all the soil that makes the streams muddy is washed away, never to return to the land. (The water returns by the water cycle, but there is no soil cycle.) Emphasize the importance of taking care of our soil.

HELPS FOR THE TEACHER

Introducing the Lesson

Begin class by discussing floods. You may even have a newspaper clipping of a recent flood to show. Explain that floods are not usually mysterious, unexplainable events. Inland floods are often caused by an unusually large amount of rainfall or snowmelt. Floods on islands and coastal areas are often caused by storms, earthquakes, and volcanoes. Emphasize God's control over all these natural forces. You may read Scriptures, such as Psalm 148:8 or Nahum 1:3.

You might also show pictures of the Grand Canyon and/or some badlands. The contrast between the height of people and the size of huge canyons can help the students understand the even greater contrast between God's power and man's frailty.

Water can be powerful, but God is always greater. Do you remember how God saved Noah in the great Flood? He also used the same flood-waters to destroy the rest of the world. God destroyed it because of man's sinfulness. He used water to do His will.

Today God still uses water to do His will. Floods may destroy many houses, but we know that God is still greater than floods. Our faithful God is able to save us from them. And we know that God promised Noah that He would never again destroy the whole earth with a flood. "The waters shall no more become a flood to destroy all flesh" (Genesis 9:15).

A flood can ruin land in a very short time. But there is another way in which land is ruined. It happens quietly right before our eyes. Often it happens so slowly that we do not notice. What is it?

Did you ever see a muddy stream in the springtime? After a hard rain, did you ever notice little ditches cut into the land? You were seeing some *erosion.*

The raindrops hit the ground. Some water soaked in, but the rest knocked off bits of soil. The water ran off, picking up more bits of soil as it went. This made the ditches that you saw. The more hilly the land was, the more ditches that were made.

The water carries the soil to streams. The streams carry some of the soil to rivers. The rivers dump some of the soil into the ocean. You learned in Lesson 4 that the water will return as rain, but the soil will not return to the land.

Does erosion matter? We barely notice it. But if the land were not protected, a farm could be ruined in this way. Erosion can carry away many truckloads of soil from a farm in a year! Yes, erosion does matter.

Badlands of South Dakota

Mention that we do not know when God formed the canyons, whether at the Creation or at the Flood. Either time would show God's power.

Discuss the significance of the flood of Noah's time. Explain that proud, wicked men needed to be punished. They needed to realize that God is Lord of all creation.

Materials needed:
• *newspaper clipping of a flood*
• *pictures of Grand Canyon and some badlands*

Extra Information

Did you know—

. . . that in 1937, the greatest flood in United States history killed over 135 people, left about a million people homeless, and destroyed about $400 million worth of property in the Ohio and Mississippi river valleys?

. . . that waves in a volcano-caused flood at a seacoast have measured 50 feet high?

. . . that in one test, a bare field lost 65 tons of soil per acre while a nearby woods lost only four pounds per acre?

. . . that the best soil protection is to leave natural plant life untouched?

. . . that erosion causes the gorge of Niagara Falls to move upstream, sometimes up to six feet a year?

Field Trip

Today would be a good time for a field trip or hike. If this is practical for you, you could show erosion in a nearby field, on a streambank, or under a waterspout. You could pour a bucket of water on an exposed bank to show how even a little water can move much soil.

Reading on Your Own

If erosion happens all the time, why do we still have so many farms? Most farms lose only a little soil. The soil is protected with plants. The plant leaves and roots keep the soil safe.

But in some areas, the land has few plants. Erosion causes little ditches to become bigger and wider. We call a big ditch a *gully.* If the gully becomes very wide and deep, we call it a *canyon.*

One beautiful canyon is the Grand Canyon. It looks like a great big crack in the earth. In some places, it is over a mile deep and eighteen miles wide. We do not know how God made the Grand Canyon. Canyons may have been formed during the Flood in Noah's time. The heavy rains and great floodwaters would have caused much erosion.

Badlands are other areas of wasted land. Erosion has cut deep gullies into thousands of acres of land. Although the shapes look interesting, the land can never be used to grow crops. That is why they are called badlands. They are bad for growing crops.

Men could not begin to make canyons and badlands into good land again. They cannot make the rivers bring back the soil they carried away. But they can protect the soil they still have. If men had always taken good care of the soil, they would have more good land for their crops today.

How can farmers take care of their land? First, good farmers do not plow too much land at once. A heavy rain could wash away the newly plowed soil.

Instead of plowing one big field, the farmer plows his field in different strips. Another crop such as hay or wheat grows next to the plowed strips. If the rain washes soil from the bare, plowed ground, the strips of hay or wheat will catch the soil. This is called strip-cropping.

In a bare field, the farmer may also plant a *cover crop.* Cover crops do not grow in rows like corn and beans. The plants spread all over the field. Their strong, thick roots hold the soil tightly. Hay and wheat are examples of cover crops.

Unit Project

The directions for constructing a miniature "water world" are given on pages 15 and 16 in this teacher's guide. This unit project can now be used to demonstrate various principles of erosion and its prevention.

Push the twigs upside-down into the soil of one of the hillsides. They are pretend roots. Scatter the small leaves over the hill to cover any bare spots. On another hill, leave the soil bare.

With a sprinkling can, rain the same amount of water on one hill at a time. Dip the extra water out of the "ocean" between sprinklings. Which hill loses more soil? Explain why.

Practice "contour plowing" in your water world. Make deep furrows across one hill with a pencil. Make furrows up and down the side of another hill. With the sprinkling can, rain the same amount of water on one hill at a time. Which hill loses more soil? Why?

Try some "strip-cropping" in your water world. Put pieces of sponge or moss in strips across a bare hill. To keep them in place, push broken toothpicks through them into the soil. Now make it rain with the sprinkling can. Do the sponge or moss strips help catch the soil? Of course, roots work even better in a real field.

A pretend flood can happen in your water world. First, place some of the houses close to the ocean and some in the hills. Then use the sprinkling can to make a fast rain. Keep pouring water until it floods some of the houses. Could you have done anything to keep the water away from the houses? ("Stop the rain" does not count, because people cannot stop rain in real life.) If this were real, what would the people in the houses do? How would they feel? Have the students tell or write a story about it. Study "Floods" in *The World Book Encyclopedia* to help you.

Materials needed:
• *about 8 small twigs with forks*
• *small leaves or pieces of large leaves*

Good farmers also plow around the hills. This is called *contour plowing.* If they would plow up and down the hills, the soil would wash away much faster.

If a field is too hilly, a farmer may not plow it at all. He may use it for pasture for his cattle. Then the grass will hold the soil. Good farmers want to take care of God's gift of soil.

Answers for "Test Your Reading"

1. When we have too much water at once
2. Because of man's sinfulness
3. Erosion happens when running water washes away soil.
4. Plant roots and leaves
5. By leaving land bare or by plowing too much land at once
6. Plant cover crops, plow around hills (contour plowing), and practice strip-cropping (3)
7. yes
8. yes
9. no
10. no   *(Total: 12 points)*

Comments on "Extra Activity"

The soil cannot all be shaken off, because the roots hold it very tightly.

——————————— **Test Your Reading** ———————————

How well did you read your lesson? Answer these questions that test your understanding.

1. When is water a danger?
2. Why did God destroy the world with a flood?
3. How does erosion happen?
4. What helps keep the soil from washing away?
5. How can farmers waste land?
6. How can farmers protect the soil? Name three ways.

Write yes *or* no *for each sentence below.*

7. Floods destroy crops, animals, buildings, and people.
8. Gullies are formed by erosion.
9. Badlands and the Grand Canyon make good farmland.
10. Corn and beans are cover crops.

Extra Activity

Do this activity as your teacher directs.

Would you like to see how tightly roots hold the soil? Dig up a small weed, carefully keeping the soil with the roots. Try shaking off all the soil from the roots of the weed. Can you do it? Why not? Soak the roots in a glass of water. When the soil has been carefully washed away, hold the roots against a piece of black paper. Use a magnifying glass to look at them. Can you see the tiny roots and the many root hairs that hold tightly to the soil?

Materials needed:
• *glass of water*
• *black paper*
• *magnifying glass*
• *small weed, carefully dug out with soil on roots*

• *sprinkling can with fine holes*
• *small cup or dipper*
• *pencil or sharp stick*
• *pieces of sponge or moss*
• *toothpicks*

QUIZ

Ask the students to use their New Words for this quiz. Some are used more than once.

1. It happens every time it rains. *(erosion)*
2. It can cause much damage to houses and people. *(flood)*
3. It is a deep and beautiful valley. *(canyon)*
4. It means plowing around hills. *(contour plowing)*
5. It is a big ditch caused by erosion. *(gully)*
6. It removes much soil from the land. *(erosion)*
7. It is a field of plants that hold the soil well. *(cover crop)*
8. It can teach people their weakness and God's greatness. *(flood or canyon)*

Water Pushes Up

New Words

ark (ark), a large ship.

buoyant force (boi′ ənt fôrs), the upward force of water.

cubit (kū′ bit), a Bible measure of length about 18 inches long or
   1/2 meter.

float (flōt), to be held up by water.

sink (singk), to go down in water.

Reading Together

Does the title of this lesson seem strange to you? In Lesson 5, you learned that water pushes down. How can it push up at the same time?

If you push a wooden block under the water and then let go of it, the block will be pushed back up to the top. You know that you did not push it up. What made it come up?

You learned in Lesson 5 that water pushes on things under water. You learned that the push of water is called pressure. The deeper the water, the greater the pressure. This pressure is not only pushing down on the top of the block, but it is also pushing up on the bottom. The bottom of the block is deeper than the top of the block. So there is more pressure pushing up on the bottom than down on the top. This extra push on the bottom is what makes

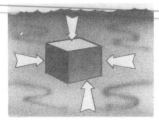

the wooden block come to the top.

This force of water pushing up is called **buoyant force**. Anything in water will be pushed up by buoyant force. Sometimes the buoyant force is more than the weight of the object. Then the object will be forced to the top. This is what happened to the wooden block. We say that the object **floats** when the buoyant force makes it come to the top of the water.

35

Lesson 7

CONCEPTS TO TEACH

- The upward force of water is called buoyant force.
- Objects float because of this upward force.
- An object sinks if the upward force is less than its weight.
- Boats and ships are held up by buoyant force.
- To carry a heavy load, a boat must have a wide bottom surface.
- God knew how large the ark would need to be to safely carry Noah, his family, the animals, and enough food.

HELPS FOR THE TEACHER

Introducing the Lesson

This lesson can be among the most interesting to students because it deals with objects and forces they can see and feel. However, it will be more difficult for some students to grasp because of its technical concepts. For this reason, concrete illustrations are especially good to use in teaching the lesson.

As you read the lesson together, stop occasionally to illustrate with a bowl of water and a wooden block. Let the students feel the water pushing the block upward. Try to float various objects, such as paper clips, erasers, and crayons. Compare the floating of cork, Styrofoam, wood, and ice. Which has the most volume above water? Which has the least?

Give them some idea of the size of Noah's ark, even if you cannot do Activity 4. You could show a cubit's length on a yardstick and then measure the chalkboard in cubits. Measure the length of

You know that not everything will float. If you put a stone in the water, it will go all the way to the bottom. This is because the stone weighs more than the buoyant force. Objects that weigh more than the buoyant force will **sink**. The water is still pushing up on the stone, but the stone weighs more than the upward force.

A stone sinks, but wood floats. Why?

Reading on Your Own

You could probably name many things that will float: Styrofoam, wax, and ice. You can name many more things that will sink: rubber, iron, glass, and lead. Does plastic float? A simple test will give you the answer. Drop some plastic in the water to see if it will float.

The ships that float on the ocean are made of iron. Of course, iron itself will sink. But the ships that are made of iron float. How can that be? The iron ships are made hollow with a lot of air space on the inside. The ships are made to take up a lot of space. This makes a lot of buoyant force when they are in the water. The buoyant force is more than the weight of the ship and all the people in it, and so it floats.

Sometimes a ship gets a hole in its bottom. Then the water comes in and begins filling up the empty space. If the men on the ship cannot stop the leak and remove the water faster than it comes in, the ship will become so heavy with water that it will sink. The captain of a big ship tries not to hit anything that will make a hole in his ship. He wants his ship to float and not to sink.

You have learned about buoyant force, but God knew all about it long ago. He told Noah how to build a large ship called an **ark**. Noah obediently built the ark. It was three hundred cubits long, fifty cubits wide, and thirty cubits high. One *cubit* equals about eighteen inches or one-half meter. Today we would say that the ark measured 450 feet (150 meters) long, 75 feet (25 meters) wide, and 45 feet (15 meters) high.

God knew how much buoyant force the ark would need. He made sure that its size would make enough buoyant force so that it would float. God told Noah to cover the inside and the outside of the ark with pitch. Pitch helped to seal the wood and the cracks so that the water could not leak in.

The ark carried Noah, his family, and their food and clothes for a year. Besides that, the ark carried hundreds of animals and all their food for that year. It must have weighed thousands of pounds, but it floated. The ark kept them safe during the long flood. How glad Noah must have been that he built the ark the way God had told him!

the schoolhouse in cubits. Then tell the students how many times longer the ark was.

Materials needed:
- *bowl of water*
- *wooden block*
- *various "floaters" and "sinkers"*

Extra Information
Did you know—

. . . that at one time, a cubit was the length from a man's elbow to the tip of his middle finger?

. . . that the largest tanker ships, over 1,000 feet long, are more than twice as long as Noah's ark?

. . . that steel ships replaced wooden ships because they were safer, stronger, and actually lighter?

How can a huge iron boat float?

──────── Test Your Reading ────────

Fill each blank with a word from your lesson.
1. The upward force of water is called ── ──.
2. The ── on the bottom of a wooden block in water is greater than the pressure on the top.
3. A stone sinks because the buoyant force is ── than its weight.
4. A ship's size must be ── enough for it to float.
5. Noah's large ship was called an ──.
6. The ark was planned by ──.

Choose the best ending for each sentence. Write the letter on your paper.
7. *Float* means
   (a) to go down in water.
   (b) to go up in water.
   (c) to be held up by water.
8. *Sink* means
   (a) to go down in water.
   (b) to go up in water.
   (c) to be held up by water.
9. Iron can float if
   (a) it has enough empty space inside.
   (b) it is small enough.
   (c) it does not have a hole in it.
10. A cubit is about (choose two)
   (a) 18 inches.   (d) 2 meters.
   (b) 28 inches.   (e) 1 1/2 meters.
   (c) 38 inches.   (f) 1/2 meter.

Answers for "Test Your Reading"
1. buoyant force
2. pressure
3. less
4. big
5. ark
6. God
7. c
8. a
9. a
10. a, f   *(Total: 11 points)*

QUIZ

Have the students say or write the New Word they think of when you give the phrases below.
1. Eighteen inches or one-half meter   *(cubit)*
2. A ship   *(ark)*
3. Pushes up   *(buoyant force)*
4. Held up by water   *(float)*
5. Goes down in water   *(sink)*
6. Makes things float in water   *(buoyant force)*

Comments on "Extra Activities"

1. You can float more marbles by using a bigger cup.

2. The stone will feel lighter when it enters the water.

3. The aluminum foil is no heavier; it only takes up less space. The aluminum foil sank because it was too small to cause enough buoyant force. This is a striking demonstration of the fact that buoyancy is determined by density, not by weight.

4. You could also measure the length of the schoolhouse and compare its length with the length of the ark.

Extra Activities

Do these activities as your teacher directs.

1. You can see buoyant force at work. Put enough marbles into a paper cup until it floats upright in a big bowl of water. Then add one marble at a time, and notice how the cup sinks deeper each time you add a marble. When the weight of the marbles is more than the buoyant force, the cup sinks. How could you make even more marbles float?

   Materials needed:
   * *paper cup*   * *large bowl*
   * *marbles*   * *water*

2. You can feel buoyant force in action. Tie a string onto a stone weighing about one pound. Hold the stone by the string, and close your eyes. Then have a friend bring a small bucket of water up under the stone. Can you feel when the stone enters the water? Does buoyant force make the stone feel heavier or lighter?

   Materials needed:
   * *string*   * *bucket*
   * *one-pound stone*   * *water*

3. Do you want to see more buoyant force in action? Shape a sheet of aluminum foil into a boat. Fold the corners together tightly so that water cannot get in. Float the boat in a bowl of water. Then squeeze the boat into a ball. See how it floats deeper? Next, step on it a few times, and then float it. Last, pound it with a hammer. Make it so flat that it will sink. Is it heavier now than it was at first? Why does it sink?

   Materials needed:
   * *aluminum foil*   * *water*
   * *large bowl*   * *hammer*

4. Would you like to see how big Noah's ark was? With your teacher's help, go outdoors and make a rectangle 450 feet (150 meters) long and 75 feet (25 meters) wide. Drive a stake or place a large rock in each corner to show the size of the ark. Ask your teacher about how many feet or meters high your school building is. Then compare the height of your school building with the height of the ark, which was 45 feet (15 meters). Can you imagine a boat that big?

   Materials needed: * *hammer*
   * *4 stakes*   * *50-foot tape measure or string*

Lesson 8

Do You Remember What You Learned?

Match the letter that finishes the sentence best.

1. To dissolve
2. To melt
3. A solution
4. To boil
5. A liquid
6. To freeze
7. A cycle

   a. changes shape but not size.
   b. means to change a solid to a liquid.
   c. means to change a liquid to a solid.
   d. means to change a liquid to a gas.
   e. means to mix something with water until it disappears.
   f. happens again and again.
   g. is a clear liquid mixture.

Match the letter that finishes the sentence best.

8. State
9. A solid
10. Ice
11. A gas
12. Steam
13. Property

   h. keeps its size and shape.
   i. changes both size and shape.
   j. tells what something is like.
   k. tells how something acts in size and shape.
   l. is a gas.
   m. is solid water.

Decide whether each sentence is true, and write yes *or* no.

14. All solutions are clear.
15. Good taste is a property of water.
16. We drink solid water.
17. Different solids melt with different amounts of heating.
18. The water cycle keeps the rivers flowing and supplies us with fresh water.
19. Water in the air cools and makes clouds.
20. A tall water tower increases the buoyant force.
21. Water pressure can push water uphill.
22. The Flood came because of man's sinfulness.
23. Much erosion happens on bare soil.
24. A ship floats because of buoyant force.
25. The cooler the water, the faster it evaporates.

39

ANSWER KEY

Match

1. e
2. b
3. g
4. d
5. a
6. c
7. f
8. k
9. h
10. m
11. i
12. l
13. j

Decide

14. yes
15. yes
16. no
17. yes
18. yes
19. yes
20. no
21. yes
22. yes
23. yes
24. yes
25. no

Lesson 8

Spend this class period in reviewing vocabulary words and key concepts, as given in "Concepts to Teach." Quizzes related to areas of student weakness could also be repeated.

Although you may do some reviewing as a class, the students should know how to review on their own. Refer to "How to Study for a Test" on page 5 of the textbook (page 11 of this manual). Ask the students to memorize the key words given in italics and listed at the beginning of the lessons. Encourage them to go through these steps for every test that they take.

Fill
26. sink
27. float
28. cover crop
29. contour plowing
30. weight
31. ark
32. Canyon
33. flood
34. buoyant force
35. cubit
36. Evaporation
37. Erosion
38. Condensation
39. gully
40. Pressure

Choose
41. b
42. a
43. c
44. a

Fill the blanks with a word or phrase from the box.

ark	cover crop	flood
buoyant force	cubit	gully
canyon	erosion	pressure
condensation	evaporation	sink
contour plowing	float	weight

26. A penny will ——— because the upward force of the water is less than the weight of the penny.
27. A ship will ——— if its size will cause enough buoyant force.
28. A ——— ——— is spread all over a field.
29. A wise farmer practices ——— ——— on his hilly fields.
30. Your ——— tells how heavy you are.
31. God taught Noah how to build the ———.
32. We could not farm in the Grand ———.
33. Too much water causes a ———.
34. Things in water are pushed up by ——— ———.
35. A ——— is about 18 inches long.
36. ——— is water going into the air.
37. ——— is soil wearing away.
38. ——— is water coming out of the air.
39. A big ditch is a ———.
40. ——— is the force of water.

Choose the best answer.

41. All living things need
    (a) ice.   (b) water.   (c) milk.
42. The state of water is changed
    (a) by heating or cooling it.
    (b) by pouring it.
    (c) by making solutions with it.
43. When enough heat is added to liquid water, it changes to
    (a) clouds.   (b) ice.   (c) steam.
44. If water in the ocean would not evaporate, we would have no
    (a) rain.
    (b) buoyant force.
    (c) pressure.

45. The weight of water makes
    (a) erosion.   (b) pressure.   (c) floods.
46. Many animals cannot live at the bottom of the ocean because
    (a) the water pressure is too great there.
    (b) the water pressure causes too much buoyant force there.
    (c) the water pressure is not great enough there.
47. Gullies and badlands are caused by
    (a) pressure.   (b) erosion.   (c) evaporation.
48. A huge, deep gully is a
    (a) cycle.   (b) canyon.   (c) cubit.
49. Good farmers
    (a) plow much land at once.
    (b) plow up and down hills.
    (c) plow around hills.
50. Water pressure would be greatest
    (a) under 100 feet of water.
    (b) under 10 feet of water.
    (c) under 50 feet of water.

Write the answers.

51-54. Name four uses of water.
55-59. Name five places God put water.
60-63. Label the picture of the water cycle. Use these words: *ocean, evaporation, clouds,* and *condensation.*

45. b
46. a
47. b
48. b
49. c
50. a

Write

51-54. (Any four) drinking, washing, making things, making solutions, putting out fires (*4 points*)
55-59. (Any five) sky or clouds, ground (spring or well), streams, rivers, lakes, oceans (*5 points*)
60. clouds
61. condensation
62. evaporation
63. ocean   (*4 points*)

(*Total: 63 points*)

Unit Two

God Gave Us the Materials We Need

"Make thee an ark of gopher wood . . . and . . . pitch it within and without with pitch" (Genesis 6:14).

Suppose everything were hard as a rock. The rain would be hard. Your clothes would be hard. Even your food would be hard! How awful it would be to live in such a hard world.

What if everything were soft? Your pencil would be soft. The table would be soft. The floor would be soft. The whole house would be soft! No, that would not work either. The house would tumble down. The floor would not hold you up.

What if everything were sticky or crumbly? You would not like it at all. God knew that you needed the things in your world to be different from each other.

In this unit, you will study some materials that God has given to us. Each has its own special properties. Some materials are hard. Some are soft. Some things are usually solids. Some are usually liquids. Others are gases. God gave us all these different materials. He created the different properties of these materials.

You will also learn how Noah used materials. He used wood that had the properties of being strong and easily cut. The pitch he used was sticky and would seal out water. God provided these materials to help save Noah and his family from the Flood.

Noah was blessed when he used God's materials right. We are happy, too, when we use materials carefully. If we are thankful for God's materials, we will not waste them.

42

Unit Two
God Gave Us the Materials We Need

For Your Inspiration

"In the beginning God created the heaven and the earth. . . . And God saw every thing that he had made, and, behold, it was very good" (Genesis 1:1, 31).

How glibly we can quote these simple statements. But within the span of these two verses, God created *every* material in our earth. He created—

. . . dozens of different metals with various properties of strength and electrical conductivity.

. . . hundreds of different kinds of rocks and minerals, choosing each color combination and degree of hardness.

. . . 20,000 different kinds of trees, designing each tree's leaf, flower, fruit, and wood-grain pattern.

. . . vast coal and petroleum deposits and their countless possibilities for useful fuels and products.

. . . 326 million cubic miles of water plus the components of every other liquid.

. . . billions of tons of air, natural gas, and every other gas, with their diversity of properties and uses.

These materials alone are sufficient to inspire awe in our hearts, not to mention the thousands of different animals. And think of man, the most intricate of God's earthly creation. How infinitely creative is the mind of our God!

Wood Is a Useful Material

New Words

bark (bärk), the rough covering on trees.

grain (grān), the lines and markings in wood.

hardwood (härd' wood), wood from trees with flat leaves.

lumber (lum' bər), wood that is cut into boards for building.

pulpwood (pulp' wood), wood that is chopped into small pieces for making paper.

softwood (sôft' wood), wood from trees with needlelike leaves.

Reading Together

You see it every day. It is strong. You can burn it for fuel. You can paint it. You can cut it. You can pound nails into it. What is it?

It is wood! We use wood to build houses. We use wood for toothpicks, pencils, and fence posts. Special parts of wood are used to make medicines, paint, soap, and even cloth!

Wood is classed into two groups: *softwood* and *hardwood.* As you might think, most hardwood is harder than softwood. It is easier to drive nails into softwood than into hardwood.

Trees such as pine, cedar, and redwood give us softwood. These trees have needlelike leaves. They usually grow cones. They are sometimes called evergreen trees because they keep their leaves all year.

Trees such as oak, maple, and walnut give us hardwood. Hardwood trees have broad, flat leaves. They usually lose their leaves in autumn. Hardwood trees have flowers and fruit.

43

Lesson 1

CONCEPTS TO TEACH

- The kind of wood is determined by the kind of tree it comes from.
- The grain of wood is its pattern of lines and markings.
- The evergreen trees like pine, cedar, and redwood give us softwood.
- The broadleaf trees like oak, maple, and walnut give us hardwood.
- Wood has many properties, such as ease of cutting, fastening, and finishing, that make it ideal for building.
- Lumber comes from the trunk and limbs of trees.
- Pulpwood is wood that is cut into small pieces to make paper.
- The bark of trees is used to tan leather.
- God wisely instructed Noah to use gopher wood to make the ark.

HELPS FOR THE TEACHER

Introducing the Lesson

Ask the students to open their books to the beginning of Unit Two. Read the introduction together, and discuss the picture and its meaning. Now turn to Lesson 1 and notice its title. Tell them that they are touching something made of wood right now (the book), and see if they can guess what it is. Ask them to name other things in the classroom that are made of wood.

If you live in the eastern United States or in Canada, tell your students that long ago, most of the land they can see was covered with trees. The early settlers burned many trees to clear the land. Stress the importance of taking good care of our remaining forests. Point out that people who carelessly start forest fires cannot be very thankful for God's gift of trees. You may also discuss some picnic rules, such as not littering, and making sure all fires are put out before leaving the picnic area.

Both softwood and hardwood trees are sawed into boards. The boards are called *lumber.* Softwood lumber is used to build the frames of houses and other buildings. It is also used to make boxes and poles. Some softwood is good for cupboards, chests, and other furniture.

Hardwood lumber often has a beautiful *grain.* The grain of wood is its lines and markings. Wood grain is caused by the way a tree grows. Each year a new ring of growth is added to the wood of the tree. When the tree is sawed into boards, the rings make lines or grain in the wood.

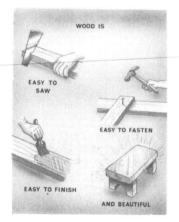

Wood grain comes from growth rings.

Because of its hardness and grain, hardwood is used to make fine furniture, floors, and paneling. Hardwood also makes strong baseball bats and tool handles.

Reading on Your Own

Making lumber is an important business. Many people are needed to do all the work. Trees must be cut down. The logs must be cut into lumber. Different sizes of lumber must be sorted. The right kind and amount of lumber must be made ready for each buyer.

Why do people keep using so much lumber? Why do builders like to work with wood? They like wood because of its good properties.

First, wood is easy to cut and shape. Did you ever saw wood? Maybe you thought it was hard work. But think of cutting rocks or steel! Wood is cut much more easily than rocks or steel.

Wood pieces are easy to fasten together too. Nails, screws, and bolts

Extra Information

Did you know—

. . . that the famous General Sherman Tree in Sequoia National Park in California contains at least 600,000 board feet of lumber?

. . . that some bristlecone pine trees are believed to be at least 4,000 years old?

. . . that the world's tallest trees are 360-foot redwoods (as tall as four 90-foot silos stacked on top of each other)?

. . . that hardwood trees conserve water when they shed their leaves? Leaves give a tree a much larger surface for evaporation. By shedding its leaves, a tree loses much less water.

Bulletin Board

Is it time for another bulletin board? Entitle this one *A Tree Gives Us Many Good Things.* Draw a softwood tree big enough to cover most of the bulletin board. (A softwood tree is better for this than a hardwood tree because softwood has a greater variety of uses.) Put pictures, signs, or small wood products on each part of the tree. They should show the use of that particular part. For example, put pictures of furniture on the trunk and biggest branches; put a small bottle of glue on the bark. Find "Forest Products" in *The World Book Encyclopedia* to help you. Include appropriate Scripture verses, such as Psalm 104:16, Psalm 1:3, or Matthew 7:17.

fasten wood well. Wood can also be glued together.

Last of all, wood is easy to finish. You can paint it any color you wish. Or maybe you want the pretty wood grain to show. Then you stain the wood, and brush a shiny sealer on top.

Lumber for building comes from the trunk and big limbs of a tree. But what happens to the smaller branches, the sawdust, and the *bark*? Must they be wasted?

No, the scrap wood can be used to make many useful things. A special material made from bark is used to tan leather. Sawdust can be used to make glue and plastics.

Both scrapwood and whole trees are used to make *pulpwood.* Pulpwood is wood that is finely chopped.

It is used to make paper. In fact, pulpwood was used to make the paper for this page.

People use very much paper. Because of this, the pulpwood business has become very important. Only the lumber business uses more wood than the pulpwood business.

Noah may not have used paper, but he did use wood. God told Noah, "Make thee an ark of gopher wood."

What was gopher wood? Some people think it was wood from a softwood tree. Gopher wood was probably easy to cut and fasten together. God knew that gopher wood was strong enough to carry the ark through the long flood. Noah used the kind of wood God chose, and he and his family were saved. God was glad that Noah obeyed.

Test Your Reading

Number your paper from 1 to 12. Choose the best answer. Write the letter beside the matching number.

1. The lines and markings in wood	a. softwood
2. Wood from a pine tree	b. pulpwood
3. Wood from an oak tree	c. hardwood
4. Boards cut from trees	d. lumber
5. Wood used for making paper	e. bark
6. The outside covering of a tree	f. grain

If a sentence below is true, write yes. *If it is not true, write* no.

7. Wood is used to make some cloth.
8. Hardwood trees have needles and cones.
9. Wood is easy to cut and finish.
10. Lumber is made from sawdust.
11. More wood is used to make paper than to make lumber.
12. Noah used gopher wood to build the ark.

Answers for "Test Your Reading"

1. f
2. a
3. c
4. d
5. b
6. e
7. yes
8. no
9. yes
10. no
11. no
12. yes   *(Total: 12 points)*

QUIZ

Write the New Words on the chalkboard. Ask the students to say or write the word they think of when you give the phrases below.

1. Trees with needles   (*softwood*)
2. Markings in wood   (*grain*)
3. Boards   (*lumber*)
4. Wood used for making paper   (*pulpwood*)
5. Trees with leaves   (*hardwood*)
6. Outside covering of a tree   (*bark*)

Comments on "Extra Activities"

1. Use your own judgment as to the students' ability to use a hammer by themselves. If they drive the nails, emphasize the need for consistence: they should hold each nail straight and always hit with the same amount of force. Have extra nails available to use if the first ones become crooked or bent.

   The results of this activity may be added to the display for Unit Two, suggested in Activity 3.

Extra Activities

Do these activities as your teacher directs.

1. You can test the hardness of different kinds of wood. Get pieces of four or five different kinds of wood. Ask someone older to help you drive a nail into each piece. Hit each nail three times. Then compare the pieces of wood. Which nail went the farthest into the wood? That wood is the softest. By looking at the nails, put the pieces of wood in order from the softest to the hardest.
   Materials needed: • *hammer*
   • *different kinds of wood scraps*   • *nails about 2" long*

2. Your family or your class could visit a lumberyard, a cabinet shop, or a paper mill. Tell or write what you see and learn.

3. Here is your project for Unit Two. Make a display of the materials discussed in each lesson. Hang up a large sign that says *God Gave Us Good Materials.*

   For this lesson, make a display about wood. Try to find many kinds of things made from wood to put on a shelf or table. Your lesson can give you some ideas. Also find "Forest Products" in the *World Book Encyclopedia* for more ideas. To show big things, such as furniture, ships, or buildings, look for pictures in catalogs, calendars, or magazines. Glue the pictures onto a large sheet of paper to make a poster. At the top of the poster, write "Wood Is a Very Useful Solid."

   If a cabinet shop or lumberyard is nearby, perhaps you could get different kinds of wood from their scraps. Label each piece of wood like this:

   Maple   Cedar
   Hardwood or Softwood

   Materials needed: • *pictures of larger wood products*
   • *small wood products*   • *large sheet of paper*
   • *shelf or table*   • *different kinds of wood scraps*

4. Play a "wood memory" game. All the players form a line. The first person touches something wooden, like a door. Then he goes to the end of the line. The second person touches the door and another wooden thing, like a desk. He also goes to the end of the line. The third person touches the door, the desk, and another wooden thing, like a pencil. And so the game goes on and on. As soon as someone gets mixed up and touches the wrong thing, he is out of the game. The one who stays in the longest is the winner. (This activity could be used as a rainy day recess activity.)

Lesson 2

God Gave Us Many Useful Solids

"Iron is taken out of the earth, and brass is molten out of the stone" (Job 28:2).

New Words

aluminum (ə • loo′ mə • nəm), a plentiful, light-gray metal.

coal (kōl), a black rock burned as fuel.

copper (kop′ ər), a red-brown metal.

glass (glas), a clear material that breaks easily.

iron (ī′ ərn), a strong, silver-gray metal.

metal (met′ əl), a hard, shiny material.

mining (mīn′ ing), the work of digging coal or ore from the earth.

ore (ôr), rock or soil that has metal in it.

raw material (rô mə • tēr′ ē • əl), a material in the earth from which man makes the things he needs.

rock (rok), a hard, stony material.

Reading Together

Take a look around you. What do you see in your classroom? Do you see pencils and paper? Do you see walls and windows? Do you see desks and doors?

All of these things come from trees, sand, stones, and other *raw materials.* In fact, everything you have and use comes from raw materials. Raw materials are taken from the earth where God placed them. Men use these raw materials to make the things we need.

There are many materials in a classroom.

47

Lesson 2

CONCEPTS TO TEACH

- God created all materials.
- All the things we use are either raw materials or are made from raw materials.
- Coal is a raw material that is mined from the ground.
- Because coal will burn, it is useful as a fuel.
- Metals are taken from ores that are mined from the earth.
- Most metals are very hard and shiny.
- Iron is used to make strong bridges and buildings.
- Copper is used to make electric wire.
- Aluminum is used to make pans and ladders.
- Limestone, sandstone, and granite are examples of useful rocks that we get from the earth.
- Glass is made from limestone and sandstone.
- The properties of a material determine its usefulness.

Note: The main emphasis of this lesson should be that (1) everything we use has been made from materials that God created, and that (2) the uses of materials are determined by their properties.

HELPS FOR THE TEACHER

Introducing the Lesson

To illustrate the right and wrong use of metal, briefly relate two Bible stories. First, tell the story of the golden calf (Exodus 32) and then give the account of the serpent of brass (Numbers 21). The brass mentioned in the Bible was probably pure copper or copper mixed with tin.

Use this lesson to explain that all materials are good, but man chooses to use them for either right or wrong purposes. One example of this is a book. Men use the same kinds of paper and ink to make Bibles as they do to make books on witchcraft.

A car is made from many raw materials.

Some raw materials are used without being changed very much. Some *rocks* are crushed into small pieces. Then they are used to build roads. Log cabins are made from tree trunks cut to certain lengths. The rocks and logs are changed very little.

Other raw materials are changed very much. Think of a car. It is made of rock, wood, sand, sheep's wool, plant parts, and many other raw materials. These raw materials look very different from the finished car.

Cars are made by men. But God gave men the raw materials. He also gave them good minds. Men can only work with the gifts God gives them. They have studied the properties of different raw materials. They have learned how to change raw materials into useful machines, tools, furniture, and many other things.

Reading on Your Own

Did you know that black *coal* is a kind of rock? This plentiful material comes from deep in the earth. It is found between layers of other kinds of rock. Digging the coal out of the earth is called *mining.*

Coal gives much heat when we burn it. Sometimes it is used to heat houses, stores, and factories. But most coal that is burned provides power to make electricity.

Many of the things we use are made of *metal.* A metal is a very hard, shiny material that does not crumble or break easily. This makes it a very useful building material. Nails, bicycles, stoves, and tractors are made of metal. Because metals carry electricity, they are also used to make electric wire.

Like coal, metals are mined from the earth. But they do not come in

Extra Information
Did you know—

. . . that every person uses an average of 12 pounds of coal every day by using electricity, steel, plastic, and other products?

. . . that in the 1800s, aluminum was considered a very precious metal? A French emperor, Napoleon III, used aluminum tableware for his most important guests, while less honored guests used gold or silver cutlery.

. . . that today more iron is produced than any other metal? Aluminum is next in importance.

. . . that a special kind of concrete is so light that it will float? It is used in thermal insulation.

Nature Hike
If you have time, today might be a good day for a short nature hike. Ask the students to identify all the raw materials they can find. As they name raw materials, ask them to name products made with that particular material.

Examples:

rocks	clay (bricks, pottery)
sand	cotton
coal	sheep (wool)
cows (leather)	water (paper, plastic)
trees	

big lumps like coal. Metals are found in special rocks called *ore.* Different ores give us different metals. The metal called iron comes from iron ore. Copper comes from copper ore, and aluminum comes from aluminum ore.

Iron is an important building metal. It makes very strong bridges and buildings. Iron is also used to make knives, cooking pans, and many other things in our homes.

Do you have any pennies in your bank? If you do, you have some *copper.* Pennies are made of copper. The water pipes in your home might also be made of copper. Copper pipes do not rust like iron pipes do.

What else is special about copper? Though iron and most other metals have a silvery color, copper has a red-brown color. Copper also carries electricity better than most other metals. For this reason, most copper is made into electric wire. Electric motors have much copper wire inside them.

Another important metal is *aluminum.* Aluminum weighs less than copper or iron. Like copper, aluminum will not rust.

These properties make aluminum very useful. Aluminum makes strong, lightweight airplanes. Some farmers put aluminum roofs on their buildings. Builders use aluminum nails and aluminum siding. All of us use things made of aluminum in our homes. We use aluminum cake pans, ladders, baseball bats, aluminum foil, and many other things.

Things made of iron

Things made of copper

Things made of aluminum

QUIZ

Write the New Words on the chalkboard. Ask the students to say or write the word that is described by the phrases below.

1. Something that is hard and shiny   *(metal)*
2. Man makes things from it   *(raw material)*
3. A very strong metal   *(iron)*
4. A lightweight metal   *(aluminum)*
5. Rock with metal in it   *(ore)*
6. Digging solid material from the earth   *(mining)*
7. Stone   *(rock)*
8. A clear material that breaks easily   *(glass)*
9. A black, solid fuel   *(coal)*
10. A metal used to make electric wire   *(copper)*

Things made from rocks

As you have learned, metals come from special rocks. However, rocks themselves are also used as building materials. Like metal, most rocks will not burn. They are cut from the earth in big chunks.

Limestone and sandstone are two kinds of useful rock. Most limestone is gray; sandstone is often brown or yellow. Both have been used in the past to build houses. Both are crushed into small pieces and used to make concrete for sidewalks, streets, buildings, and bridges. Both are used to make **glass** for windows. Think of it—clear glass comes from rocks!

Granite is another very useful rock. It is even stronger than limestone and sandstone, and it is harder to cut. Granite is used in some heavy bridges and buildings.

Have you seen gravestones made of granite? The granite has pretty sparkles in it. It is often a reddish-brown or gray color. Granite makes good gravestones because it does not crumble easily. The writing on granite gravestones will not wear off for hundreds of years.

Rocks are important, but they do not make good wires. Metals would never make good fuels. Coal would not make good houses. No, each material has its own special properties. Each material's properties help us decide how to use it. God wants us to use these wonderful gifts wisely.

Answers for "Test Your Reading"

1. The *raw materials* which God placed in the earth are made into many useful things.
2. *Coal* is a rock that we can burn for heat.
3. *Mining* is taking coal or ore from the ground.
4. *Metals* are hard and shiny and can carry electricity.
5. Clear *glass* is made from sandstone and limestone.
6. Gravestones are made of *granite*.
7. The *properties* of a material help men decide its uses.

——————————— **Test Your Reading** ———————————

Copy each sentence below. Choose words from your lesson to fill the blanks.

1. The —— —— which God placed in the earth are made into many useful things.
2. —— is a rock that we can burn for heat.
3. —— is taking coal or ore from the ground.
4. —— are hard and shiny and can carry electricity.
5. Clear —— is made from sandstone and limestone.
6. Gravestones are made of ——.
7. The —— of a material help men decide its uses.

Which metal fits best with each sentence below? Write I *for iron,* C *for copper, and* A *for aluminum.*

8. It is a very lightweight metal.
9. It is used mostly for electric wires.
10. It makes strong buildings and bridges.
11. It will rust.
12. It has a red-brown color.
13. It is used to make airplanes.

8. A
9. C
10. I
11. I
12. C
13. A   *(Total: 13 points)*

Extra Activities

Do these activities as your teacher directs.

1. Do you live in an old house? Check your basement walls to see whether they are made of limestone or sandstone blocks. Ask your parents if you are not sure which kind of rock was used. Or you can do the limestone test in Activity 2.

2. You can know whether or not a rock is limestone. First, scrape off some grains of the rock. Make a little pile of them in a shallow dish. Then drop a little vinegar on the pile. If the rock is limestone, it will start to bubble. But the bubbles may be too tiny to see. Hold your ear close. Can you hear a fizzing sound? If you can, the rock is limestone.
   Materials needed:
   • *limestone rock*
   • *dull knife*
   • *small shallow dish*
   • *vinegar*

3. Visit an old graveyard. Can you tell which gravestones are made of granite? Granite has many little crystals of different colors. Try to find other gravestones with the writing almost worn off.

4. To add to your unit project, make a big sign that says: "We Need Many Solids." Make two smaller signs that say Made by God and Changed by Man. Then bring raw materials, such as rocks, coal, and soil. Also bring things such as glass, a spoon, a toy car, a toy airplane, copper wire, and a brick. On a small table or shelf, put your materials with the correct sign.
   Materials needed:
   • *poster board*
   • *various raw materials*
   • *various manufactured items*

Lesson 3

Petroleum Is a Useful Material

New Words

asphalt (as′ fôlt), a black, heavy material used to seal out water.
gasoline (gas′ ə • lēn), a light, clear liquid fuel.
oil (oil), a slippery liquid.
oil well (oil wel), a deep hole drilled in the earth to get petroleum.
petroleum (pə • trō′ lē • əm), a thick, oily liquid found in the earth.
plastic (plas′ tik), an easily shaped material.
refinery (ri fī′ nər • ē), a place where petroleum is changed into
    useful fuels, oils, and greases.

Reading Together

How are candles, soap, paint, and crayons alike? They look very different from each other. But all of them come from a special liquid God gave us. This dark, strong-smelling liquid is called *petroleum.*

Long ago, Noah used petroleum to seal the ark. God told him, "Make thee an ark . . . and . . . pitch it within and without with pitch." Pitch was a natural *asphalt* that came from petroleum. When the thick, sticky asphalt dried, it sealed the cracks between the boards of gopher wood. During the Flood, the asphalt or pitch kept Noah's family and the animals dry inside the ark.

Do you know the Bible story of Joseph? His jealous brothers sold

The Egyptians used petroleum to grease their chariot wheels.

him, and he became a servant in Egypt. After Joseph became a ruler, he rode in a chariot. The Egyptians greased their chariot wheels with petroleum.

The people long ago used much less petroleum than we use today. The little bit they used, they got near

52

Lesson 3

CONCEPTS TO TEACH

- The pitch that Noah used to waterproof the ark was a natural asphalt.
- Petroleum is a natural liquid that is a mixture of many liquids.
- Oil wells are drilled deep into the earth to get petroleum.
- The petroleum is separated into its parts at an oil refinery.
- Black asphalt from petroleum is used to make roads.
- Useful oils and greases come from petroleum.
- Useful fuels come from petroleum.
- Plastic is made from petroleum, coal, wood, and other raw materials.

HELPS FOR THE TEACHER

Introducing the Lesson

Are there any oil wells in your community? A sample of crude oil would make this lesson come alive to your students. Ask them to describe how it looks and smells.

Ask the class to notice the lesson title. Ask, "Is petroleum as a raw material a solid, a liquid, or a gas?" On the picture of the fractionating tower, show the students that things made of petroleum exist in all three states: solid, liquid, and gas. If possible, have samples of various products of petroleum: paraffin, asphalt, grease, oil, fuel oil, diesel fuel, kerosene, gasoline, or propane (ordinary bottled gas).

Use a globe to show the major oil reserves in the world. They include the Middle East, central Soviet Union, central North America, northwestern Africa, and western Europe.

the top of the ground. But most petroleum is trapped between rocks, far below us. Today deep holes are drilled into the earth to reach the petroleum. Such a hole is called an *oil well.* The petroleum is pumped up through metal pipes in the oil well.

Raw petroleum is a mixture of many liquids. Petroleum must be taken to a *refinery* before it becomes useful to us. There the different liquids are separated from each other.

Do you remember evaporation and condensation from Unit One? In an oil refinery, evaporation and condensation are very important because they separate petroleum into different liquids. Each liquid needs its own certain amount of heating to evaporate and its own certain amount of cooling to condense.

An oil well pump

Reading on Your Own

At the refinery, the petroleum is heated in a furnace connected to a tower. It is heated until most of it evaporates into a gas. But asphalt and the heaviest oil do not evaporate. They settle to the bottom of the tower. There, pipes carry them away. The oil and the asphalt are used to pave roads. They help keep water from getting under the road where it

An oil refinery

Materials needed:
- *sample of crude oil*
- *various petroleum products*
- *globe*

Extra Information
Did you know—

. . . that King Nebuchadnezzar used asphalt to join the bricks of the Great Wall of Babylon?

. . . that the Greek word *petra* ("rock") and the Latin word *oleum* ("oil") form our word *petroleum*?

. . . that the American Indians used oil as a remedy for illnesses?

. . . that in the 1800s when kerosene was the chief petroleum product, gasoline was considered a nuisance and was dumped into rivers?

. . . that one of the deepest oil wells ever drilled was 5 1/2 miles deep?

would freeze and break up the road. Asphalt roads are sometimes called blacktop roads.

As the petroleum gas rises in the tower, it starts to cool. The first to condense is a thick, heavy oil. This oil is used to help cars, tractors, and machines of all kinds to run smoothly.

The petroleum gas keeps rising toward the middle of the tower where it is cooler. There a lighter oil condenses. It is the fuel oil used to heat houses, schools, and other buildings.

A yet lighter fuel oil cools and condenses next. This oil is burned as fuel in trains, ships, and jet planes. You burn this oil too if you burn an oil lamp.

The lightest liquid fuel is *gasoline*. It cools and condenses almost at the top of the tower. You probably see this fuel often because it is burned in lawn mowers, cars, trucks, and tractors. People use more gasoline than any other liquid made from petroleum.

After the gasoline has condensed, some gas is still left. This gas is so light that it does not condense even at the top, which is the coolest part of the tower. But the gas is not wasted. It is burned to heat houses and other buildings.

After the different parts of the petroleum have separated from each other in the tower, they are cleaned and changed even more. Some of the parts are used to make soap, crayons,

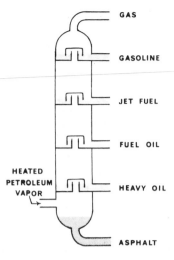

A tower to separate petroleum into different liquids

and hundreds of other useful things.

Some petroleum parts are used to make *plastic*. Plastic is also made from other raw materials, such as wood, coal, limestone, and water. Plastic may be hard or soft; it may be smooth or rough; it may be clear or brightly colored. Think of all the things we have that are plastic—toys, dishes, and even clothes! But all the different kinds of plastic have this same property: they are easy to shape.

What good things can come from the greenish-black liquid, petroleum! It is one of God's gifts to us.

Discussion Suggestion

You could have a profitable discussion about safety today. Caution the students that some petroleum products can be dangerous and flammable, such as gasoline, cleaning supplies, oily rags, and exhaust fumes.

Field Trip

Your class would probably enjoy watching an oil well being drilled or visiting an oil refinery if any are in your area.

———————————— **Test Your Reading** ————————————

The sentences below tell what happens to oil before people use it. Copy the sentences. Choose a word from the box to fill each blank.

condenses	oil well
evaporates	refinery

1. Because petroleum is deep in the earth, ——s are drilled to reach it.
2. The petroleum is taken to a —— to be separated into useful liquids.
3. First, the petroleum is heated until most of it ——; then as it cools, it —— and separates into different liquids.

Number these phrases about petroleum. Put them in the same order as they condense in the refinery tower, beginning with the heaviest. The first one is done for you.

4. _____ Fuel for ships and jet planes
5. _____ Gasoline for cars
6. _____ Oil to make machines run smoothly
7. __1__ Asphalt to pave roads
8. _____ Light gases to heat buildings
9. _____ Heavy oil to heat buildings

Four main uses for petroleum were given in this lesson. Each sentence below tells one of the uses. Copy the sentences. Fill each blank with a word from the box.

fuel	raw material
oil	seal

10. Petroleum is the —— from which candles, paint, and plastics are made.
11. Petroleum burned as —— keeps us warm and runs our cars.
12. Modern machines need —— from petroleum to run smoothly.
13. Noah used asphalt to —— out water.

Answers for "Test Your Reading"

1. Because petroleum is deep in the earth, *oil wells* are drilled to reach it.
2. The petroleum is taken to a *refinery* to be separated into useful liquids.
3. First, the petroleum is heated until most of it *evaporates*; then as it cools, it *condenses* and separates into different liquids.
4. 4
5. 5
6. 2
7. (1)
8. 6
9. 3
10. raw material
11. fuel
12. oil
13. seal   *(Total: 13 points)*

QUIZ

Write the New Words on the chalkboard. Ask the students to choose one to fit each sentence below.

1. To keep the ark dry inside, Noah used *(asphalt)*.
2. To help their chariots run smoothly, the Egyptians used   *(petroleum)*.
3. A thick, heavy liquid used to make cars and other machines run smoothly is   *(oil)*.
4. Greases and fuels are separated in a   *(refinery)*.
5. Your lawn mower burns   *(gasoline)*.
6. Today petroleum is pumped from an   *(oil well)*.
7. Petroleum and other raw materials are used to make   *(plastic)*.

Comments on "Extra Activities"

2. Yes. The oil stops the squeaking because it keeps the metal parts from rubbing against each other.

Extra Activities

Do these activities as your teacher directs.

1. Find "Petroleum" in the *World Book Encyclopedia*. Look at the pictures, and read the words underneath the pictures. Think of some questions about petroleum to ask your teacher or parents.

2. Is any door squeaking in your home or school? Ask for some household oil to put on the hinges of the door. Use only a little oil at the place where the two parts of the hinge rub together. Then listen as you open and close the door. Does the oil make any difference? Why?

   Materials needed:
   • *household oil*

3. To add to your unit project, make a display about petroleum. First, make a big poster that says "Petroleum Is a Special Liquid." On the poster, glue pictures of cars, trucks, jet planes, tractors, and other farm machinery. Beneath the pictures, write: Fuel to Run Many Machines. Bring a picture of a highway. Beneath it, write: Asphalt for Roads. Bring pictures of a house, a school, and a city. Beneath them, write: Fuel to Heat Many Buildings. Put your poster upright on a shelf or table. Ask your parents to help you find small things made of petroleum. Put them on the shelf or table. You could bring crayons, candles, an oil lamp, soap, a shingle, Vaseline, an enamel paint can, household oil, something made of plastic, or nylon clothing.

   Materials needed:
   • *large sheet of poster board*
   • *pictures that show uses of petroleum*
   • *various petroleum products*

God Gave Us Many Useful Liquids

New Words

alcohol (al′ kə • hôl), a clear liquid that makes good solutions.
distill (dis • til′), to boil and then condense back to a liquid.
mercury (mėr′ kyər • ē), a heavy liquid metal.
turpentine (tėr′ pən • tīn), a clear liquid distilled from pine trees.

Reading Together

Which are more important, solids or liquids? What a hard question! We live in solid houses. We like solid ground beneath us. But we need liquids too. We drink liquids when we are thirsty. We want liquids to make solutions. We need liquids to be clean. How could we clean ourselves, our clothes, and our houses without liquids?

Although water is our most important liquid, we also use other liquids. In Lesson 3, you studied about the liquid, petroleum. *Alcohol* is another useful liquid. Alcohol can help to make you well when you are sick. It can kill the very tiny living things that make you sick. Do you use rubbing alcohol when you have an itchy rash? If you have a cough, do you take cough syrup? It often has alcohol in it. If you cut your finger, your mother may paint a red alcohol solu-

Some medicines containing alcohol

tion on your finger. Many medicines are alcohol solutions because alcohol can dissolve many things. Dissolving things is one of alcohol's good properties.

57

Lesson 4

CONCEPTS TO TEACH

- Liquids are important for cleaning things and for making solutions.
- Water is our most important liquid.
- Alcohol is made by allowing wood or grain to rot and then distilling the liquid.
- Alcohol is used as a fuel, to make medicines, and to make many kinds of solutions. (Some people use alcohol wrongly to become drunk.)
- Turpentine is distilled from the sap of pine trees.
- We use turpentine to thin paints and to clean paintbrushes.
- Mercury is a liquid metal that is used in thermometers and electric switches.

HELPS FOR THE TEACHER

Introducing the Lesson

Again it would be helpful to bring samples of the liquids you are studying. A clinical thermometer would provide a sample of mercury. Or if you have fluorescent lighting in your school, tell the students that a gas made from mercury is inside the glass tubes.

If you bring turpentine, be especially careful to put it out of reach of the students after class.

If you have a spirit duplicator in your school, you could show the duplicator fluid as an example of alcohol. Rubbing alcohol would be another example. The students may be surprised to learn that alcohol has many good uses; perhaps they have only thought of alcohol as something people drink. Discuss this wrong use of alcohol. Do not allow the students to mock drunkards, but teach them to show compassion like Jesus.

There are many kinds of alcohol and many uses for alcohol. Some alcohols will burn. Your teacher may use an alcohol burner to do science experiments. Alcohol is used to keep the water in cars from freezing in the winter.

Alcohol does not come from petroleum, like gasoline. Alcohol can be made from parts of plants, such as wheat, corn, and potatoes. Some is made from the wood of trees. First, the plant parts are allowed to rot until they become a soupy liquid. Then the plant liquid is boiled. The alcohol boils off first. This alcohol gas is caught. Then it is cooled until it condenses from a gas back to a liquid.

To boil and then condense a liquid in this way is to *distill* it. Why does the plant liquid need to be distilled to make alcohol? As the plant material rots, only part of the soupy liquid is alcohol. Distilling separates the alcohol from the other parts.

Yes, alcohol can be a very helpful liquid. But some people do not use alcohol rightly. They drink it until they are drunk. Then they may say foolish things. They may hurt people because they cannot think rightly. God does not want alcohol to be used badly. The Bible says, "Wine [which contains alcohol] is a mocker, strong drink is raging: and whosoever is deceived thereby is not wise" (Proverbs 20:1).

Reading on Your Own

Turpentine is a useful liquid that comes from pine trees. It comes from the sap of pine trees, just as maple syrup comes from the sap of maple trees. The sap looks thick and gummy. It must be distilled to remove the part that we want. After the turpentine is boiled and condensed, it is thin and clear like water. Its sharp smell makes us think of pine needles.

Turpentine is useful to us. If some paint is too thick, turpentine will make it thinner. Turpentine will clean paintbrushes. One kind of turpentine is used in medicines.

Like alcohol, turpentine can be either a friend or an enemy. It can catch fire easily. It can make us very sick if we swallow it. If it gets into our eyes, it can hurt very much.

Turpentine is used to thin paint.

Mercury is a silver-colored metal. It is sometimes called quicksilver because it is the only metal that is usually a liquid. Because mercury is a metal, it can carry electricity. Because it is a liquid, it can quickly change its shape.

Materials needed:
- *mercury thermometer*
- *turpentine*
- *rubbing alcohol or spirit duplicator fluid*

Extra Information

Did you know—

. . . that antifreeze for automobiles is the alcohol, ethylene glycol?

. . . that about one–third of the traffic deaths in America are alcohol related?

. . . that a solid alloy of mercury and silver is used for filling teeth?

. . . that of the 89 naturally occurring elements, only mercury and bromine are liquid at room temperature?

Mercury is used in some thermometers.

These properties make mercury very useful to us. It can be used in electric switches. It can be used in a thermometer to measure how hot or cold something is. The thermometers that are used to take our temperature have mercury in them. The silvery liquid is inside a glass tube. Other thermometers sometimes have a red or blue liquid inside. This liquid is colored alcohol.

Now, imagine that we have four cups that are exactly the same. The cups are filled with the metals, iron, copper, aluminum, and mercury. Which do you guess is heaviest?

Mercury is heaviest! Did you guess right? This tells us another property of mercury. It is a very heavy metal. A cup of liquid mercury is over thirteen times as heavy as a cup of liquid water. It is almost twice as heavy as solid iron.

Today you have learned about alcohol, turpentine, and mercury. These are only a few of the many useful liquids that God has given us. God planned each liquid's own special properties. He wants us to use each one in the right way.

--- **Test Your Reading** ---

Copy each sentence. Then find a word in your lesson to fill the blanks.
1. We —— liquid water to stay alive.
2. We make —— with liquids when we dissolve other materials in them.
3. We need liquids to —— ourselves and our clothes.
4. Our most important liquid is ——.
5. We —— liquids by boiling and then condensing them.
6. Distilling —— liquids into different parts.

Which liquid is it? Write A *for alcohol,* T *for turpentine, and* M *for mercury.*
7. It can be burned as a fuel.
8. It is a metal.
9. It is used to thin paints.
10. It is heavier than the other liquids.
11. It is used to make solutions for medicines.
12. It is distilled from pine tree sap.
13. It is distilled from the liquid of rotting plant parts.

Answers for "Test Your Reading"
1. We *drink* liquid water to stay alive.
2. We make *solutions* with liquids when we dissolve other materials in them.
3. We need liquids to *clean* ourselves and our clothes.
4. Our most important liquid is *water*.
5. We *distill* liquids by boiling and then condensing them.
6. Distilling *separates* liquids into different parts.
7. A
8. M
9. T
10. M
11. A
12. T
13. A   *(Total: 13 points)*

QUIZ

As before, write the New Words on the chalkboard. Ask the students to choose one for each question.
1. Which liquid comes from pine trees?   *(turpentine)*
2. Which word means to separate parts of a liquid?   *(distill)*
3. Which liquid is very good for dissolving things?   *(alcohol)*
4. Which liquid is used to thin paints?   *(turpentine)*
5. Which two liquids are used in thermometers?   *(mercury and alcohol)*

Comments on "Extra Activities"

1. No. Distilling separated the water from the salt.
2. Though rainwater is safe to drink, it tastes flat. As rainwater soaks into the earth and flows in rivers, it dissolves tiny amounts of minerals from rocks. These minerals give water its good taste. But these minerals are not present in rainwater or distilled water.

Extra Activities

Do these activities as your teacher directs.

1. Would you like to distill water from "ocean water?" Add 2 teaspoons of salt to 2 cups of water. After all the salt has dissolved, the water will be as salty as ocean water. Put the water into a teakettle, and boil it on a hot plate or stove. Put 6 ice cubes into a cake pan. Hold the pan over the steam that comes from the spout of the teakettle. Slant the pan just enough to make the condensed water run to one end and drip into another cake pan. Taste the distilled water in that pan. Can you taste any salt? Why not?
Materials needed:
  - *measuring cup*
  - *water (2 cups)*
  - *measuring teaspoon*
  - *salt (2 teaspoons)*
  - *teakettle*
  - *hot plate or stove*
  - *2 cake pans*
  - *ice cubes*

2. Rainwater is the same as the distilled water in Activity 1. If you catch rainwater before it touches the ground, is it good to drink? Why does it not taste as good as well water?

3. See how many different things you can find at home and school that contain small amounts of alcohol. Look on the labels of medicines and flavorings. Make a list of the different things you can find that contain alcohol. Or you may choose to add them to your display for Activity 4.

4. To add to your unit project, make a display about liquids. If you have room, you may put it near your display about petroleum. Collect different kinds of liquids, and put them in baby food jars. Label the jars, writing the name on masking tape. Arrange the jars on a table or shelf with this sign: "We Need Many Liquids." If you can, get the liquids you studied about today, and also some others. Here is a list to help you.

cough syrup   tincture of iodine   water
rubbing alcohol   cleaning liquids   vinegar
turpentine   any fruit juice   condensed or evaporated milk
tincture of Merthiolate or Mercurochrome
Materials needed:
  - *various liquids*
  - *baby food jars*
  - *masking tape*

Air Is a Useful Material

New Words

atmosphere (at′ mə • sfēr), the air around the earth.

nitrogen (nī′ trə • jən), a gas that makes up most of the air.

oxygen (ok′ sə • jən), a gas that all living things need.

Reading Together

Is air real? You cannot see, taste, or even smell pure air. Yet air is just as real as you are. You can hear it. Listen. If you breathe deeply, can you hear yourself breathing? Air is going in and out, in and out of you. Can you sometimes hear the wind whistling? The wind is only moving air.

When you feel the wind, you are feeling air. It can be very powerful. Moving air can make a tall tree or a strong house crash to the ground!

Although we do not usually talk about a pound of air, air does have weight. It would take about ten bushels of air to weigh just one pound.

Air takes up space, just as you do. You can see this when you blow up a balloon. You cannot see the air, but you can watch the balloon become bigger and bigger. It keeps stretching to make more room for the air.

How does air hold up a car?

Do you play with air? If you play with a balloon, air is helping you to play. And it is not much fun to bounce a flat basketball, is it?

Air does work for us. Do you vacuum the rugs for your mother? The vacuum cleaner needs air, or it would not clean the dirty rugs. If a big truck stops near you, do you hear a loud *hiss?* Air helps the brakes work.

We even ride on air! If a car tire is flat, we feel a rough bumping. But with air in the tires, our ride is smooth. Of course, we can also ride on air in an airplane.

61

Lesson 5

CONCEPTS TO TEACH

- The wind is moving air.
- The air that surrounds the earth is called the atmosphere.
- Air is a mixture of oxygen and nitrogen.
- God wisely made both oxygen and nitrogen colorless and odorless.
- We need the oxygen in the air for breathing.
- We use the oxygen in the air for burning.
- The nitrogen in the air keeps fires from burning too fast.

HELPS FOR THE TEACHER

Introducing the Lesson

Show a picture of a diver or astronaut. Ask why he wears a helmet around his head and a tank on his back. Explain that God put air on earth for us to breathe. When men go where there is no air, they must take it along, or they will die. You could also mention that, as far as we know, the earth is the only planet with air. This will emphasize the fact that God created the earth for man. Neither earth nor man just happened.

Materials needed:

- *picture of a diver or astronaut*

MORE THAN 10 MILES

What happens in the atmosphere?

Reading on Your Own

Do you remember learning about water pressure? Do you remember that water pressure is greatest at the bottom of the ocean? The air around the earth, called the **atmosphere,** is like a big ocean. We live on the earth at the bottom of this great ocean of air. Many miles of air are pressing down on top of us. But our bodies are used to this pressure. If suddenly the air pressure would be gone, our bodies could not stand it. We would die.

A fish in the ocean knows where the top of the water is. It can swim upward only so far until the water stops. But the "air ocean," or atmosphere, is a gas, not a liquid. If we would travel straight upward through the atmosphere, the air would not stop suddenly. It would slowly become less and less the farther we would travel from the earth. The air pressure on us would also become less and less.

What is air made of? It is made of gases mixed together. God wisely made these gases clear so that we can see things clearly through them. They have no smell so that we can smell other things.

Oxygen is a very important gas in the air. When you run a race, soon you breathe hard and fast. Why do you pant? Your body needs lots of oxygen right then. If you suddenly had no more oxygen, you could live only about three minutes. Both

Extra Information
Did you know—

. . . that we get the nitrogen we need from our food, not from breathing it in like oxygen?

. . . that winds are caused by the sun? Differences in temperature cause differences in pressure. Winds are simply air masses moving from high pressure areas to low pressure areas.

. . . that the air pressure is always pushing on our bodies with almost 15 pounds on every square inch?

. . . that the 1 per cent of air that is not nitrogen and oxygen is mostly argon with very small amounts of 8 or more gases?

QUIZ

Ask the students to choose a New Word to fit each sentence. Some will be used twice.

1. It is like the ocean. *(atmosphere)*
2. A fire needs it. *(oxygen)*
3. It will not burn. *(nitrogen)*
4. It presses against your body. *(atmosphere)*
5. People breathe it. *(oxygen)*

people and animals breathe oxygen.

Fire does not breathe, but it needs oxygen too. It needs oxygen to burn. Fire warms us and cooks our food. It runs our machines and burns our trash. But without oxygen, fire could not do these things for us.

Do you wonder, "Why is not all the air made of oxygen?" If all the air were oxygen, things would burn much too fast. Too much oxygen in the air would cause terrible fires. We could not stop them.

This is why we need *nitrogen* in the air. In fact, the air has almost four times as much nitrogen as oxygen. Nitrogen does not burn. It keeps fires from burning too fast. How thankful we can be that God made our air exactly right for us!

Test Your Reading

Write yes *if the sentence is true. Write* no *if it is not true.*

1. Moving air is wind.
2. The atmosphere is the air around the earth.
3. Our bodies need air pressure.
4. The farther away from the earth, the greater the air pressure is.

Give the answers.

5. Name two gases that make up most of the air.
6. Why is it good that we cannot see or smell air?
7. Name two reasons why oxygen is important.
8. Why is nitrogen important?
9. Think about what you learned in this lesson. Then explain Mark's problem. Mark's family lives near some mountains. Sometimes they drive part of the way up a mountain. Then they hike trails to the mountaintop. Mark notices that he pants more quickly on the mountaintop. He has a harder time getting his breath. Is Mark just tired, or can you think of another reason for this?

Extra Activities

Do these activities as your teacher directs.

1. Does air really have weight? This activity can help you find out. Make a noose with a piece of yarn, and tie it around the middle of a yardstick. Hang the yardstick by tying this yarn to an open cupboard door handle or other support. With yarn tie two empty balloons the same size, one on each end of the yardstick. Adjust the balloons until they balance. Now carefully untie the one balloon and blow it up. Tie it back on the yardstick at exactly the same

Answers for "Test Your Reading"

1. yes
2. yes
3. yes
4. no
5. oxygen, nitrogen (2)
6. So that we can see and smell other things.
7. A fire needs oxygen to burn. People need oxygen to breathe. (2)
8. Nitrogen keeps fires from burning too fast.
9. The air is thinner on top of the mountain because Mark and his family traveled upward through the atmosphere.   *(Total: 11 points)*

Comments on "Extra Activities"

1. Yes. Air has weight. The balloon that has been blown up is heavier and makes the one end of the yardstick hang down.

2. No. The air inside the glass takes up space.

3. Yes. The liquid pours faster with two holes in the can. With only one hole, the air must go in the same hole that the liquid comes out, and it takes more time. With two holes, the air can "pour" in one hole as the liquid pours out the other hole.

4. The candle under the quart jar goes out because it uses all the oxygen.

   After the candle goes out, ask the students whether any gas is still in the jar. What is its name? (nitrogen)

Note: Activities 3 and 4 are short and simple enough to do during class if you have time.

place. What happens to the yardstick? Does air have weight?
Materials needed:
• *yardstick*
• *yarn*
• *2 balloons of equal size and shape*

2. Does air really take up space? You can find out. First, float a cork in a big bowl of water. Then turn a clear glass upside down over the floating cork. Push the glass straight down into the water, without tipping it. Keep pushing the glass straight down, and watch the cork. It tells you how high the water rises inside the glass. Does the water fill the glass? Why not?
Materials needed:
• *small cork*   • *clear drinking glass*
• *big, clear bowl*   • *water*

3. Try this activity about air taking space. Ask your teacher or parents to punch one hole near the edge on the top of a can of juice or milk. Then try to pour the liquid. Ask them to punch another hole on the other side of the top of the can. Now try pouring the liquid. Is there a difference? Why?
Materials needed:
• *can of fruit juice or condensed milk*
• *can opener*

4. Does a fire need air? You can find out. Ask your teacher or parents to light 2 candles. Then put a jar over one candle. Watch the candles for a while. What happens? Why?
Materials needed:
• *2 short candles*
• *matches*
• *quart jar*

5. For your unit project, make a poster showing some of the ways we use air. Find pictures that show air used for automobile tires, for burning, for breathing, and for flying airplanes. Fasten a balloon to your poster.
Materials needed:
• *large sheet of poster board*
• *pictures of using air*
• *balloon*

God Gave Us Many Useful Gases

New Words

ammonia (ə • mō′ nyə), a strong-smelling gas that can be used for cleaning when dissolved in water.

carbon dioxide (kär′ bən dī • ok′ sīd), a heavy gas that will not burn.

helium (hē′ lē • əm), a very light gas used in balloons.

natural gas (nach′ ər • əl gas), a fuel gas found in the earth.

propane (prō′ pān), a heavy fuel gas made from oil or natural gas.

Reading Together

God gave us many kinds of gases on the earth. Can you tell them apart? Many of them have no color or smell. You cannot tell them apart by feeling them or by listening to them.

Some people have studied gases very carefully. They have learned that different gases have different properties. They have even changed every gas into its liquid and solid states. Then they could see them! In these ways, they learned how to tell all gases apart. But today you will study only a few of them.

Natural gas is a gas that comes from deep in the earth. Often it is found on top of petroleum in oil wells. Pure natural gas has no smell of its own. But breathing natural gas can make people very sick. For this rea-

The flame of a natural gas stove

son, sometimes a bad smell is put into natural gas before it is sold. Then people can smell the gas and know that their pipes have a leak.

Natural gas gives much heat when it burns. This makes it very useful in homes and cities. Does your mother cook on a gas stove? Do you see the hot blue flames? Natural gas is also burned for heating water and drying clothes. It can warm our homes in the winter.

Propane is another fuel gas. It is made from petroleum or natural gas. Because propane is a heavy gas, it is easy to change it into a liquid. The

65

Lesson 6

CONCEPTS TO TEACH

- Men tell gases apart by studying their different properties.
- Natural gas is a fuel that comes from deep in the ground.
- Propane comes from both natural gas and petroleum.
- Propane is forced into bottles and sold as fuel for torches.
- Helium is a gas found in some natural gas wells.
- Helium is a very light gas used in lighter–than–air balloons.
- Ammonia gas dissolves in water to make a cleaning material.
- Carbon dioxide can be used to put out fires.
- Carbon dioxide helps green plants to grow.
- We breathe out carbon dioxide.
- Carbon dioxide makes the holes in cake and bread.

Note: Your students may wonder why natural gas could not also be bottled like propane. You could answer that a bottle of natural gas, to make enough heat, would be so big that it would be unhandy to take anywhere. Propane is especially useful for hard-to-reach or sparsely settled areas away from natural gas pipelines.

liquid propane is forced into bottles. This makes it easy to carry anywhere that we need it. It makes good fuel for torches, trucks, and homes.

What can a propane torch be used for?

Reading on Your Own

Did you ever get a special balloon that pulled upward on its string? If you would stand outdoors and let it go, the balloon would keep rising high into the sky. Why does it always want to go up?

The gas in the balloon is *helium.* It wants to go up because helium is lighter than air. Remember how buoyant force pushes things upward in water? Buoyant force pushes the helium balloon upward too. Buoyant force works in air the same way it works in water.

Helium is used in very large balloons. Some of them are bigger than your house. Some helium balloons help men study the weather.

Helium is even lighter than natural gas. It is found in some natural gas wells. Natural gas burns, but helium will not burn. It is used for keeping metal from burning when it is being welded.

Do you think that *ammonia* is a liquid? Your mother may use it to clean. But she does not use pure ammonia gas. She uses ammonia that has been dissolved in water. It cleans very well. Be careful when you use ammonia. Like breathing natural gas, breathing ammonia can make you sick. It has a very strong, stinging smell. Do not put your nose close to an ammonia bottle. Use your hand to sweep some of the gas up to your nose. Whew, one sniff is enough!

Like helium, ammonia is a gas that will not burn, although it can soak up lots of heat when it is changed from a liquid to a gas. This makes ammonia useful in large refrigerators or ice makers for cooling things.

Ammonia is made from coal, nitrogen, and other things. A little ammonia also comes from rotting plants and animals. Long ago, some people made ammonia from deer antlers.

Carbon dioxide is a heavy gas that will not burn. You know that a fire needs air to burn. Carbon dioxide can put out fires by shutting off the air. The carbon dioxide settles over the fire like a blanket.

Green plants need carbon dioxide to grow. They take carbon dioxide

What does this carbon dioxide fire extinguisher have in it?

HELPS FOR THE TEACHER

Introducing the Lesson

Show the class two fruits, such as an orange and an apple. Ask whether they have any problem getting them mixed up. Why not? Discuss the differences in color, shape, taste, and so forth.

Now hold up two similar balloons, one filled with air and the other with helium. (Check with your local florist for helium.) Tell the students that the balloons hold two different gases. Ask them whether they can tell the difference between the gases. Explain that neither gas can be seen, smelled, or tasted. Then release both balloons. As the students watch one balloon rise while the other falls, explain that we tell gases apart by the way they act or by their properties. (If a helium balloon is not available, you could design a similar demonstration with two other gases, comparing their odor or ability to support burning.)

Materials needed:
- *2 kinds of fruit*
- *helium-filled balloon*
- *air-filled balloon*

into their leaves and give off oxygen.

It is just the opposite for us. We breathe in oxygen and breathe out carbon dioxide. God wisely planned it this way. Green plants use the gas that people and animals give off, and people and animals use the gas that green plants give off.

When your mother bakes a cake, carbon dioxide helps her. She puts the heavy, sticky batter into the oven. While it bakes, carbon dioxide bubbles form in the batter. They make the cake rise. You can eat light, fluffy cake because of carbon dioxide bubbles!

Do not forget that God made carbon dioxide, ammonia, helium, and all the other gases on the earth. God gave them their useful properties.

Test Your Reading

For each sentence below, choose the gas or gases that fit it. Write A for ammonia, C for carbon dioxide, H for helium, N for natural gas, and P for propane. Give two answers for sentences 1 and 8.

1. It makes a good fuel. (2)
2. Green plants need it to grow.
3. It is a very light gas.
4. It is a good cleaner.
5. It is used in balloons.
6. We breathe it out.
7. It makes the holes in cake and bread.
8. It can be taken out of the earth. (2)
9. It cools other things.

Choose the best ending for each sentence below. Write both the letter and the complete sentence.

10. Propane can be carried anywhere because
    (a) it makes a good fuel.
    (b) it can be put into bottles.
    (c) it is a very light gas.
11. A helium balloon rises because
    (a) it is pushed up by water pressure.
    (b) it is lighter than air.
    (c) it will not burn.
12. Carbon dioxide puts out fires because
    (a) it shuts off air.
    (b) it soaks up heat.
    (c) it is lighter than air.

Answers for "Test Your Reading"

1. N, P
2. C
3. H
4. A
5. H
6. C
7. C
8. N, H (also P, indirectly)
9. A
10. b
11. b
12. a

(Total: 14 points)

Extra Information

Did you know—

. . . that dry ice is carbon dioxide that has been cooled and compressed into a solid?

. . . that the ancient Chinese obtained salt by boiling seawater, using natural gas as their fuel?

. . . that early Russian temples had "eternal flames" fueled by natural gas?

. . . that to become a liquid, helium needs more cooling than any other gas? If liquid helium (at −269°C or about −452°F) is put into an open container, it will flow upward over the sides.

QUIZ

As you read these questions, call on students at random to give the answers.

1. How can men tell gases apart? *(by studying their properties)*
2. How is natural gas used? *(It is burned as a fuel.)*
3. In what way is propane better than natural gas? *(It can be carried around in bottles.)*
4. Which gas helps men study the weather? *(helium)*
5. What might happen if you breathe natural gas or ammonia? *(It could make you very sick.)*
6. Which heavy gas can put out fires? *(carbon dioxide)*

Extra Activities

Do these activities as your teacher directs.

1. Pick one of the places listed below:
   - garage or shed (for car or tractor)
   - pantry or basement (home-canned food)
   - cleaning closet
   - refrigerator

   On a sheet of paper, write the headings, *Solid, Liquid,* and *Gas.* Ask an older person to help you make a list of the things in your chosen place, and put each item under the correct heading. You will hardly see any gases, but you can smell and think of them. If you do not know the name of a gas, write *"the smell of . . ."* or *"a gas from . . ."*

2. Would you like to learn more about helium balloons? Find "Airship" or "Balloon" in the *World Book Encyclopedia.* Study the pictures. Tell or write what you learn.

3. For your unit project, make a display about gases. If possible, get a helium balloon, an empty propane bottle, and a carbon dioxide fire extinguisher, or find pictures of them. Label them *Helium, Propane,* and *Carbon Dioxide.* Also bring a piece of bread or cake. Label it like this: Carbon dioxide caused this bread (or cake) to rise.

   The rest of your display may be things to smell, such as brown sugar, a geranium plant, cinnamon, candles, flowers, pepper, glue, an onion, perfume, vinegar, and household ammonia mixed with water. Arrange these things on a table or shelf with this sign: "We Need Many Gases." On the same sign, in smaller letters, write: You cannot see many gases. But you can smell some of them. The smell of something is caused by a gas. If you have room, put your display about air from the last lesson beside this display.

   Materials needed:
   - *various items to smell*
   - *helium balloon*
   - *propane bottle (empty for safety reasons)*
   - *carbon dioxide fire extinguisher*
   - *slice of bread or cake*

Do You Remember What You Learned?

Match each word on the right to the correct word group on the left.

1. Wooden boards	a. aluminum
2. Wood for paper	b. carbon dioxide
3. Black rock that burns	c. coal
4. Strong metal for bridges	d. copper
5. Electric-wire metal	e. gasoline
6. Lightweight metal	f. iron
7. Oily liquid in the earth	g. lumber
8. We breathe it out	h. oil well
9. Deep hole to reach petroleum	i. petroleum
10. Separates petroleum into its parts	j. pulpwood
11. Fuel for cars	k. refinery

Match each word on the right to the correct word group on the left.

12. Material that is easily shaped	l. alcohol
13. Many things can be dissolved in it	m. ammonia
14. Makes paint thinner	n. asphalt
15. Heavy liquid metal	o. atmosphere
16. The ocean of air surrounding us	p. helium
17. We need it from the air to live	q. mercury
18. Keeps fires from burning too fast	r. nitrogen
19. Fuel for torches	s. oxygen
20. Very light gas	t. plastic
21. Blacktop roads	u. propane
22. Good for cleaning and cooling	v. turpentine

69

ANSWER KEY

Match

1. g
2. j
3. c
4. f
5. d
6. a
7. i
8. b
9. h
10. k
11. e
12. t
13. l
14. v
15. q
16. o
17. s
18. r
19. u
20. p
21. n
22. m

Lesson 7

Ask questions to help the students grasp the unit as a whole, such as "What was the main idea of this whole unit? Can you name the solids we studied? How many liquids (or gases) can you name without looking in the book?" Help the students appreciate the great variety of materials that God has provided.

Again, emphasize that the properties of a material determine its uses. Give plenty of examples that they have studied. One way to do this together is to make a chart on the chalkboard, like the one below. You could place the solids, liquids, and gases in groups.

Materials	Properties	Uses
coal	will burn	fuel
mercury	liquid	thermometers
	metal	electric switches
helium	lighter than air	weather balloons

Together, review the steps given in "How to Study for a Test," found on page 5 of the textbook (page 11 of this manual).

Fill each blank with a word or phrase from the box.

alcohol	hardwood	oil
bark	metal	ore
distill	mining	rock
glass	natural gas	softwood
grain		

Fill

23. hardwood

24. softwood

25. grain

26. bark

27. metal

28. Ore, mining

29. rock, glass

30. oil

31. distill

32. alcohol

33. natural gas

23. Maple and walnut trees are —— trees.
24. Cedar and redwood trees are —— trees.
25. The pretty —— in wood is caused by a tree's rings of growth.
26. The rough, outer covering on a tree is its ——.
27. A hard, shiny material is a ——.
28. —— is a rock containing metal. This rock is gotten by ——.
29. Different kinds of —— are used for building and for making clear ——.
30. Grease and —— keep machines running smoothly and quietly.
31. To make alcohol and turpentine, we —— it by boiling and then condensing the liquid.
32. The red medicine that is put on cuts is a solution of ——.
33. A gas that gives much heat when it burns is ——.

Choose

34. a

35. a

36. b

37. c

Choose the best answer.

34. Lumber comes from
    (a) a tree's trunk and limbs.
    (b) a tree's bark and roots.
    (c) pulpwood and scrap wood.
35. Noah built the ark with
    (a) gopher wood.
    (b) redwood.
    (c) cedar wood.
36. Baking pans, ladders, and airplanes are made of
    (a) copper.
    (b) aluminum.
    (c) iron.
37. The pitch Noah used was natural
    (a) alcohol.
    (b) ammonia.
    (c) asphalt.

38. A wrong use of alcohol is
    (a) becoming drunk.
    (b) making medicines.
    (c) burning it as fuel.
39. Air is mostly made of
    (a) helium and oxygen.
    (b) nitrogen and oxygen.
    (c) carbon dioxide and oxygen.
40. Moving air is called
    (a) wind.
    (b) atmosphere.
    (c) nitrogen.
41. Helium comes from
    (a) petroleum.
    (b) the air.
    (c) natural gas wells.

Decide whether each sentence is true, and write yes *or* no.

42. A material from bark is used to tan leather.
43. Everything we have comes from raw materials.
44. Both coal and metal ores are mined from the earth.
45. The properties of a material help us decide how to use it.
46. Gasoline is made of many liquids mixed together.
47. Oil for cars and machines comes from petroleum.
48. Petroleum is our most important liquid.
49. A fire cannot burn without oxygen.
50. We can smell nitrogen.
51. Natural gas comes from the earth.

Write the answers.

52-54. Give three reasons why people like wood for building.
55. Explain how to tell hardwood trees and softwood trees apart.
56-58. Name three useful rocks. Explain how each is used.
59. Tell how alcohol is distilled.
60-62. In what three ways is carbon dioxide useful to us?

Be sure to follow the four steps given on page 5, "How to Study for a Test."

38. a
39. b
40. a
41. c

Decide

42. yes
43. yes
44. yes
45. yes
46. no
47. yes
48. no
49. yes
50. no
51. yes

Write

52-54. (Any three) Wood is easy to cut (or saw).

Wood is easy to fasten (or nail, bolt, and screw).

Wood is easy to finish (or paint and stain).

Wood has a beautiful grain.

(3 points)

55. Hardwood trees have flat leaves, but softwood trees have needles and cones. (They may also mention that hardwood trees lose their leaves in autumn and bear flowers and fruit.)

(2 points)

56-58. (Any three) Coal—used as fuel.

Sandstone or limestone—used for building and making glass.

Granite—used for building and for making gravestones. *(3 points)*

59. First, the plant parts are allowed to rot. The plant liquid is boiled. The gas that boils off is caught and cooled. When it condenses, the liquid is alcohol. *(2 points)*

60-62. Carbon dioxide is needed by plants to grow.

It can put out fires.

It makes our bread and cakes rise.

(3 points)

(Total: 64 points)

Unit Three

God Promised to Protect
His Creation

"I do set my bow in the cloud" (Genesis 9:13).

Can you keep your promises? You might promise your teacher, "I will bring some red roses for you tomorrow." But maybe your sister has just given the last red rose in your garden to your grandmother. You cannot keep that promise.

Or you might promise your mother, "Yes, I will rake the leaves right now." But when you look for the rake, you cannot find it. The rake was left at the church on cleanup day.

Sometimes we can keep our promises. Sometimes we cannot. This is why we say things like this: "The Lord willing, we plan to . . ." or "If the weather is nice, I want to . . ."

God's promises are different from our promises. God can always keep His promises. God never says, "If I can, I will . . ." or "Tomorrow, if nothing happens, I will . . ."

God made some promises to Noah. These promises were also made to Noah's children and all their children after them. In fact, these promises were even made to us! We are all children of Noah's children's children . . . and on and on, down the long line of families.

What are these promises God made to Noah and to us? God said, "While the earth remaineth, seedtime and harvest, and cold and heat, and summer and winter, and day and night shall not cease. . . . The waters shall no more become a flood to destroy all flesh." With these promises, God was promising to protect His children.   **72**

Unit Three

God Promised to Protect His Creation

For Your Inspiration

"Yet He Abideth Faithful"

If God has faithfully
  Kept another flood
    From engulfing the earth,
Can He not faithfully
  Keep floods of problems
    From engulfing my classroom?

If God has faithfully
  Provided seedtime
    And bountiful harvest,
Can He not faithfully
  Supply creative ideas
    That my teaching may flourish?

If God has faithfully
  Sent a warm summer
    After each bleak winter,
Will He not faithfully
  Give me a warm love
    For this problem child?

If God has faithfully
  Changed every dark night
    Into bright, clear day,
Will He not faithfully
  Reveal His clear truth
    To my searching mind?

—*Naomi Lapp*

"If we believe not, yet he abideth faithful: he cannot deny himself" (2 Timothy 2:13).

"Faithful is he that calleth you, who also will do it" (1 Thessalonians 5:24).

God Promised
Seedtime and Harvest

New Words

climate (klī′ mit), the kind of weather an area has from year to year.

crop (krop), plants raised in a field for food or other uses.

germination (jėr′ mə • nā′ shən), growing from a seed into a young plant.

growing season (grō′ ing sē′ zən), the part of the year during which crops and gardens can grow.

Reading Together

Do you pull weeds from your garden? Do you pick peas, beans, and strawberries? If so, you already know that a good harvest does not happen by itself. We need to work hard for a good harvest.

What must we do if we want a good harvest? First, we break up the soil. We may use a shovel or a garden tiller to do this. A farmer may use a plow and a disc harrow to break up the soil in his fields.

After we plant the seeds in the soft soil, we may add plant food or fertilizer. This helps the plants grow.

Somehow we must get rid of the weeds. In a garden, we may pull them. Or we may uproot them with a hoe or a garden tiller. We can also smother the weeds with sheets of

73

Lesson 1

CONCEPTS TO TEACH

- Man has a part in making a harvest possible. He breaks up the soil, plants seeds, removes weeds, and harvests at the right time.
- God's part of the harvest is much greater than man's. He provides sunshine, rain, soil, germination, warmth, minerals, and a growing season.
- The climate of each area determines the crops that are grown.
- Man is dependent on the harvest for food.

HELPS FOR THE TEACHER

Introducing the Lesson

First of all, view the unit as a whole. You may page through the unit, noticing the headings and illustrations. Then read the unit introduction together.

For this lesson, read Leviticus 23:10–12, 22 to the class. Discuss these Old Testament harvest laws: (1) Israel was to give some of their first harvest to the Lord through the priest, and (2) those who harvested were to leave some grain for the poor and the strangers.

In a sense, we still keep these laws today. We give our first fruits to God when we love and obey Him above all others. We also give time and money to the Lord's work. (Give some examples of the Lord's work in your area.) Giving reminds us that all our harvest comes from God. In fact, everything we have comes from God.

If we live on a farm, we can invite people to glean our cornfields. If we have a garden, we can share fruits and vegetables with others. We can give to the poor. Wherever we live, we can always invite visitors to our home to share our food.

Bean seeds that have germinated

black plastic or with a thick layer of leaves.

Then we wait until our gardens and field *crops* are ripe. We must not harvest them too soon, or they may be small, hard, and tasteless. We must not wait too long, or they will spoil.

All of this takes much hard work. It means working on warm, sticky days. It means feeling tired and sweaty at times.

Yet with all our work, we still would have no harvest if God had not done some important things. First of all, God gave living plants the wonderful ability to make more plants. The dead things that man makes cannot do this. For example, your coat cannot make more coats. Your pen cannot make more pens. But a plant can make more plants just like itself.

How can a plant do this amazing thing? God has caused each grown plant to make little seeds. The seeds can sprout and grow into tiny plants. This is called *germination.*

When does germination happen? The seeds must be placed in warm, moist soil. As the hard, dry seeds become wet, they begin to swell. Then tiny roots and leaves start pushing out of the seeds.

After germination, the seedlings grow bigger and stronger. They keep receiving warmth and light from the sun. They keep taking in water through their roots.

The young plants also take in small amounts of plant food or fertilizer. Some of this food is made of minerals, such as iron and copper. Minerals and other plant food come from the air, the water, and the soil.

As plants grow, they make food that we can eat. We need to wait until this food is ripe; then we gather it. This is our harvest.

Only God can make such a harvest possible. Only He can give plants what they need: light, warmth, water, minerals, air, and soil. Only He can make plants able to germinate, grow, and make food and seeds. You can see that God's part of the harvest is much greater than our part.

Bean plants ready to harvest

Extra Information

Did you know—

. . . that the largest wheat field on record covered 35,000 acres in Alberta, Canada?

. . . that one Michigan farmer harvested a record-breaking 352 bushels of corn from one acre?

. . . that an average North American eats up to 70 tons of food in his lifetime?

QUIZ

Ask the students to say or write the correct New Word when you say each phrase below.

1. Sprouting of a seed   *(germination)*
2. Plants grown in a field   *(crop)*
3. Usual kind of weather   *(climate)*
4. Length of time when gardens grow   *(growing season)*

Reading on Your Own

God has done still more to give us a harvest. He has provided a *growing season* for plants. The growing season is the time when the ground stays warm enough for seeds to germinate and plants to grow. The growing season begins after the last heavy frosts in the spring. It ends with the first heavy frosts in the fall.

Some parts of the world have a short growing season. In these areas, it is warm for only a short part of the year. It is cold for many months of the year.

The people there live in a cold *climate*. They must grow crops that will grow in a cold climate. They may raise wheat, oats, potatoes, and carrots. These crops ripen quickly enough to be harvested at the end of a short growing season.

Other parts of the world have a long growing season. In these areas, it is warm and rainy most of the year. Because of this mild, wet climate, the people who live there can raise many kinds of fruits and vegetables. They can raise oranges, bananas, pineapples, rice, and sugar cane.

The growing season where you live may not be very long or very short. Your climate may be warm part of the year and cold part of the year. But whatever the climate, we raise only crops that are suitable for it. We grow plants that will become ripe before the growing season is over.

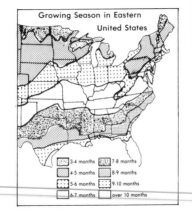

Growing Season in Eastern United States

3-4 months   7-8 months
4-5 months   8-9 months
5-6 months   9-10 months
6-7 months   over 10 months

The length of the growing season is from the last killing frost in the spring to the first killing frost in the fall.

We can be very glad that God gave us a growing season. He did not make the earth like the moon. On the moon, every day is broiling hot. Every night is bitter cold. If the earth were like the moon, all the plants would either burn or freeze. We could not have a harvest.

Why do we need a harvest? We need a harvest because it gives us food. If we had no food, we would starve.

How thankful we should be for each harvest! How glad we should be for such a faithful God! Today He is still keeping the promise He made long ago to Noah: "While the earth remaineth, seedtime and harvest . . . shall not cease."

Answers for "Test Your Reading"

1. G
2. G
3. M
4. G
5. M
6. G
7. G
8. M
9. M
10. G
11. G
12. b When a seed germinates, it becomes a tiny plant.
13. c A growing season may be long or short.
14. d A climate may be cold, wet, warm, or dry.
15. a For crops to grow well, they must be suitable for the climate.
16. e We need a harvest because we need food to eat.

(Total: 16 points)

Comments on "Extra Activities"

1. The *warm and wet* climate is best for germination.

——————— Test Your Reading ———————

Below is a list of the work needed for a harvest. Write M for the things man needs to do. Write G for the things God did or does.

1. Make the soil
2. Provide a growing season
3. Break up the soil
4. Send the sunshine
5. Harvest when the crop is ripe
6. Make plants that can germinate
7. Send the rain
8. Plant the seeds
9. Remove the weeds
10. Make the minerals
11. Provide warmth

Match each sentence beginning to the right ending. On your paper, write both the correct letter and the complete sentence.

12. When a seed germinates, it becomes
13. A growing season may be
14. A climate may be
15. For crops to grow well, they must be suitable for
16. We need a harvest because we need

a. the climate.
b. a tiny plant.
c. long or short.
d. cold, wet, warm, or dry.
e. food to eat.

Extra Activities

Do these activities as your teacher directs.

1. You can watch bean seeds germinate. You can also make different climates to learn what seeds need in order to germinate. Get four jars. Put three bean seeds, folded in a paper towel, into each jar. Wet the paper towels in only two of the jars. Put lids on all the jars. Label the jars that have wet paper towels inside them. Label the one *warm and wet;* label the other *cold and wet.* Label the two jars that have dry paper towels. Label the one *warm and dry;* label the other *cold and dry.* Then put the jars labeled *cold* into a refrigerator. (If the weather is cold, you may put them outdoors.) Put the other two jars on a table or shelf in your classroom but not in direct sunlight. Cover them with a dark cloth or a box.

   Look at all your seeds every day for about a week. Use a magnifying glass to look at them closely. Which seeds germinate first? Which climate is best for germination? What do seeds need in order to germinate?

   Materials needed:
   - *4 small glass jars with lids*
   - *12 bean seeds*

• *4 paper towels*   • *refrigerator*
• *water*   • *dark cloth or box*
• *masking tape*   • *magnifying glass*

2. Do all seeds germinate in the same way and in the same amount
   of time? You can find out with vegetable seeds. Choose four kinds
   of seeds, such as corn, bean, radish, pea, carrot, or similar seeds.
   Put the seeds in folded paper towels inside four jars, just as in
   Activity 1. All the paper towels should be damp. Label each jar
   with the name of the seeds that are inside. Screw on the lids. Then
   cover the jars with a dark cloth or a box.

   Look at your seeds each day for a week or two. Be sure to keep
   all the paper towels moist. As the seeds germinate, look at them
   with a magnifying glass. Compare the roots and leaves of the different sprouts. How are they different from each other? Which
   seeds sprout quickly? Which seeds take more time to germinate?
   Write a paragraph about what you see and learn.
   Materials needed:
   • *4 kinds of vegetable seeds*   • *water*
   • *4 paper towels*   • *masking tape*
   • *4 glass jars with lids*   • *dark cloth or box*
                                      • *magnifying glass*

3. Make a list of the fruits, vegetables, and field crops that are grown
   in your area. Make another list of some that are not grown where
   you live. Can you find out why these do not grow well in your area?
   Ask your parents or teacher to help you.

4. Your project for Unit Three is to make models of the earth, the
   sun, and the moon. By doing this project, you will have a better
   idea of what the real sun, earth, and moon look like in space.

   For this lesson, draw a small picture of a seed of corn. Label
   it *Seedtime*. Then draw a small picture of a full-grown cornstalk.
   Label it *Harvest*. Glue your pictures onto toothpicks. Stick the
   toothpicks into Styrofoam balls. If you use Ping-Pong balls, tape
   the pictures onto the balls.

   After the next lesson, your teacher will help you put the model
   earths around a model sun.
   Materials needed:
   • *drawing paper*   • *glue*   • *toothpicks*
   • *2 Styrofoam balls* or *Ping-Pong balls (Cracked or dented Ping-
   Pong balls can be used.)*

4. Wait to arrange the model earths
   until the next lesson. However, it
   would be helpful to study the project activities in succeeding lessons
   and to observe the diagram on
   page 85.

Lesson 2

God Promised Day and Night

New Words

axis (ak′ sis), the imaginary line through the center of the earth,
    around which the earth turns.

day (dā), the time it takes for the earth to rotate once; daylight;
    the part of the day when the sun is in the sky.

rotation (rō • ta′ shən), turning on an axis.

tilt (tilt), a slant; not straight up and down.

Reading Together

Do you like to ride a merry-go-round? Round and round you spin until you are dizzy. You shout, "Stop! I want off!"

Right now we are spinning on something much, much bigger than a merry-go-round. We are spinning around faster than the speed of a fast jet airplane. Yet we do not feel dizzy. How strange!

Our merry-go-round is the earth. We do not feel dizzy because the whole earth spins with us. The whole earth is spinning on its *axis*, just as a merry-go-round spins on its center pole.

The earth's axis is not a pole or a line that we can see. It is just the center of the earth around which the rest of the earth spins.

God did not put the earth's axis straight up and down. Instead, He tipped the axis a little to one side. We call this the *tilt* of the earth. The earth always stays tilted in this same way.

The earth always turns toward the east. Because of this turning, the sun seems to rise in the east and move westward across the sky. Then it sets in the west.

How much time does it take for one complete turn or *rotation* of the earth? It takes one whole *day*. God planned it this way. He planned that one rotation, or one day, would be used to measure time.

The earth rotates on its axis once in a day.

78

Lesson 2

CONCEPTS TO TEACH

- The sun rises in the east and sets in the west because the earth is rotating in a west–to–east direction.
- We measure time by the earth's rotation; one rotation is one day.
- We have daylight when our side of the earth faces the sun, and night when we are turned away from the sun.
- The sun rises three hours later in California than it does in New York.
- Day and night and sunrise and sunset are always happening somewhere on the earth.

HELPS FOR THE TEACHER

Introducing the Lesson

Today a demonstration will be a valuable aid to the students' understanding of the rotation of the earth. Darken the classroom as much as possible, except for a bright lamp. Attach a small lump of clay at your geographical location on a globe. Demonstrate the earth's rotation by spinning the globe in an eastward direction. Show how the lamplight moves westward across the globe, just as the sun seems to move westward across the sky.

Notice that half of the globe is always lighted and the other half is always shadowed. In the same way, half of the earth has day while the other half has night.

Explain that sunrise, noon, and sunset are names for the sun's positions in the sky, as we see the sun from the earth. Rotate the globe, and point out when the spot marked by the clay has sunrise, noon, sunset, and midnight.

We have day when our side of the earth is toward the sun; we have night when our side is away from the sun.

Reading on Your Own

The word *day* has two meanings. As you know, it means one rotation of the earth. But God used the word *day* to mean daylight. The Bible says, "And God called the light Day, and the darkness he called Night. And the evening and the morning were the first day."

Today we still call the light day. We have daylight when our side of the earth is turned toward the sun. We still call the darkness night. We have night when our side of the earth is turned away from the sun. Day and night keep coming because the earth keeps turning on its axis.

When the sun sets in the west, it is nighttime for us. But it is not nighttime everywhere. On the other side of the earth, the sun is starting to rise in the east. There, the day has only begun.

You could find this out for yourself. Right now you could call people in India. But they would need to get out of bed to answer the telephone. They might say, "Who's calling in the middle of the night!"

Sometimes people in New York call people in California. Perhaps they call after dark. But their friends in California say, "We still have daylight here."

The sun always sets three hours later in California than it does in New York. It always rises three hours later too. Lunch time in California is three hours later than lunch time in New York. In fact, everything is three hours later in California. Everything is later because people in California see the sun rise later than the people in New York.

The sun is always rising somewhere on the earth. It is always setting somewhere. Always there is day somewhere. Always there is night somewhere because the earth never stops rotating.

All of these things happen because of our wise, powerful God. Because of Him, the earth keeps

Materials needed:
- *bright, unshaded lamp*
- *globe*
- *clay*

Extra Information
Did you know—

. . . that in the 1800s, Wisconsin had 38 different local times in different parts of the state?

. . . that the most accurate clocks today measure time by atomic vibrations and are so accurate that in 300 years, they would lose or gain only one second?

. . . that the earth's speed of rotation is about 1,000 miles per hour at the equator?

. . . that every few years, a "leap second" is added because the earth has rotated slightly more slowly?

rotating. We never wonder whether the sun will rise each morning. Because of God, the earth always rotates toward the east. We do not wonder whether the sun might rise in the north one day and then set in the south.

It all happens in such a smooth, orderly way. But that does not surprise us if we know God. He is an orderly God. He is keeping His promise to Noah: "While the earth remaineth, seedtime and harvest . . . and day and night shall not cease."

A sunrise. What is moving to make the sun come up?

Answers for "Test Your Reading"

1. rotation
2. tilt
3. night or darkness
4. three
5. time or the day
6. b The earth turns on its axis.
7. b One rotation of the earth takes one day.
8. c The earth rotates toward the east.
9. a When we are having sunset, the people on the other side of the earth are having sunrise.

(Total: 9 points)

—————————— **Test Your Reading** ——————————

On your paper, write a word to fill each blank below.

1. The earth's spinning movement is called ——.
2. The slant of the earth's axis is called its ——.
3. We have —— when our side of the earth is turned away from the sun.
4. The sun rises —— hours later in California than it does in New York.
5. We measure —— by the earth's rotation.

Finish the sentences by choosing the best ending. Write both the letter and the complete sentence.

6. The earth turns on its
   (a) tilt.   (b) axis.   (c) pole.
7. One rotation of the earth takes one
   (a) month.   (b) day.   (c) year.
8. The earth rotates toward the
   (a) west.   (b) south.   (c) east.
9. When we are having sunset, the people on the other side of the earth are having
   (a) sunrise.   (b) night.   (c) noon.

Additional Demonstrations

Can you obtain a gyroscope? It makes an interesting demonstration of rotation on an axis. A spinning gyroscope can balance on a string or on the tip of a pencil.

Your students may need help to understand why the earth turns eastward when the sun seems to move westward. Demonstrate this concept by asking a few students to stand in the middle of the room. Tell them to turn around a few times while they watch the walls. Ask them which way the walls seemed to move. Then point out that they themselves had turned the opposite way. This can help them understand why the earth turns one way while the sun seems to move the opposite way.

Materials needed:
• *gyroscope*
• *pencil*

QUIZ

Write the New Words on the chalkboard. Ask the students to give the New Words they think of when you say the words and phrases below.

1. Spinning   *(rotation)*
2. Line through the earth   *(axis)*
3. Slant   *(tilt)*
4. One whole rotation   *(day)*

Extra Activities

Do these activities as your teacher directs.

1. Do you know your directions? Make signs for your classroom. Write *North*, *South*, *East*, and *West* on small cards. Also write *Sunrise* and *Sunset* on cards. Ask your teacher to help you hang them in the right places in your classroom. Try to learn them all by memory.
   Materials needed:
   • *6 index cards (3″ x 5″)*

2. This activity will teach you about the earth's rotation. Tape a ruler in a vertical position in the middle of a window. Now look around your classroom. Where is the ruler's shadow? Mark it with a piece of paper.
   Then wait for an hour or two. Again, look for the shadow. Is it in the same place? What does this tell you about the earth's rotation?
   Materials needed:
   • *12-inch ruler*
   • *masking tape*

3. For your unit project, paint half of a Styrofoam or Ping-Pong ball black. Label the black half *Night* and the white half *Day*. Blow up a yellow balloon, and label it *Sun*. Cut apart the individual compartments of an egg carton. You will need four compartments today, but save the rest for the following lessons.
   Ask your teacher to help you place the models on a large piece of poster board to show what makes day and night.
   Materials needed:
   • *Styrofoam ball*
   • *black poster paint*
   • *paintbrush*
   • *paper*
   • *tape*
   • *round yellow balloon*
   • *Styrofoam egg carton*
   • *toothpicks*
   • *poster board or large piece of cardboard*

Comments on "Extra Activities"

2. The earth's rotation will cause the shadow to move.

   If you have made the direction cards, as suggested in Activity 1, you will be better able to describe the eastward or westward movements of the sun and the earth.

   If your classroom is not on a side of the school where sunlight can enter the window, you can set up a mirror outdoors to reflect the light into your classroom.

3. Glue or tape the compartments of the egg carton to the poster board in the positions shown below. Fasten the model earths and the sun to the compartments with toothpicks. If you use Ping-Pong balls, you may need to pierce them with a pin before you can insert the toothpicks. Make sure that the day side of the day/night model faces the sun. The extra compartments are for the coming lessons.

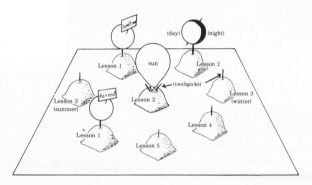

Lesson 3

God Promised Summer and Winter

New Words

leap year (lēp yēr), a year with one extra day.

Northern Hemisphere (nôr' thərn hem' ə • sfēr), the upper half of the earth.

orbit (ôr' bit), the path that the earth takes as it travels around the sun.

revolution (rev' ə • lōō' shən), one whole trip in a circle around a center point; the earth's movement around the sun.

Southern Hemisphere (suth' ərn hem' ə • sfēr), the lower half of the earth.

year (yēr), the time it takes for the earth to circle the sun once.

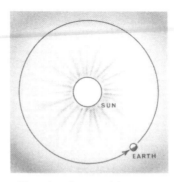

The earth revolves around the sun once a year.

Reading Together

You know that the earth is spinning. But it is also moving forward. Right now the earth is traveling forward eighteen miles every second!

Where is the earth going? It is speeding along a special path called an *orbit*. This orbit is a big circle around the sun.

In the picture, you see a circle that shows the earth's orbit. But we cannot really see the earth's orbit. It is not a road or a railroad track. Yet the earth stays on that orbit, just as a train stays on its tracks. Each trip around the sun is one *revolution*.

82

Lesson 3

CONCEPTS TO TEACH

- The earth revolves around the sun in a big circle that is called an orbit.
- We measure time by the earth's revolution; one revolution is one year.
- The earth turns 365 times on its axis as it revolves around the sun once.
- We add an extra day to our calendar every four years because the earth turns slightly more than 365 times a year.
- Because the earth is tilted on its axis, the Northern Hemisphere points toward the sun during half of its orbit, which makes summer.
- The Northern Hemisphere is tilted away from the sun during the other half of its orbit, which makes winter.
- The seasons in the Southern Hemisphere are opposite from those in the Northern Hemisphere.

- Two things make winter colder than summer:
  (1) We have less hours of daylight.
  (2) We have more slanting rays of sunshine because the sun is lower in the sky.

In summer the Northern Hemisphere is tilted toward the sun.

its axis while it revolves only once around the sun. This is why there are 365 days in a year.

Every year the earth turns a little more than 365 times on its axis. The extra turning is not even half a day. But in four years, the extra amounts of rotation added together make one whole day. Every fourth year, this extra day is added to the end of February. Such a year has 366 days and is called a *leap year.* So if your calendar shows February 29, you know that this year is a leap year.

In the last lesson, you learned that we measure time by the earth's rotation; one rotation is one day. We also measure time by the earth's revolution around the sun. One revolution is one *year.*

You know that a year is much longer than a day. That is because one revolution of the earth around the sun takes much longer than one rotation of the earth on its axis. In fact, the earth rotates 365 times on

Reading on Your Own

Look at the picture on the left. Do you see how the earth is divided into two halves? The upper half is called the *Northern Hemisphere.* The lower half is called the *Southern Hemisphere.*

We live in the Northern Hemisphere. During part of the earth's orbit, the Northern Hemisphere is tilted toward the sun. Then we have summer. But during the other part of the earth's orbit, it is tilted away from the sun. Then we have winter.

Summer in the Northern Hemisphere

HELPS FOR THE TEACHER

Introducing the Lesson

Who besides God has actually seen the earth revolving around the sun? Even the most brilliant scientist only believes what he has read or else has learned by indirect evidence. Small wonder then that not all third graders will find this concept easy to grasp.

However, the use of models can make this lesson surprisingly easy to understand. Begin by showing your geographical location on the globe. Fasten a small lump of clay on that place. Then darken the room except for a bright lamp in the center of the room. Explain that our earth would be dark and cold if we did not have the sun, which is like the lamp. Spin the globe to review *rotation.* Then walk around the lamp to explain the term *revolution.*

Now point to the axis of the globe. With the axis held perpendicularly, walk around the lamp. Meanwhile, explain that if the earth's axis were ac-

tually perpendicular, the earth would not have any seasons. Our climate would always be like springtime unless we lived near the equator or the poles.

Then tilt the globe at its usual angle. Explain that you will show how your area, which is marked by the clay, has seasons. Holding the globe, walk around the lamp again, being careful to always keep the axis pointed northward. Point out the clay's position (representing your area) during each of the seasons. (You will need to rotate the globe so that the clay appears in the light during each season.) Notice especially the difference between the summer position and the winter position. The clay will appear noticeably lower and in more direct light in the summer position.

Materials needed:
- *globe*
- *clay*
- *bright lamp without shade*

In winter the Northern Hemisphere is tilted away from the sun.

People who live in the Southern Hemisphere also have seasons. But their seasons are exactly opposite from ours. The Southern Hemisphere has summer when the Northern Hemisphere has winter. While we are making snowmen, the children in the Southern Hemisphere may be outdoors, running barefooted. Their hemisphere is tilted toward the sun when ours is tilted away from it.

You know that winter comes when the Northern Hemisphere tilts away from the sun. But what difference does the tilt make? Why are winters colder than summers?

Because of the earth's tilt, the sun is hidden more in the winter. Then we have longer nights and shorter days. We have more hours of darkness and less hours of daylight. For this reason, winter is colder than summer.

Think of the sunshine at noon. How warm is it? Now think of the sunshine in the evening. How warm is it? You know that the sunshine is warmer at noon. When the sun is high in the sky, its bright rays shine straight down on us. But in the evening, the rays of sunshine are more slanted. The evening sunshine is not as warm as the noon sunshine, even though the same sun shines at both times.

This can help you understand another reason why winter is colder than summer. Because of the earth's tilt, winter sunshine is always more slanted than summer sunshine. For this reason, the winter sunshine is

Winter in the Northern Hemisphere

Extra Information

Did you know—

. . . that if our solar system could shrink until the earth were the size and weight of a Ping-Pong ball, the sun would still measure over four yards across and weigh about three fourths of a ton?

. . . that because the earth's gravity and centrifugal force are never quite balanced, the earth moves at changing speeds, which causes it to travel in an elliptical orbit?

. . . that because of the earth's elliptical orbit, the Northern Hemisphere is about three million miles *closer* to the sun during the winter?

Additional Activity

This activity allows the students to feel how much warmer vertical sunlight is than slanting sunlight. Drape a dark sweater over a globe. Fasten one safety pin onto the sweater over the general area where you live. Fasten the other pin onto the sweater over the center of South America. Place the globe in a sunny window. Point the globe's axis away from the sun. Wait a few minutes for the sun to warm the globe.

During this time, explain the purpose of this activity and the advantage of using a dark color to absorb the heat faster. Tell the class that soon you will compare the warmth of the two areas. Your area is receiving slanting light, and South America is receiving direct light. Ask the class to predict which area should feel warmer.

After a few minutes, feel the two areas. Blindfold a student and place his hands on the areas. Ask him which feels warmer.

Finally, position the sweater and globe so that

spread out over a larger area. This makes winter colder than summer.

Why do we have seasons? Seasons are caused by the tilt of the earth. This tilt causes one hemisphere to receive less hours of sunshine and more slanted sunshine than the other hemisphere.

It is God who gives us our seasons. He made the sun and the earth. He set the earth on just the right tilt. God is the one who keeps the earth on its orbit.

All this is God's way of keeping His promise to Noah: "While the earth remaineth, seedtime and harvest, . . . and summer and winter, and day and night shall not cease."

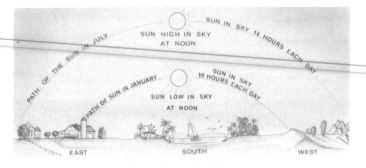

—————— **Test Your Reading** ——————

Draw a picture for each exercise.
1. Draw the shape of the earth's orbit.
2. Draw the earth, and label the Northern and Southern hemispheres.
3. Draw the sun. Draw the earth to the right of it. Show which way the earth's axis tilts when the Northern Hemisphere has winter.
4. Draw something we do or see outdoors in the Northern Hemisphere while the Southern Hemisphere has summer.

Give the answers.
5. What is the name of the earth's trip around the sun?
6. How long does it take the earth to make one complete circle around the sun?
7. What is the name of a year with 366 days? Why is an extra day added to this year?
8. Give two reasons why winters are colder than summers.

Answers for "Test Your Reading"

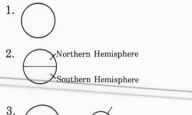

1.
2. Northern Hemisphere / Southern Hemisphere
3. sun   earth
4. drawing of snowflakes, icicles, snowmen, sledding, and so forth
5. revolution
6. one year
7. leap year

Each year the earth turns a little more than 365 times. In four years, the extra amounts of turning added together make the extra day.   (2)
8. There are less hours of sunshine. The sunshine is more slanting (or spread over a greater area).   (2)

(Total: 10 points)

the axis points toward the sun. Follow through as before. Notice that the seasons are now reversed. Emphasize the reason for the difference in temperature. The same sunlight strikes both areas, but because of the globe's roundness, some areas receive more sunlight than other areas.

Materials needed:
• globe
• 2 safety pins
• dark sweater

QUIZ

Write the New Words on the chalkboard. Ask the students to choose one for each question below.
1. Which one means the earth's path around the sun? *(orbit)*
2. Which one means the top half of the earth? *(Northern Hemisphere)*
3. Which one means one complete circle of the earth around the sun? *(revolution)*
4. Which one means the time it takes the earth to circle the sun? *(year)*
5. Which one means the bottom half of the earth? *(Southern Hemisphere)*
6. Which one means a year with one extra day? *(leap year)*

Comments on "Extra Activities"

1. The spot of slanting light is larger and fainter, but the spot of direct light is smaller and brighter. In the winter, slanting light is not as bright and warm as direct light in the summer.

4. Make sure that the axis of the winter model earth is tilted away from the sun, and that the axis of the summer model is tilted toward the sun.

Extra Activities

Do these activities as your teacher directs.

1. It is easy to see the difference between slanting light and direct light. Darken the classroom as much as possible. Shine a strong flashlight straight at the chalkboard. With a chalk, draw a circle around the spot that is lighted. Notice how bright it is.

   Then shine the flashlight so that the light slants toward the chalkboard. Again circle the spot that is lighted, and notice how bright it is.

   Which spot is larger? Which spot was brighter? What does this tell you about slanting sunlight in the winter? What does it tell you about direct light in the summer?

   Materials needed:
   • *flashlight with bright beam*

2. Ask your teacher, parents, or minister to help you get the name and address of a school in the Southern Hemisphere. Perhaps your church has a mission in Paraguay or Brazil in South America.

   Write a letter to this school. Tell the children there that you are studying about the seasons. Tell them what your season is like now. Write what you like to do during this season.

   Then ask the schoolchildren to write back to you. Ask them to tell about the season they are having right now. What do they like to do during this season?

3. Draw a picture that shows your home or farm in the summer. Then draw another picture that shows your home or farm in the winter. Tell about the differences in your pictures.

4. For your unit project, paint half of each Styrofoam ball one color. Paint the other halves another color. Label the halves that are alike *Northern Hemisphere.* Label the other halves that are alike *Southern Hemisphere.* Take the two halves that are labeled *Northern Hemisphere,* and write *Winter* on the one label and *Summer* on the other label. Push a toothpick axis through each model earth. Fasten the models to the Styrofoam stands with more toothpicks. Also, draw arrows on the poster board to show the direction in which the earth is traveling.

   Materials needed:
   • *2 Styrofoam or Ping-Pong balls*   • *paper*
   • *2 colors of poster paint*   • *tape*
   • *paintbrush*   • *toothpicks*

God Gave Us the Moon

New Words

crescent moon (kres′ ənt mōōn), the phase of the moon when it looks
like a thin slice.

full moon (fool mōōn), the phase of the moon when it looks like
a whole circle.

gravity (grav′ ə • tē), the downward pull of the earth, sun, or
moon.

new moon (nōō mōōn), the phase of the moon when it is dark.

phases (fāz′ əz), the different shapes of the moon.

quarter moon (kwôr′ tər mōōn), the phase of the moon when it looks
like a half circle.

tides (tīdz), the daily rise and fall of the oceans caused by the pull
of the moon.

Reading Together

We all say that the moon shines.
But the moon cannot make any light.
It does not burn like the sun does.

Moonlight is really light from the
sun. The sunlight strikes the moon.
Some of it bounces down to earth.
Then we can see the sun's light even
at night.

The moon is like a great ball of
rock. One side of it always receives
sunlight, just as one side of the earth
always receives sunlight. But most
of the time, we see only part of the
moon's lighted half. And sometimes
we cannot see any of the moon's
lighted half. What causes this?

Full moon

87

Lesson 4

CONCEPTS TO TEACH

- The moon shines because the sun shines on it.
- The moon revolves around the earth in 29 1/2 days, which is almost a month. (You might also tell the class that the word *month* comes from the word *moon*.)
- Because the moon changes position in relation to the sun and earth, the moon appears to change shape.
- The first crescent and the first quarter moon can be seen in the evening; the last quarter and the last crescent moon can be seen in the early morning.
- The full moon can be seen all night.
- The gravity of the earth holds us to the ground.
- The gravity of the earth keeps the moon in orbit.
- The moon also has gravity that pulls on the earth.
- The moon's gravity causes the ocean to rise and fall several feet every day.
- The gravity of the sun keeps the earth in orbit.
- God gave us the moon for a little light at night.

HELPS FOR THE TEACHER

Introducing the Lesson

This demonstration can give your class an idea of the relative size and distance between the earth, moon, and sun. Cut out a circle
1/8 inch in diameter: ◯
Label it *Moon*.
Cut out another circle
1/2 inch in diameter: ◯
Label it *Earth*.
Place the circles 15 inches apart on your classroom wall.

For the model sun, tape some sheets of newspaper together. Draw a circle 4 1/2 feet in diameter, using a pencil and a 27-inch string as a compass. (Allow extra string for tying around the

The moon is always moving around the earth. It revolves around the earth, just as the earth revolves around the sun. As the moon moves from place to place, the part that we can see keeps changing. To us, it looks like the moon's shape is changing. These changes are called *phases*.

When the moon's darkened half faces the earth, we cannot see any moonlight. This phase is called *new moon*. During new moon, the night seems very dark.

After new moon, the moon's lighted side slowly turns toward us. Then it looks like a thin sliver of light. This is the first *crescent moon*. We can see a first crescent moon in the evening.

As the moon keeps moving in its orbit, we keep seeing more of its lighted side. Soon we can see half of it. This phase is the first *quarter moon*. Like the first crescent, the first quarter can be seen in the evening.

Every night we can see more and more of the moon. When we see all of the lighted part, the moon looks like a large, shiny coin in the sky. This phase is called *full moon*. A full moon seems very bright. We can see it all night.

After full moon, the moon's lighted side begins to turn away from us. Every night the moon seems to shrink. When the moon is again a half circle, the phase is called the last quarter. The last quarter is seen in the morning.

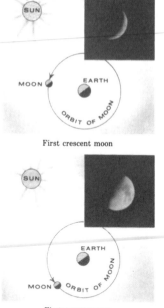

First crescent moon

First quarter moon

On and on, the moon keeps moving around the earth. Finally we see only a thin slice again. This phase is the last crescent. Like the last quarter, it can also be seen in the morning.

In a few days, it will be time for the new moon again. Then the moon will be right back where it started in its orbit. It will have finished one revolution in 29 1/2 days. This is almost one month.

---

pencil, and hold the loose end of the string in place on the circle's center.) Label this circle *Sun*. If possible, place some kind of marker about 485 feet (162 yard–long steps) from the classroom where you will present the earth and moon models.

Begin class by showing the earth and moon models. Explain that the sun, earth, and moon are all so large that you will pretend that they are many, many times smaller than they are. In this way, they can understand them better. Inform the students that if the earth and moon were the same size as your models, they would be located just as far apart as you have placed them (15 inches).

Now show the sun model. How far away should it be? Tell the class that even at this small scale, the sun would be far out on the playground. If it is not suitable to take your class outdoors now, tell them to look for your marker when you dismiss them for recess. Or if you have not placed a marker, point out a landmark about 450 to 500 feet away.

Materials needed:
- *paper*
- *pencil*
- *scissors*
- *yardstick*
- *several sheets of newspaper*
- *tape*
- *string*

Extra Information
Did you know—
- . . . that the moon's average speed is 2,300 miles per hour?
- . . . that the moon actually moves from west to east in the sky? However, the moon seems to move from east to west because its revolution takes much longer than the earth's rotation.
- . . . that although the moon appears to circle around the earth, actually they both weave back and forth around their barycenter, which is their common center of gravity?

Whose ball will fall into the glove? Why?

Reading on Your Own

Look at Jerry and Beth. Both of them hold a ball near the glove. Both of them will open their hands at the same time. Which ball will move? That is easy to answer. Jerry's ball will move. It will fall right into the glove. Beth's ball will stay in her hand. It will not move.

Why does Jerry's ball fall? It falls because the earth pulls it down. But why and how does the earth pull? No one knows. That is one of God's secrets.

The pull of the earth is called *gravity.* Gravity pulls down on everything we can see. It holds us and everything else to the earth.

The earth's gravity keeps the moon in orbit. It pulls hard enough so that the moon will not go speeding away from the earth. But it does not pull so hard that the moon comes crashing down into the earth.

The moon is smaller than the earth. The moon's gravity is not as strong as the earth's gravity. But the moon still pulls at the earth. We especially notice the moon's pull on the oceans. Every day the moon causes part of the ocean to rise several feet. The other parts of the ocean sink several feet. This daily rise and fall of the oceans is called the *tides.* The gravity of the moon causes these tides.

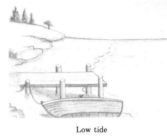

High tide   Low tide

. . . that tides have been harnessed to produce electricity for the Canadians, the French, and the Russians?

Study the illustration below. Although it is not drawn to scale, it illustrates the paths taken by the moon and earth.

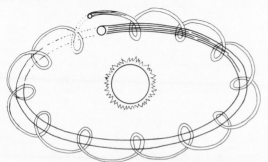

While the moon is orbiting around the earth, the earth itself is orbiting the sun. This gives the moon a looping path as the earth and the moon travel together around the sun. Why would the moon's path have twelve loops in it?

Additional Demonstration

This demonstration may be helpful to students who have trouble understanding that the moon's position causes its phases.

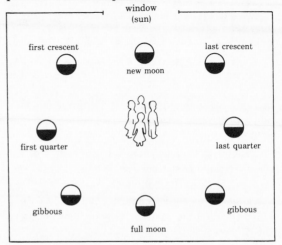

Use poster paint or a Magic Marker to blacken

The sun also has gravity. Because the sun is very large, it has very much gravity. The sun's gravity has a much stronger pull than the gravity of the earth or the moon.

We are very glad for the sun's gravity. It keeps the earth in its orbit. Without the sun's gravity, the earth would fly far away into dark, cold, empty space. Nothing could live that far away from the sun.

The amount of gravity between the sun, earth, and moon is just right because God knew just how large to make them. He knew just how far apart to place them. He knew just how fast to make them travel in their orbits.

Why did God give us the moon? He wanted to give us a little light at night. The Bible says, "And God made two great lights; the greater light to rule the day, and the lesser light to rule the night."

Answers for "Test Your Reading"

1. no
2. yes
3. yes
4. yes
5. no
6. yes

——————————— **Test Your Reading** ———————————

Read each sentence below. Write yes *if it is true. Write* no *if it is not true.*

1. The sun gets its light from the moon.
2. The moon's shape seems to change because we see different amounts of its lighted side.
3. The moon revolves around the earth in 29 1/2 days.
4. The gravity of the moon causes tides.
5. The gravity of the earth keeps the sun in orbit.
6. God made the moon so that we have some light at night.

Make a chart of the moon's phases like the one below. Write the name of each phase, draw its shape, and tell when it can be seen. The first ones are done for you.

Name	new moon	first crescent	first quarter	full moon	last quarter	last crescent
Shape:		)	7.	9.	11.	13.
When seen:	is not seen	in the evening	8.	10.	12.	14.

Name:	new moon	first crescent	first quarter	full moon	last quarter	last crescent
Shape:		)	7. D	9. ○	11. (	13. (
When seen:	is not seen	in the evening	8. in the evening	10. all night	12. in the morning	14. in the morning

(Total: 14 points)

half of a white Styrofoam ball. Then punch a thin nail into the line between the two halves. You can hold your "moon" by this nail.

Have the students stand in the center of the room. Explain that they should think of the window as the sun, the ball as the moon, and themselves as the earth. When facing the window, they are in the daytime position. Having their backs to the window is like being turned away from the sun at night.

Show how you will hold the moon so that the white side always faces the window. Of course, this resembles the moon's lighted side that always faces the sun.

Your first position is in front of the window. Can they see the lighted side of the moon from where they are standing? No, they cannot. The moon's phase is a new moon. Then move counterclockwise until you stand in line with the first corner of the room. Can they see the moon now? Ask them to describe the shape of the white part. Identify this as the first crescent phase.

Extra Activities

Do these activities as your teacher directs.

1. Show the movements of the earth and moon with two friends. Ask one friend to stand in the middle as the sun. Ask the other friend to be the earth. He should keep turning as he walks around the "sun." Then you be the moon and walk around the "earth." Can you do it without becoming mixed up or dizzy?

2. If it is not cloudy, you can look at the moon tonight. First, check a calendar that shows the phases of the moon. By studying such a calendar, you can know which day of the month to look for each phase of the moon. If you know the moon's phase, you can know what time of the night to look for it. Use a pair of binoculars or a telescope. Can you see the mountains and craters on the moon? The craters are the bowl-shaped holes on the moon.

   Materials needed:
   • *calendar showing the phases of the moon*
   • *binoculars or telescope*

3. Make a poster about gravity. Write the heading, "Gravity at Work." Draw pictures to show the power of gravity. Here is a list of ideas to help you start.

rain falling	waterfalls
a ball falling	a bicycle rolling downhill
gravel being unloaded from a dump truck	children sledding

   Materials needed:
   • *large sheet of poster board*
   • *crayons, markers, or poster paints*

4. To add to your unit project, use clay to model a moon about as big as a marble, and fasten it with a toothpick to a model earth. Fasten the earth to an egg carton compartment glued on the poster board, as shown below.

   Materials needed:
   • *clay or Play-Doh*
   • *Styrofoam ball*
   • *toothpicks*
   • *glue*

Comments on "Extra Activities"

1. If there is snow on the ground, this activity may be done outdoors. Ask the students to walk very carefully in the snow, with the "earth" and "moon" a few yards apart. Then you can see that the moon's path is not a series of circles but of S-curves.

🌑 New Moon
🌒 waxing crescent
🌓 first Quarter
🌔 waxing gibbous
🌕 Full moon
🌖 Waning gibbous
🌗 last Quarter
🌘 Waning crescent

Continue in the same way for the other phases, as shown in the illustration on page 93. Remember to keep the white half of the moon facing the window.

You could also ask the students to slowly rotate once during each moon phase. This will help them understand the earth's day and night and the evening and morning phases of the moon.

Materials needed:
• *white Styrofoam ball or worn-out softball*
• *black poster paint*
• *thin nail*
• *4 3" x 5" index cards*

QUIZ

Make a set of flash cards with simple outlines of the moon's phases. To tell the new moon and the full moon apart, color the inside of the new moon black. Draw rays around the full moon. The students may also need help in telling the first and last quarters and the crescent moons apart. You could explain that the moon always 'fills up" from the right, and always "empties" from the right. Remember this little rhyme:

   The moon at night
   Fills from the right.

Here is another tip. The "first" phases are seen in the first part of the night (before midnight); the "last" phases are seen in the last part of the night (after midnight).

Lesson 5

God Gave Man a Sign of His Promise

New Words

prism (priz′ əm), a clear object that separates sunlight into its colors.

rainbow (rān′ bō), a curved band of different-colored light in the sky.

spectrum (spek′ trəm), all the colors found in white light.

Reading Together

How kind and faithful God was to Noah! God had showed him how to build the strong, watertight ark. God had kept Noah and his family safe during the long flood. He had provided all their needs.

Noah wanted to show God how thankful he was. So after the Flood, he built an altar to God. He gave many birds and animals to God as burnt offerings.

God was pleased with Noah's offerings and made a special promise to him. God promised to never again send a flood to destroy all the earth. As a sign that He would keep His promise, God set a lovely *rainbow* in the clouds.

Noah had never seen a rainbow before. What did he think when he saw those shining stripes of color? Maybe he thought, "How beautiful! I will never forget this. I will always remember God's promise." (Look on the first page of this unit for a picture about this story.)

Ever since the Flood, God has kept His promise. Never again has there been such a great flood. The earth has always had seedtime and harvest. It has always had summer and winter. It has always had day and night.

We still see rainbows today. They make us think of God's promise. They help us remember His faithfulness. They remind us that everything God makes is beautiful and orderly.

How is a rainbow orderly? First of all, each rainbow has these same colors: red, orange, yellow, green, blue, and violet. Besides this, the colors always come in the same order, as given above. Red is on the outside of the rainbow, and violet is on the inside.

92

Lesson 5

CONCEPTS TO TEACH

- God has been faithful to the promise He made to Noah.
- The rainbow reminds us of God's promise.
- The rainbow shows us the order and beauty of God's handiwork.
- Sunlight is made of many colors.
- A prism will separate the colors of sunlight into the spectrum.
- Rainbows and other spectrums from white light show these colors in this order: red, orange, yellow, green, blue, and violet.

HELPS FOR THE TEACHER

Introducing the Lesson

Read Genesis 8:20–9:17 to your class.

It is a good practice to read Bible stories such as this. If you always tell a Bible story in your own words, your students may unconsciously think of it as just another story. To them, it may be on the same level as all the other stories they hear or read. You can remind your students of the absolute truth of this and other Bible stories by reading directly from the Bible.

However, you will want to make sure that your students understand what you read. You could pause in your reading to discuss verses such as 8:22, 9:11, and 9:16.

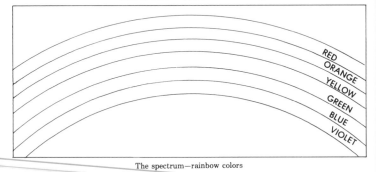

The spectrum—rainbow colors

Reading on Your Own

When is the best time to see a rainbow? Watch for bright sunlight during or after a shower of rain. Stand with your back to the sun, and look at the sky. If the rainfall was heavy, the rainbow may look brighter and spread farther than usual. Both of its ends may seem to touch the earth.

Sometimes a rainbow looks like a whole circle! But such a rainbow can only be seen from a high mountain or from an airplane. The sun must be low in the sky. Its rays must strike the raindrops just right. Then the rainbow looks like a bright wheel of color.

Rainbows can often be seen near a large waterfall, such as Niagara Falls. The mist rising from the falls works like the raindrops in other rainbows.

You can even help to make a rainbow. Do you have a garden hose on an outdoor faucet? As before, stand with your back to the sun. Then spray a fine mist of water into the air. Do you see a little part of a rainbow?

You know that rain and sunlight are needed to make a rainbow. But how can that be? How can clear rain and white sunlight make a colorful rainbow?

Sunlight is really made of many colors. Usually the colors are all mixed together. This makes the light look white.

Sometimes the rays of sunlight strike the raindrops with just the right slant. Then the sunlight is scattered. The different colors are separated from each other. They form a rainbow in the sky.

All the colors of the rainbow make a *spectrum.* But we do not need to wait for the next rainbow in order to see a spectrum. We can use a *prism.* A prism does the same work as the raindrops. It separates white light into the colors of the spectrum.

Extra Information

Did you know—

. . . that a rainbow over North Wales lasted more than three hours?

. . . that moonlight can cause faint rainbows?

. . . that by studying the spectrum of a star, scientists can discover its temperature, chemical composition, and direction of travel?

. . . that because of spectrochemical analysis, which is the analysis of materials according to their spectrums, air and water pollution can be measured, the presence of metal can be detected, the quality of molten metal can be tested, and criminals can be convicted?

QUIZ

Ask the students to copy the New Words on a piece of paper, making sure to spell them correctly. Then ask them to choose a word to match each sentence below. Some words will be used more than once.

1. It is a sign of God's promise. *(rainbow)*
2. It separates white light into its colors. *(prism)*
3. It is the band of colors found in any white light. *(spectrum)*
4. It is a spectrum in the sky. *(rainbow)*
5. It can be carried in your hands. *(prism)*

A prism is shaped like a wedge. It is made of a clear material such as glass. When sunlight enters the prism, the rays of light are bent and scattered. The light spreads out into the bright colors of the spectrum. Of course, the colors are always in the same order as in a rainbow: red, orange, yellow, green, blue, and violet.

We know a little about the way white light makes a spectrum of color. But we know so much less than God knows. Only He could plan and create light and color.

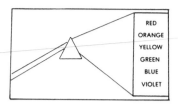

A prism used to make a spectrum

These beautiful gifts should cause us to bow before God in worship. We should thank Him for keeping His promises so faithfully.

Answers for "Test Your Reading"

A. Noah should not be offering fruits and vegetables.

The colors of the rainbow are in the wrong order.

The sun should not be beside the rainbow, facing Noah. (3)

B. 1. destroy the whole earth with a flood.

2. promises.

3. beautiful and orderly. (Answers may vary.) (2)

4. many colors.

5. all the colors in a rainbow.

6. separate white light (or sunlight) into its colors.

(Total: 10 points)

Test Your Reading

See pupil's book for color.

A. *Look at the picture above. It shows some things that you studied in your lesson. Can you find three things that are wrong in the picture?*

B. *Finish each of the sentences below.*

1. God promised Noah that He would never again ——.

2. God has always kept His ——.

3. Rainbows remind us that God's works are both —— and ——.

4. Although sunlight looks white, it is made of ——.

5. A spectrum is made of ——.

6. Both raindrops and prisms can ——.

Extra Activities

Do these activities as your teacher directs.

1. Make a little rainbow by spraying water, as explained in the lesson. Or blow some soap bubbles with wire that is bent into a circle. On the bubbles, you can see tiny spectrums of color.
   Materials needed:
   • *bubble solution: 1/4 cup dish detergent in 1 quart water (Let it "age" for several days for best results.)*
   • *thin wire*
2. If you have a prism, use it to make a spectrum on the wall. If you do not have a prism, use a container made of clear glass. Set the container on the edge of a windowsill in bright sunlight. Fill it with water almost to the brim. Put white paper where the spectrum appears so that you can see the colors more clearly.
   Here are some interesting activities to do with the spectrum.
   a. Watch your hand, your pencil, and other things change color when you hold them in front of the spectrum.
   b. Draw a red "happy face" on paper. On top of that, draw a green "sad face." Watch what happens when you hold it in front of the red or green light of the spectrum.
   c. Get some different colors of clear glass or plastic. Watch what happens when you hold them in front of the spectrum.
   d. Place the prism so that the spectrum shines on a certain spot on the wall. Any marked spot such as a picture or a strip of paneling is fine. Watch how fast the spectrum moves away from that spot. This is how fast the earth rotates on its axis.
   Materials needed:
   • *prism or clear glass container*   • *pencil*
   • *water*   • *crayons*
   • *white paper*   • *colored glass or clear plastic*
3. Your unit project is almost finished. Today draw two small pictures: a child and a rainbow with some raindrops. Glue the pictures onto toothpicks. Ask your teacher to help you place them correctly into the model earth. Fasten the model earth to the last egg carton compartment on the poster board.
   When you have finished, use all of your models to help you remember what you have learned. See if you can tell about each lesson by looking at the models.
   Materials needed: • *glue*   • *Styrofoam ball*
   • *drawing paper*   • *toothpicks*

Comments on "Extra Activities"

2. The glass container should be completely plain, with no etchings or designs. Set it out as far as possible on the edge of the windowsill. Because the glass container should be filled to the brim, you may want a towel nearby to wipe up any spills.
3. Help the students to stick the pictures correctly into the last model earth. Place the child so that he faces the rainbow and raindrops and has his back toward the sun.

Answer Key

Match

1. l
2. c
3. b
4. f
5. a
6. i
7. d
8. k
9. h
10. j
11. g
12. e

Fill

13. climate
14. growing season
15. axis
16. day
17. year
18. leap year
19. crescent
20. full
21. new
22. Gravity
23. tides
24. rainbow

Lesson 6

Do You Remember What You Learned?

Match each word on the right to its meaning on the left.

1. Slant of the earth's axis	a. crop
2. Upper half of the earth	b. germination
3. Changing from seed to tiny plant	c. Northern Hemisphere
4. Separates white light into colors	d. orbit
5. Plants raised in a field	e. phases
6. Turning on an axis	f. prism
7. Path of the earth or moon	g. quarter moon
8. All the colors of a rainbow	h. revolution
9. One complete journey around the sun	i. rotation
10. Lower half of the earth	j. Southern Hemisphere
11. Half of a full moon	k. spectrum
12. Shapes of the moon	l. tilt

Fill each blank with a word or phrase from the box.

axis	full	new
climate	gravity	rainbow
crescent	growing season	tides
day	leap year	year

13. A —— may be warm, cold, wet, or dry.
14. Our —— —— is the part of the year when the weather is suitable for raising plants.
15. The earth spins on its ——.
16. One —— is one rotation of the earth on its axis.
17. One —— is one revolution of the earth around the sun.
18. In a —— ——, one extra day is added to the year.
19. A —— moon is shaped like a slice of an apple.
20. A —— moon is completely round.
21. During —— moon, we cannot see the moon.
22. —— holds us to the earth.
23. The moon's gravity causes —— in the oceans.
24. God made a —— to remind us that He keeps His promises.

96

Lesson 6

Discuss the unit as a whole. Review the vocabulary words and key concepts of this unit. Although you need not insist that students spell every vocabulary word correctly, they should have a reasonable amount of accuracy.

If you did the unit project, you may ask a few students to use it to explain some basic concepts of a lesson that they choose. By occasionally having a student "teach" the class like this, the concepts will be reinforced clearly in his mind. Sometimes also, when a student puts the concepts in his own words, it can help the other students grasp the concepts.

Decide whether each sentence is true, and write yes *or* no.

25. We need a harvest because we need food to eat.
26. People all over the world raise crops that are suited to their climate.
27. Time is measured by the rotation and revolution of the earth.
28. In California midnight is three hours earlier than in New York.
29. The sun is always rising somewhere on the earth.
30. During one year, the earth rotates 536 times on its axis.
31. The earth revolves around the moon in one month.
32. The earth's gravity keeps the sun in orbit.
33. God promised that never again would the earth have any floods.

Choose the best answer.

34. When the Southern Hemisphere is tilted toward the sun, it has
    (a) summer.   (b) fall.   (c) winter.
35. When the Northern Hemisphere has fall, the Southern Hemisphere has
    (a) summer.   (b) winter.   (c) spring.
36. When our side of the earth is turned toward the sun, we have
    (a) night.   (b) sunset.   (c) daylight.
37. The sun rises in the east because the earth rotates
    (a) toward the west.   (b) toward the south.   (c) toward the east.
38. The moon gets its light from
    (a) the earth.   (b) the sun.   (c) the stars.
39. The moon has different phases because
    (a) at times the earth shuts off its light.
    (b) the sun does not always shine on it.
    (c) it moves to places where we see more or less of its light.
40. God gave the moon to us
    (a) so that we have a little light at night.
    (b) so that we have more heat.
    (c) so that we can see the stars.

Write the answers.

41-43. Name three things that man needs to do to have a harvest.
44-46. Name three things that God has provided for a harvest.
47-48. Give two reasons why winters are colder than summers.

Draw these pictures.

49-50. Draw and color a rainbow. Be sure to put the colors in the right order.
51-53. Draw these phases of the moon: full moon, first quarter, and last quarter. Under each phase, tell when it can be seen.

Decide

25. yes
26. yes
27. yes
28. no
29. yes
30. no
31. no
32. no
33. no

Choose

34. a
35. c
36. c
37. c
38. b
39. c
40. a

Write

41-43. (Any three) He must break up the soil.
He must plant the seeds.
He must remove the weeds.
He must harvest at the right time.   *(3 points)*

44-46. (Any three) sunlight, warmth, rain, soil, minerals, germination, growing season

(3 points)

47-48. In the winter, there are less hours of sunshine (or shorter days). In the winter, the sunshine is more slanting (or the sunshine is spread over a larger area).   *(2 points)*

Draw

49-50. See the illustration on page 93 of the textbook.   *(6 points)*

51-53. See the answer key on page 94 of the teacher's manual.   *(6 points)*

(Total: 60 points)

Unit Four
God Gave Us Heat and Cold

"While the earth remaineth . . . cold and heat . . . shall not cease" (Genesis 8:22).

Look at the picture above. How can you tell that there is heat in the picture? Noah and his family do not seem to be shivering. But you do not need to look at Noah's family. Can you find four other things in the picture that show us there is heat?

The sun is shining. It gives off heat. You can also see the fire burning on the altar. You know that a fire makes heat. But what about the plants? Do you remember that green plants need warmth before they will grow? Since these plants have grown, they must have received heat. Look at the clouds. You know that clouds are made of water. How did the water get up into the sky? Heat caused the water to evaporate. After that, the water cooled and condensed into clouds. Heat was needed to make the clouds.

The picture above has helped you think about heat. In this unit, you will learn more about it. In fact, you have already been learning about heat. In Unit One, you learned that heat is used to distill alcohol and to separate petroleum into useful liquids. In Unit Three, you learned that different amounts of the sun's heat cause warm summers and cold winters.

This shows you how important heat and cold are to us. God knew this. After the Flood, He promised Noah, "While the earth remaineth, . . . cold and heat . . . shall not cease." God has kept His promise. We still have cold and heat. Every day heat and cold are very much a part of our lives.

98

Unit Four

~~God Gave Us Heat and Cold~~

For Your Inspiration

The heavens declare the glory of God;
    and the firmament sheweth his handywork.
Day unto day uttereth speech,
    and night unto night sheweth knowledge.
There is no speech nor language,
    where their voice is not heard.
Their line is gone out through all the earth,
    and their words to the end of the world.

In them hath he set a tabernacle for the sun,
Which is as a bridegroom coming out of his chamber,
    and rejoiceth as a strong man to run a race.
His going forth is from the end of the heaven,
    and his circuit unto the ends of it:
And there is nothing hid from the heat thereof.

Psalm 19:1-6

We Measure Temperature

New Words

boiling point (boi′ ling point), the temperature at which a liquid boils.

degree (di • grē′), the unit for measuring temperature.

freezing point (frē′ zing point), the temperature at which a liquid freezes.

temperature (tem′ pər • ə • chər), how hot or cold something is.

thermometer (thər • mom′ ə • tər), a tool that measures temperature.

Reading Together

We say, "Let's eat before the food gets cold." We also say that snow is cold. How cold is cold? We talk about a hot stove and about the hot sun. How hot is hot?

Hot and *cold* tell about *temperature.* But these words can mean very different temperatures. Snow is much colder than the cold food on our table. The sun is many times hotter than the hottest stove.

When we want to know exactly how hot or cold something is, we use a *thermometer.* A thermometer measures temperature.

One kind of thermometer looks like a clock. Around the edges are many small marks that are numbered. The marks are all placed the same distance apart. Sometimes the

distance from one mark to the next is one *degree;* sometimes it is two degrees.

This thermometer is like a clock with only one hand. The hand is fastened to a spring that is made of two metals. When the weather becomes cooler, the spring curls up more

99

Lesson 1

CONCEPTS TO TEACH

- We tell how hot or cold something is with a thermometer.
- Temperature is measured in degrees on either the Fahrenheit scale or the Celsius scale.
- Some thermometers use liquid mercury or colored alcohol.
- Other thermometers have a metal spring that moves a pointer on a dial.
- Some important points on a thermometer are:

freezing point of water:	0°C	32°F
boiling point of water:	100°C	212°F
room temperature:	20°C	68°F
body temperature:	37°C	98°F

Note: The students should memorize these temperatures by making flashcards or card pairs to match.

HELPS FOR THE TEACHER

Introducing the Lesson

First, introduce the unit. The students may read the introduction, page through the unit, and look at the pictures.

Now focus on Lesson 1. Show various thermometers, such as a candy thermometer, a fever thermometer, a weather thermometer, or a meat thermometer. Include at least one with the Celsius scale.

Use a weather thermometer to see whether your room temperature is the same as the normal room temperature. Have all the students learn to read the weather thermometer.

Use a fever thermometer to take several students' temperatures. (Remember to sterilize the thermometer between uses.) Point out that the normal body temperature is slightly higher than 98°F. But for their lesson today, 98° is close enough.

Materials needed:

- *various thermometers*
- *alcohol (to sterilize thermometer)*

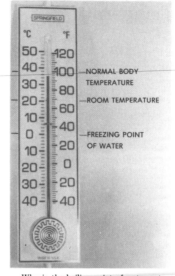

—NORMAL BODY
TEMPERATURE

—ROOM TEMPERATURE

—FREEZING POINT
OF WATER

Why is the boiling point of water not
labeled on the thermometer?

In this kind of thermometer, we can tell how warm the weather is by seeing how high the liquid rises in the tube. It has degree marks with numbers along the glass tube.

One scale of degree marks was made by a man named Fahrenheit (far′ ən • hīt). Fahrenheit's scale is probably on the thermometers in your home.

Reading on Your Own

When you go to town, you may see 45°F on a flashing sign. Can you guess what that means? The little circle means degrees. The *F* stands for the Fahrenheit scale. As you can see, 45°F is just a quick way to write "45 degrees Fahrenheit."

You may also see 15°C on a sign. The *C* stands for the Celsius (sel′ sē • əs) scale. This scale was made by a man named Celsius. Celsius degrees are a little farther apart than Fahrenheit degrees.

Many people like the Celsius scale better than the Fahrenheit scale. On the Celsius scale, water freezes at zero degrees. This temperature, 0°C, is called the *freezing point* of water. The temperature at which water boils, or the *boiling point* of water, is 100°C. Of course, 0°C and 100°C are easy to remember. This is why many people like the Celsius scale.

On the Fahrenheit scale, the freezing point of water is 32°. The boiling point of water is 212°.

Your body's temperature is very

tightly. The hand points to a lower number. But when the weather becomes warmer, the metal spring loosens. Then the hand points to a higher degree of temperature.

An even more common weather thermometer has a thin glass tube that holds a liquid. In many thermometers, the liquid is alcohol that has been colored red or blue. In some thermometers, the liquid is silver-colored mercury. Do you still remember that mercury is the only metal that is a liquid?

Extra Information
Did you know—

... that thermography, the process of translating heat rays into colored pictures, enables doctors and scientists to "see" in complete darkness?

... that tiny heat sensors all over your body are continually sending temperature messages to your brain? When you flush, sweat, or shiver, your brain is using information from the heat sensors to regulate your body temperature.

... that Anders Celsius always used his scale upside-down from the way we use it? He chose 0° as the boiling point of water and 100° as the freezing point, but his colleagues inverted the scale after his death.

important. Usually it is about 98°F or 37°C. This is called normal body temperature. But if you are sick, your temperature may rise. Then your mother slides a fever thermometer under your tongue. She may do this every few hours. Taking your temperature helps her to know whether you are becoming better or worse.

When the air around you becomes 98°F or 37°C, you feel too warm. You do not want the air around you to be the same temperature as your body temperature. You feel better when the air is about 68°F or 20°C. This temperature is called room temperature, because many people keep the rooms in their houses about 68°F or 20°C.

The boiling and freezing points of water, your body temperature, and room temperature are four important temperatures to remember. How can knowing these temperatures help us?

You already know that your body temperature tells whether you are sick or healthy. Knowing the freezing point of water can also help us. It helps us know whether or not our garden plants will freeze outside. Then we will not plant our gardens too early.

Knowing about room temperature can even help us. It helps us know how warm to make our homes in the wintertime. In these and many other ways, knowing certain temperatures can be useful to us.

─────────── **Test Your Reading** ───────────

Copy each sentence below. Write and underline the missing words.

1. We use a ──── to measure ────.
2. A thermometer is divided into many small parts called ────.
3. A round thermometer has a metal ──── curled up inside that moves a single hand.
4. Other thermometers have either colored ──── or the liquid metal ──── sealed in a thin glass tube.

Match each temperature below with one of the phrases on the right. Write the correct letter beside each number.

5. 0°C	a. room temperature
6. 100°C	b. normal body temperature
7. 98°F	c. freezing point of water
8. 37°C	d. boiling point of water
9. 32°F	
10. 68°F	
11. 212°F	
12. 20°C	

Answers for "Test Your Reading"

1. We use a *thermometer* to measure *temperature*. (2)
2. A thermometer is divided into many small parts called *degrees*.
3. A round thermometer has a metal *spring* curled up inside that moves a single hand.
4. Other thermometers have either colored *alcohol* or the liquid metal *mercury* sealed in a thin glass tube. (2)
5. c
6. d
7. b
8. b
9. c
10. a
11. d
12. a   *(Total: 14 points)*

Temperature Demonstration

The following demonstration shows how unreliable our sense of touch is. Blindfold one or more volunteers. Fill three containers with water: one very warm, one lukewarm, and one cold. Put the volunteer's right hand into the very warm water and his left hand into the cold water. Wait about two minutes.

Next, place the lukewarm water before the volunteer. Remove his hand from the cold water, and place it into the lukewarm water. Ask him how it feels. (He will probably say it feels warm.)

Then have the volunteer remove his hand from the very warm water and place it into the lukewarm water. Ask him how it feels. (He will probably say it feels cold.)

Materials needed:

• *blindfold*
• *3 bowls*
• *very warm water*
• *lukewarm water*
• *cold water*

QUIZ

Ask the students to write the correct New Word for each phrase below.

1. How hot or cold something is   *(temperature)*
2. A tool that measures how hot or cold something is   *(thermometer)*
3. One of the many parts of a temperature scale   *(degree)*
4. The temperature at which water begins to freeze   *(freezing point)*
5. The temperature at which water begins to boil   *(boiling point)*

Comments on "Extra Activities"

2. This activity could be done faster with more thermometers. The thermometers could then be placed in the various locations and later compared.

3. The instructions given for the heat tour are only suggestions.

Plan now where you want to place the displays for the heat tour. Most of them will take up only a little space. Because Stop 2 should be placed at a sunny south or west window, Stop 1 could be placed just before the window. If you have no sunny window for Stop 2, you may use a bright light instead, as described in the next lesson.

Instead of using index cards, the cards can be made of poster board or other thin cardboard. Five of these cards will be needed, one for each display.

Some of the answers to Test 1 will vary according to your thermometer or the room temperature. The third answer, for example, could be given as 68°–72°F or 19°–22°C.

Extra Activities

Do these activities as your teacher directs.

1. You can make the temperature change on a thermometer. First, put an alcohol or mercury thermometer into a bowl of cold water for a few minutes. Watch the line of alcohol or mercury move. What is the temperature of the cold water?

   Then put the thermometer into a bowl of warm water. Again, watch the line move. What is the temperature of the warm water?

   Materials needed:
   - *2 bowls*
   - *cold water*
   - *warm water*
   - *thermometer*

2. Is the temperature the same everywhere in your classroom? You can find out with a thermometer. Put it on your desk, then on the floor, then near the ceiling, and then on a windowsill. Leave the thermometer in each place for about 15 minutes. Record the temperature of each place. Then look at the temperatures to answer these questions.

   Which temperature was the highest? Which part of your room is the coolest? Why are some parts of your room warmer than other parts?

   Materials needed: • *thermometer*

3. For this unit, you can make a project for other children and your parents to enjoy. You can give them a "heat tour" in your schoolroom. Then they can learn some of the same things that you are learning.

   First of all, you will need to decide where to locate five different stops in the heat tour. The tops of bookcases or wide windowsills would be fine. At each stop, you will have a project or activity to do and a test to take.

   For this lesson, use poster board to make a large sign that says:

   > **TAKE A HEAT TOUR**
   >
   > How much do you know about heat? You can find out by taking our free heat tour. You may also learn some new things about heat. So get a pencil and paper, and find *Stop 1.*

   Hang this sign near the doorway where your guests can easily see it.

Next, make a big sign that says "Stop 1." Then on an index card, write:

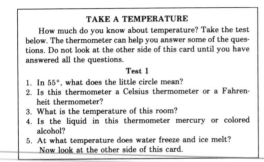

TAKE A TEMPERATURE

How much do you know about temperature? Take the test below. The thermometer can help you answer some of the questions. Do not look at the other side of this card until you have answered all the questions.

Test 1

1. In 55°, what does the little circle mean?
2. Is this thermometer a Celsius thermometer or a Fahrenheit thermometer?
3. What is the temperature of this room?
4. Is the liquid in this thermometer mercury or colored alcohol?
5. At what temperature does water freeze and ice melt?
   Now look at the other side of this card.

Write answers for the test. Ask your teacher to check your answers. Then make an answer key on the other side of the index card, as follows:

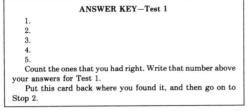

ANSWER KEY—Test 1

1.
2.
3.
4.
5.

Count the ones that you had right. Write that number above your answers for Test 1.

Put this card back where you found it, and then go on to Stop 2.

Put the "Stop 1" sign behind or above the place where you will put the index card and the thermometer. It might also help your guests to answer #5 on the test if you put a bowl of ice cubes and water at Stop 1.

Further directions for setting up your heat tour will be given in the following lessons.

Materials needed:
• *poster board or large sheet of unlined paper*
• *large index card*
• *thermometer*
• *bowl of ice cubes and water (optional)*

Lesson 2

The Sun Gives Us Heat

New Words

absorb (ab • sôrb′), to take in or receive.

radiation (rā′ dē • ā′ shən), sending energy, such as light or heat, through air or space.

solar energy (sō′ lər en′ ər • jē), heat, light, and other energy from the sun.

Reading Together

Pretend that you are on a boat in the middle of a pond. You dip your finger into the water. The water runs off your finger—*drip, drip, drip.*

Now, pretend that the pond represents all the sun's light and heat. What part of this "pond of sunlight" would the earth receive? It would receive only a few drops!

Amazing! We receive only a very tiny part of all the sun's light and heat, or *solar energy*. Yet that solar energy is enough to warm the earth. It is enough for all the plants to grow and make food. It is enough to keep the water cycle moving.

If we would receive too little solar energy, the earth would be too cold for us. Many materials would freeze. Many plants, animals, and people would die.

If we would receive too much solar energy, the light would be too bright. We might be blinded. The

A solar collector is made to heat water with energy from the sun.

earth would become too warm. Much of the ice near the North and South poles would melt and cause great floods. Of course, many plants, animals, and people would die.

But God has placed the earth and sun just far enough apart so that the amount of solar energy that reaches the earth is perfect. What a great and wise Creator He is!

104

Lesson 2

CONCEPTS TO TEACH

- The earth gets its heat from the sun.
- God gave us a bright sun that gives exactly enough light energy.
- Sunlight travels by radiation.
- When sunlight is absorbed by the earth, it changes to heat.
- Black or dull objects absorb the sun's heat better than white or shiny objects.
- Solar energy is sometimes used to heat water, to heat houses, to make electricity, and to shape metal and plastic.

HELPS FOR THE TEACHER

Introducing the Lesson

Ask the students to name ways in which they or their families use heat. Also, name the source of the heat.

Explain that most of the earth's energy comes from the sun. Of course, sunlight heats the earth directly. And solar cells use the sun's direct rays to produce electricity. But we also use solar energy indirectly in many ways. Electricity can be produced from the energy of falling water. This hydroelectricity is indirectly produced by solar energy because the falling water is a part of the water cycle that is powered by the sun.

In some places, electricity is generated by windmills. The energy of the wind comes from the sun because the uneven heating of the earth's surface produces high and low pressure areas that put the air in motion. The windmills catch this moving air with slanted blades that turn the generators.

Many people heat their homes with wood that

Reading on Your Own

The sun is very far away from the earth. Between the sun and the earth is much space. This space is mostly empty nothingness. In it there is no water or air.

How does the sunlight get from the sun to the earth? Electricity must travel through metal, water, or some other material. Likewise, sound must travel through some material. But light can travel through nothing. In one second, light zips through thousands of miles of empty space.

This kind of traveling is called *radiation*. Light, heat, and some other forms of energy travel by radiation. They can travel through space or air to something that is a distance away.

Right now the sun is radiating light and heat. It is sending many, many rays of sunlight in every direction. It takes about eight minutes for the light from the sun to reach the atmosphere of the earth. Some of these

The sun is 93 million miles from the earth, but it is hot enough to keep us warm.

SUN

Light and heat travel to us from the sun by radiation.

rays will keep traveling straight through the clear air, the clear water, and our clear windows. Then they will stop. The rays will stop whenever they strike something that is not clear. It might be a cloud, a tree, your house, or even you.

Whenever the sunlight stops, some of it changes to heat. This sunlight has been *absorbed*. It has made the cloud, the tree, your house, or you a little warmer.

Not all sunlight that is stopped is absorbed. Some of it bounces off the object it hits. For example, if sunlight strikes a white roof, much of it bounces off. Anything that is shiny or light-colored cannot absorb much sunlight.

However, if sunlight falls upon a black roof, much of it will be absorbed. The sunlight will make the black roof warmer than the white roof.

People who use solar energy want a dark-colored roof. This roof is slanted so that it can absorb much sunlight. The warm roof heats water that is stored nearby. In this way,

Which roof will get hotter on a sunny day? Why?

grew in trees with the action of the sun on their green leaves. The energy we get from food is also from the sun's energy.

We depend on the sun for our life. So when Christ said that God "maketh his sun to rise on the evil and on the good," He was calling attention to a great gift of love to us.

Extra Information
Did you know—

... that the sun's surface temperature is about 10,000° F (5500°C), and its center is about 27,000,000°F (15,000,000°C)?

... that every second, about 4,000,000 tons of solar matter become energy? This exchange happens as hydrogen becomes helium under tremendously high temperatures.

... that the total amount of energy that the earth receives from the sun in 40 minutes is roughly equal to the total amount of energy that man uses in a year?

... that already in 1774, a French chemist, Antoine Lavoisier, built a solar furnace that could become as hot as 3092°F (1700°C)?

... that the sun's mass is 99.8 percent of the total mass of our solar system?

solar energy can help to give the people hot water and a warm house.

Solar energy is also useful to workers. In one work place, the sunlight shines on many mirrors. The mirrors are turned so that most of the sunlight bounces off them onto one place in the center. This center place becomes very hot. It is hot enough to melt metal or to shape plastics. Solar energy can also be used with special materials called solar cells to make electricity.

Why do we need to use solar energy? Why do people not keep on burning coal, wood, petroleum, and natural gas? Many people forget that we are using up these fuels faster and faster. Every year more and more people are using more and more heat. They cook, heat buildings, heat water for washing, and use heat in many, many other ways. Someday, people may no longer have enough wood, coal, petroleum, and natural gas for all their needs.

But we do not need to worry that we will not have enough sunlight. God will keep the sun shining as long as He wants it to. We want to use solar energy and any other kind of energy wisely and carefully.

Answers for "Test Your Reading"

1. Without the sun's heat, the earth would be too *cold*.
2. The sun gives us just enough *heat* and *light*.
3. Sunlight changes to heat when *it is absorbed (or when it falls on a dark or dull object)*.
4. The way sunlight travels through space is called *radiation*.
5. Not much heat is absorbed by *shiny or light-colored* objects.
6. People have used solar energy in at least three ways: *to heat water, to warm houses, to make electricity, and to shape metal and plastic.* (3)
7. Mark will choose the light–blue shirt because it will not absorb as much heat as the dark–blue shirt.
8. More snow melted on the picnic table because it was darker and absorbed more heat.

(Total: 10 points)

———————————————— **Test Your Reading** ————————————————

Copy and finish each sentence below.

1. Without the sun's heat, the earth would be too ——.
2. The sun gives us just enough heat and ——.
3. Sunlight changes to heat when ——.
4. The way sunlight travels through space is called ——.
5. Not much heat is absorbed by —— objects.
6. People have used solar energy in at least three ways: ——, ——, and ——.

Answer the questions below.

7. It is a warm spring morning. Mark may wear a light-blue shirt or a dark-blue shirt to school. Both shirts are made of the same material. If Mark wants to be as cool as possible, which shirt will he choose? Why?
8. It is a cold winter morning. A light coat of snow covers the ground. In the afternoon when Lydia comes home from school, she notices something strange. Most of the snow has melted on the dark-red picnic table. But only a little snow has melted on the white chairs beside the picnic table. Both the table and chairs are made of wood. Why did more snow melt on the picnic table than on the chairs?

QUIZ

Ask the students to write the correct New Word that matches each phrase.

1. The sun's heat and light   *(solar energy)*
2. To stop sunlight and take it in   *(absorb)*
3. Sending sunlight through space   *(radiation)*

Extra Activities

Do these activities as your teacher directs.

1. You can see that light travels in straight lines, and that it can bounce. Ask a friend to help you hold a comb, a mirror, and a cardboard, as shown below. If it is a cloudy day, use a lamp without a shade for the sun.

   Materials needed:
   • *mirror*
   • *wide comb*
   • *white cardboard*

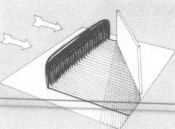

Comments on "Extra Activities"

1. Show the students that each beam of light that strikes the mirror is reflected at the same angle. Turn the mirror slightly to show how the angle of the reflected light changes.

2. The mirror and aluminum foil reflect the most light. Dark-colored cloth and paper absorb the most heat.

2. Find out which materials bounce light away and which ones absorb much heat. Lay a mirror, a piece of aluminum foil, and various scraps of paper and cloth on a table in a darkened room. Shine a flashlight on each material. Which ones send the light right up into your eyes? Which ones seem to absorb the light?

   Place the materials on a board. Leave them in bright sunshine for a few minutes, and then feel each material. Which ones seem to absorb the most heat?

   Put a piece of white cloth over one thermometer. Put a piece of black cloth over another thermometer. Leave both in the sunshine for a few minutes. What is the temperature of each thermometer?

   Materials needed:
   • *flashlight*
   • *mirror*
   • *aluminum foil*
   • *scraps of light-colored and dark-colored paper and cloth*
   • *board*
   • *white cloth*
   • *black cloth*
   • *2 thermometers*

3. Experiment with the lamp and papers until you feel certain that the light is both bright enough and close enough to cause a noticeable difference in temperature between the two papers.

You could also show the temperature difference with two identical thermometers. Glue matching pockets onto the two pieces of construction paper. Then on the index card after the sentence "Feel the two papers on the window," add this: "Read the thermometers that are in the pockets at the sides of the papers."

3. For your unit project, work on Stop 2. Make a large sign that says "Stop 2."

Label a piece of black construction paper *A* and a piece of white construction paper *B*. Tape the two pieces of construction paper side by side on a south or west window.

Hang the "Stop 2" sign nearby. Put a bright lamp close to the papers in the window. Your guests can use the lamp if the sun is not shining.

On an index card write:

FEEL HEAT FROM LIGHT

If the sun is not shining through this window, switch on the lamp and wait a few minutes. If the sun is shining, read on.

How much do you know about sunshine and heat? Feel the two papers on the window. Then answer the questions below.

Test 2

1. What is heating the papers?
2. Which paper is warmer?
3. If the sun would stop shining now, could you stay warm for a month?
4. What is the name for the way sunlight travels?

Now look at the other side of this card to check your answers.

On the other side of the card, write:

ANSWER KEY—Test 2

1. sunshine (if the sun is shining) the lamp or electricity (if the lamp is shining)
2. paper A (the black paper)
3. no
4. radiation

Count all the answers you have right. Write the number on your paper above Test 2.

Then put this card back just as you found it, and go to Stop 3.

Put the "Stop 2" sign on the window above the construction papers. Lay the index card on the windowsill.

Materials needed:
- *poster board*
- *black construction paper*
- *white construction paper*
- *masking tape*
- *floodlight*
- *large index card*

Heat Moves

New Words

conduction (kən • duk′ shən), the way heat travels when a hot material touches a cooler material.

conductor (kən • duk′ tər), a material through which heat travels quickly.

convection (kən • vek′ shən), the circling motion of liquids or gases because of a difference in temperature.

insulator (in′ sə • lā′ tər), a material that slows the movement of heat.

Reading Together

It is a warm spring evening. You and your family have just roasted hot dogs over a campfire. Now the sun is slipping down behind the trees. Because you are feeling chilly, you come close to the fire.

Soon your face and hands are tingling warm. But your back still feels cold. You turn around to warm your back. Why do you need to keep turning around to stay warm?

To answer this question, you need to remember from your last lesson how radiation works. The fire is radiating light and heat, much like the sun. These rays warm your face when it is turned toward the fire. But they cannot curve around to warm your back. Radiation moves in straight lines, not in circles or curves.

After a while, your family puts the campfire out. It is time to go home. When you enter your house, you are glad that it is warm. Warm air is rising from the stove or registers. But strangely, you do not need to face the stove, as you faced the campfire. You feel warm all over. Why is this?

109

Lesson 3

CONCEPTS TO TEACH

- Heat speeds through empty space and gases by radiation. (Review this from Lesson 2.)
- Heat moves more slowly in gases and liquids by convection.
- Convection is caused by a difference in the weight of air. Cooler air is heavier; warmer air is lighter. Cool air or water sinks; warm air or water rises.
- Heat spreads through a solid by conduction.
- Conduction happens when a hot material touches and warms all the cooler materials around it.
- We use materials called conductors when we want heat to move quickly.
- Metals, such as iron, aluminum, and copper, are good conductors.
- Heat always moves from a warm area to a cooler area.

- We use materials called insulators when we do not want heat to move.
- Wood, paper, cloth, and fiber glass are good insulators.

Convection in a room with a stove

To understand this, you must know about *convection*. Because of convection, the air moves in a big circle up, over, and down in the room. The whole room feels warm. What makes convection happen? Why does the air move in circles?

Convection happens because of a difference in temperature. The warm air is rising from the stove. As it rises farther away from the stove, it begins to cool. As the air cools, it becomes a little heavier. It becomes heavy enough to sink slowly toward the floor. Then this cool air moves over to the stove where it is heated again. Over and over it circles, heating and rising and then cooling and sinking.

Convection also happens outdoors. The warm air around the middle of the earth is always rising. The heavy cold air near the North and South poles is always sinking. When this moving air pushes against us, we do not usually say that convection is happening outdoors. We say the wind is blowing.

Convection does not only happen in the air. It happens in any gas or liquid that is being heated. Convection always happens because of a difference in temperature.

HELPS FOR THE TEACHER

Introducing the Lesson

To demonstrate conduction, hold the tip of a scissors against a heated iron. Then use a hot pad to hold the scissors against the iron. Explain that heat moves by conduction through both materials, but metal allows a much faster conduction. This is why you cannot bear to hold the scissors as long as the hot pad. The scissors is a good conductor, but the hot pad is a poor conductor. The hot pad is an insulator.

Use two candles to demonstrate convection. You will need a window that is slightly opened both at the top and bottom or a door that is slightly ajar between a warm and a cool room. Light the candles. Ask a student to hold one candle at the bottom of the window or door while you hold the other candle at the top. (You may need paper to catch the wax drippings.) The flames will point in the direction of the air flow. Of course, this will need to be done in the absence of a wind that would disturb the convection.

Demonstrate radiation by holding the heated iron above a student's hands. Ask him to tell you when he feels the heat. Explain that the heat has traveled down to his hand by radiation. It could not have been conduction, because the iron did not touch his hand, and because air is a poor conductor. Neither could it have been convection, because convection always causes heated air to move upward, not downward.

Materials needed:
* *electric iron*
* *scissors*
* *hot pad*
* *2 candles*
* *matches*

Reading on Your Own

Heat travels through space and through gases by radiation. It circles up and around in gases or liquids by convection. But heat moves through solids by *conduction*. Conduction happens when something warm touches something cooler.

Heat moves through a frying pan by conduction. First, the stove heats the bottom of the frying pan. The bottom part heats the sides of the pan. Then one side heats the handle. Now the whole frying pan is hot because of conduction. Anything that touches the pan will also be heated by conduction.

The frying pan is made of iron.

Iron is a good *conductor* of heat because heat can flow through it quickly. Aluminum, copper, and most other metals are also good conductors of heat. This is one reason why cooking pans, heaters, and stoves are made of metal. Good conductors help heat to travel quickly over short distances.

Heat always moves from something warm to something cooler. If a bowl of warm potatoes touches a bowl of cold salad, what happens? The heat flows from the potatoes into the salad. The potatoes become cooler, and the salad becomes warmer. After a while, they are both the same temperature.

Conduction in a frying pan

Extra Information

Did you know—

. . . that superconductors are metals or other electrical conducting materials that have been made so cold that they have no resistance to electricity? An electric current will flow through them endlessly without requiring any additional electricity.

. . . that convection cannot occur without conduction?

. . . that extremely strong convectional currents are created by the intense heat of a forest fire?

. . . that several layers of lightweight jackets and sweaters will keep you warmer than the same amount of material in one heavy overcoat? The air spaces between the layers provide additional insulation.

Discussion Suggestions

Give the following illustration to focus attention on the concept that heat always moves from a warm object to a cooler object.

An ice cube is in a glass of lemonade. Is the ice cube sending cold into the lemonade, or is the lemonade sending heat into the ice cube?

Ask for the students' answers. If they are not sure, give these clues: Heat is energy or force; cold is not. Heat can move; cold cannot. By this, show that the lemonade is actually "doing the work." It is sending heat into the ice cube. The ice cube only receives the heat.

For another discussion, ask this question: Does a blanket warm you, or do you warm the blanket? Ask the students to give reasons for their answers. (A thinking student may reason that an *electric* blanket warms you!) You could also suggest that they wrap a thermometer in a blanket to see whether the thermometer becomes warmer.

A well-insulated boy

Your house may have a thick blanket of fiber glass inside its walls. Inside the fiber glass are many air spaces. The trapped air keeps the heat from rushing outdoors.

Do you have a Thermos bottle in your lunch box? Between its inside and outside walls is an air space. Your hot chocolate stays warm because of the air space.

We are glad that God gave us conductors and insulators. With them, we can make heat move quickly or slowly. We are also glad for conduction, convection, and radiation. Because of them, heat can move from hot objects to places we need it.

Sometimes we wish that heat would not move at all. In the winter, it would be much easier to keep our houses warm if heat did not move outdoors. We could heat them once, and they would stay warm all winter. But, no, the heat keeps moving outdoors.

Although we cannot stop heat from moving, we can slow it down. We use an *insulator* to slow the movement of heat. Wood, paper, cloth, and fiber glass are some good insulators. Many of these insulators work well because they have spaces that hold still air. For example, air is trapped between your clothes and your body. The trapped air keeps you from losing heat too fast.

A well-insulated house

Experiment With Styrofoam

Show that Styrofoam is an excellent insulator by filling a Styrofoam cup and an ordinary drinking glass with hot water. Cover both containers and set them on a shelf. After an hour or two, allow the students to feel the water in both containers and to notice the difference in temperature. You might also use thermometers to compare the temperatures.

Materials needed:
* *Styrofoam cup*
* *drinking glass*
* *hot water*
* *flat lids to lay on containers*

QUIZ

Write the New Words on the chalkboard. Ask the students to write the New Word that is described by each sentence below. Ask them to spell correctly.

1. It does not let heat escape quickly.   *(insulator)*
2. It is caused by a difference in the temperature of the air.   *(convection)*
3. It happens when something warm touches something cooler.   *(conduction)*
4. It is a solid that lets heat move through it more quickly than many other solids.   *(conductor)*

———————————— **Test Your Reading** ————————————

For each sentence, choose the way that heat is traveling. Write the correct letter on your paper.

> a. conduction
> b. convection
> c. radiation

1. Sunlight is falling on the roof of a house.
2. A torch heats one end of a bolt, and the rest of the bolt gets hot.
3. A stove heats the air in a big room.
4. A hot stove burner heats a cooking pan.
5. The water at the top of a pan of water on a stove becomes hot.
6. Our backs feel warm when we sit with our backs to a fireplace.
7. An electric iron held above our hands warms them.

Write yes if the sentence is true. Write no if it is not true.

8. Conduction is heat that moves in circles.
9. Warm air weighs less than cool air.
10. The wind blows because of convection.
11. Two good conductors are wood and metal.
12. Heat always flows from warm areas to cooler areas.

Extra Activities

Do these activities as your teacher directs.

1. How many things can you find in your school or home that are warm? Here are some things to look for: radiator, stove, water heater, electric iron or toaster, light bulb, the back of a freezer or refrigerator. Feel the heat moving away from these things. Try to decide whether the heat is traveling by conduction, convection, or radiation. Ask your teacher or parents if you need help.
2. You can watch convection in water. Fill a pan or a Pyrex bowl with water. Sprinkle a little cornmeal or sawdust into the water.

   Now ask your teacher or parents to help you heat the pan of water on a hot plate. Watch the cornmeal or sawdust move. What makes the water move?

Materials needed:
- *aluminum pan or clear Pyrex bowl*
- *water*
- *cornmeal or fine sawdust*
- *hot plate*

Answers for "Test Your Reading"

1. c	7. c
2. a	8. no
3. b	9. yes
4. a	10. yes
5. b	11. no
6. c	12. yes

(Total: 12 points)

Comments on "Extra Activities"

1. Use this activity to stimulate the students' thinking. However, do not be overly concerned with pinpointing only one method of heat transfer for each heat source. One heat source may give off heat in two or three ways. For example, a burner on an electric stove radiates heat to our outstretched hands. It creates small convectional currents in the air above it. Of course, we most often use the burner to heat cooking pans by conduction.

2. The cornmeal moves in circles because the water moves in circles. The water circulates because part of it is warmer than the other part.

3. Air is inside the bubbles. The more fluffy cloth (fur, wool, or flannel) will make more bubbles because it has more trapped air in it. This cloth would keep you warmer because trapped air is a good insulator. The cotton cloth has fewer air spaces in it and keeps you cooler.

3. You can see that cloth has trapped air inside it. Drop a scrap of cloth into a glass of water. Quickly push it to the bottom of the glass with a long pencil. Watch for bubbles rising to the top. What causes the bubbles?

Try it again with more scraps. Which cloth makes more bubbles? Would this kind of cloth keep you warmer or cooler than the other cloth? Why?

Materials needed:
- *long pencil*
- *water*
- *clear drinking glasses*
- *scraps of cotton, flannel, wool, or fur*

4. For your unit project, make a "Stop 3" sign. Then on an index card, write:

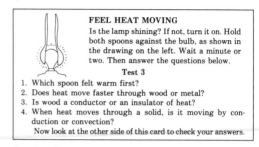

FEEL HEAT MOVING

Is the lamp shining? If not, turn it on. Hold both spoons against the bulb, as shown in the drawing on the left. Wait a minute or two. Then answer the questions below.

Test 3

1. Which spoon felt warm first?
2. Does heat move faster through wood or metal?
3. Is wood a conductor or an insulator of heat?
4. When heat moves through a solid, is it moving by conduction or convection?

Now look at the other side of this card to check your answers.

On the other side of the card, write:

ANSWER KEY—Test 3

1. the metal spoon
2. metal
3. insulator
4. conduction

Count all the answers that are right. Write the number on your paper above Test 3. Then put this card where you found it, turn off the lamp, and go to Stop 4.

Put the "Stop 3" sign, spoons, and lamp in their appropriate places.

Materials needed:
- *poster board*
- *large wooden spoon*
- *large metal spoon*
- *lamp*
- *large index card*

Lesson 4

Heat Causes Materials to Expand

New Words

contract (kən · trakt′), to become smaller.

expand (ek · spand′), to become larger.

Reading Together

Did you know that a bridge is as changeable as the weather? When the weather becomes hot, the bridge becomes longer. When the weather becomes cold, the bridge becomes shorter. In fact, a bridge over a wide river may be twelve inches shorter in the winter than in the summer.

How can this be? In the summer, heat makes the bridge *expand*. It becomes a little larger and longer. In the winter, cold makes the bridge *contract*. It becomes a little shorter and smaller.

Even though the bridge expands and contracts, you would not notice it. The bridge has some special parts. These parts push together or pull apart when the bridge expands and contracts.

The electric wires beside the roads also expand and contract. During the warm summer, the lines sag. They hang loosely because they have expanded. But in the cold winter, the wires contract. They are stretched tightly.

What will happen to this bridge on a hot day?

Did you know that thermometers would not work without expansion and contraction? The liquid mercury or alcohol expands when it is warmed and contracts when it is cooled. Expansion and contraction make the red or silver liquid "line" move up and down. In a round thermometer, the metal spring inside expands and contracts when it is heated and cooled.

115

Lesson 4

CONCEPTS TO TEACH

- When a material is heated, it expands.
- When a material is cooled, it contracts.
- Expansion and contraction make thermometers work.
- When water is cooled to its freezing point, it expands.
- Expansion can break glass, burst pipes, cause rutted roads, and cause electric wires to sag.

HELPS FOR THE TEACHER

Introducing the Lesson

Begin class with one or more of the demonstrations given below, as time permits.

Show the expansion of a solid by dropping two ice cubes into a glass of warm water. Ask the class to listen to the ice cracking. The ice cracks because it expands faster on the outside of the cube than on the inside.

To show the expansion of a liquid, fill a bottle with cold water, and add a few drops of food coloring. Then put some glass tubing through a rubber stopper, and put it firmly into the mouth of the bottle. Heat the bottle with an alcohol burner. Ask the class to explain why the colored water rises. Explain that this is actually a kind of thermometer.

To show the expansion of a gas, put a ketchup bottle into a freezer for a few minutes (or pack ice around it in an ice chest). Then quickly remove the bottle, and lay a wet quarter on the opening. Allow two students to warm the jar by wrapping their

Sometimes your mother leaves the lid on a hot cooking pan. Heat has caused the air and steam inside to expand. But as the pan cools, the air and steam contract. They pull the lid tightly to the pan. Then your mother cannot lift the lid. So what does she do? She heats the pan again to make the air and steam expand. Now she can lift the lid.

Reading on Your Own

What would happen if we touched an ice-cold pitcher to a hot burner? What would happen if we heated a piece of window glass and held it against an ice cube? We will not try these things, because the glass would break. Most glass breaks when part of it expands or contracts very quickly. But it does not break if it is heated or cooled slowly.

Most materials expand when they are heated. Most of them contract when they are cooled. But water acts differently. When water begins to cool, it contracts for a while. It contracts until its temperature is just above freezing. Then it begins to expand, taking up more space.

Because freezing water expands, it can cause problems for us. In the winter, freezing water can burst the pipes in our houses. Then we might not have running water for a while.

Freezing water can also cause bumpy, rutted asphalt roads. First, some rain falls into a small crack in the road. It causes no problem in the summer. But in the winter, the water

What made this jug bulge when the water froze?

freezes. The freezing water expands and forces the crack to open even wider. If the crack is not patched, soon more rain will fall inside. As it keeps freezing and thawing, the crack becomes larger and larger.

Even though freezing water can cause problems, we are glad that it does expand. When freezing water expands, it becomes lighter. Because ice is lighter than water, it floats. You have often seen ice cubes floating in a glass of water.

Because ice floats, all the streams and ponds freeze first on top. Why is it so important that the water freezes at the top? If it would not, the water could not keep flowing. The fish could not stay alive.

But God is very wise. We are glad that He made freezing water act differently than other freezing liquids. Because God made every material, He knows exactly how it should expand and contract.

hands around it. Warn them not to shake the quarter off. Soon the expanding air will cause the quarter to tap against the bottle.

Materials needed:

- *ice cubes*
- *warm water*
- *drinking glass*
- *bottle with a one–hole rubber stopper*
- *glass tubing*
- *cold water*
- *food coloring*
- *alcohol burner*
- *ketchup bottle*
- *freezer*
- *quarter*

Extra Information
Did you know—

. . . that a mile of railroad track may measure a yard shorter in the winter than in the summer?

. . . that rubber, leather, and many plastics contract when they are heated because of the unique structure of their molecules?

. . . that a house creaks at night because of uneven contraction after a day's expansion?

Test Your Reading

Choose the best ending for each sentence. Write the correct letter on your paper.

1. Most materials that are heated will
   (a) expand. (b) contract. (c) rise.
2. When metal contracts, it becomes
   (a) heavier. (b) larger. (c) smaller.
3. A tower is tallest in the
   (a) spring. (b) summer. (c) winter.
4. When water is cooled,
   (a) it expands and then contracts.
   (b) it contracts and then expands.
   (c) it expands and then sinks.

Use good sentences to give the answers.

5. Name two gases that expand and contract.
6. Name two problems we have because freezing water expands.
7. Explain why it is good that ice floats on streams and ponds.

Extra Activities

Do these activities as your teacher directs.

1. You can watch air expand and contract. Pull a large balloon down over the neck of an empty ketchup bottle. Then put the bottle into a bowl of hot water. Watch it for a few minutes. What happens to the balloon? Explain why it happens.
   Now put the bottle into a bowl of ice cubes. Again wait for a few minutes. What happens to the balloon? Explain why it happens.
   Materials needed:
   • *large balloon*   • *2 large bowls*
   • *ketchup bottle*   • *hot water*
                         • *ice cubes*
2. What do you do when the lid sticks tightly on a jar of food? The next time this happens, put some hot water into a bowl. Set the jar upside down into the water. After a minute or two, dry the jar. Then try to open it. What happens? Can you tell why heat helps you open the lid?
   Materials needed:
   • *jar with tight lid* • *hot water*
   • *bowl*   • *paper towel*

QUIZ

Read the sentences below. Ask the students to write *expand* or *contract* to indicate which has happened.

1. Air becomes colder. *(contract)*
2. The line of mercury in a thermometer rises. *(expand)*
3. The electric wires are stretched tightly in winter. *(contract)*
4. Water is freezing in a crack in the road. *(expand)*
5. A water pipe bursts. *(expand)*

Answers for "Test Your Reading"

1. a
2. c
3. b
4. b
5. Air and steam are gases that expand and contract. (3)
6. Freezing water can burst water pipes.
   It can cause rough roads. (3)
7. It is good that ice floats on streams and ponds because the water can still flow underneath (or the fish can still live underneath) (2)

(Total: 12 points)

Comments on "Extra Activities"

1. In the bowl of hot water, the balloon expands because the air inside the bottle expands. In the bowl of ice cubes, the balloon contracts because the air inside the bottle contracts.
2. The lid opens. If it is a vacuum-sealed lid, the heat causes the food and air inside the jar to expand. This force pushes up against the lid and makes it easier to open. If the lid sticks because of syrup or

Answers for "Test Your Reading"

Note This Change

Beginning with this lesson, the students will occasionally encounter exercises with these instructions: "Use good sentences to answer these questions." Requiring complete sentences helps the students both to understand and to remember their lesson concepts.

In the answer key for such exercises, you will notice that an extra point has been added for each question. However, no extra points are added in the exercises that require merely copying or finishing a sentence.

Complete sentences are not required, and extra points are not added in the final tests. A final test is not designed to measure a third grader's writing skills but his knowledge of science.

Write some sample questions on the board, and have the class answer in complete sentences. Explain that an extra point will be added for each complete sentence.

jelly, the heat causes the lid to expand slightly and become looser. Also, the hot water dissolves the sugar that may be keeping the lid tight.

3. First, fasten the paper bags to the yardstick, and then hang the yardstick from the ceiling. Place the lamp so that the bulb is inside Bag A. Take care that the burning lamp is not left against the paper very long. This could cause a fire.

3. Keep working on your heat tour by making a "Stop 4" sign. Then ask someone older to help you set up your project as the drawing below shows.

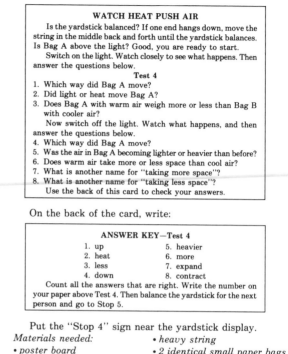

On an index card, write:

WATCH HEAT PUSH AIR

Is the yardstick balanced? If one end hangs down, move the string in the middle back and forth until the yardstick balances. Is Bag A above the light? Good, you are ready to start.

Switch on the light. Watch closely to see what happens. Then answer the questions below.

Test 4

1. Which way did Bag A move?
2. Did light or heat move Bag A?
3. Does Bag A with warm air weigh more or less than Bag B with cooler air?

Now switch off the light. Watch what happens, and then answer the questions below.

4. Which way did Bag A move?
5. Was the air in Bag A becoming lighter or heavier than before?
6. Does warm air take more or less space than cool air?
7. What is another name for "taking more space"?
8. What is another name for "taking less space"?

Use the back of this card to check your answers.

On the back of the card, write:

ANSWER KEY—Test 4

1. up	5. heavier
2. heat	6. more
3. less	7. expand
4. down	8. contract

Count all the answers that are right. Write the number on your paper above Test 4. Then balance the yardstick for the next person and go to Stop 5.

Put the "Stop 4" sign near the yardstick display.

Materials needed:
- *poster board*
- *Scotch tape*
- *yardstick*
- *heavy string*
- *2 identical small paper bags*
- *lamp with 100-watt bulb*
- *large index card*

We Use Cold to Preserve Food

New Words

evaporation (i • vap′ ə • rā′ shən), the change of a liquid to a gas.

refrigeration (ri • frij′ ə • rā′ shən), cooling or keeping something cool.

spoiling (spoi′ ling), becoming moldy or rotten.

Reading Together

Why do bananas get brown spots? What makes milk become sour and lumpy? Why does bread become moldy?

This *spoiling* of food is caused by mold and other kinds of tiny living things. Millions of these tiny living things are floating around in the air. They are sure to find our food almost anywhere we keep it.

Like all plants and animals, these tiny living things need warmth. They grow fast when they are in warm food. But they grow slowly in cool food. This is why we keep our food in a cool place. The cold keeps the food from spoiling quickly.

When we freeze food, the mold and other tiny living things cannot grow at all. Many of them are killed. This is why we put meat, fruit, and vegetables into a freezer. We can take the food out months later, and it still has not spoiled.

These foods will keep a long time if they are kept cold.

Keeping things cold is called *refrigeration*. We use refrigerators to cool food in our homes. Refrigeration also helps workers make candy, fruit juices, and ice cream. Doctors give sick people medicines and extra blood that have been kept in refrigeration.

119

Lesson 5

CONCEPTS TO TEACH

- Food spoils when tiny plants called mold grow on it.
- Keeping food cool slows spoiling.
- Freezing temperatures do not allow food to spoil.
- Before people had refrigerators, they used ice or cold spring water to keep their food cold.
- Evaporation causes cooling.
- A refrigerator has a liquid in it that evaporates quickly.

HELPS FOR THE TEACHER

Introducing the Lesson

Read Joshua 9:3–27 to your class. The Gibeonites tricked Joshua and the Israelites by claiming that their moldy bread and other provisions had been fresh at the beginning of their journey. Joshua knew that some time is required for mold to grow. He believed their story because of the mold and the rest of the "proof" they showed him. Too late, Joshua and the other Israelites realized that the Lord's counsel would have been far more trustworthy than the doubtful evidence of moldy bread.

Cutting ice

Long ago, before people had freezers or refrigerators, they cooled their food in cold water or ice. Some people kept a tank of cold spring water in their basement. Other people cut many large chunks of ice from a pond in the wintertime. In a small building, they packed the blocks of ice in sawdust. There the ice stayed frozen until the next summer. Little by little, these people would use the ice to keep their food cool.

Reading on Your Own

Today we still use ice for cooling our food. We put ice cubes into our lemonade. We use ice to make homemade ice cream. When we go on a picnic, we may keep our meat cool in an ice chest.

But for everyday cooling, most people use a refrigerator. One part of a refrigerator gets cold enough to freeze the food. The larger part of a refrigerator keeps food cool but not frozen.

What makes the food cold in a refrigerator? This is a hard question, but if you read carefully, you can learn how a refrigerator works.

You know that when you get very warm on a summer day, you begin to sweat. The sweat evaporates and cools your body. If the wind or a fan blows air over you, the sweat evaporates faster. *Evaporation* of sweat helps to cool you. When a liquid like sweat evaporates, it turns into a gas.

Evaporating sweat cools our body.

This causes much cooling. In a way, God gave your body a special refrigerator, since He made your body to sweat.

A food refrigerator makes things cold by evaporation also. But instead of sweat, it uses a special liquid that evaporates much faster than sweat. In fact, this special liquid evaporates so fast that it can make ice. After the liquid evaporates and cools the refrigerator, an electric pump squeezes the gas and puts it under high pressure.

Extra Information

Did you know—

. . . that the drug penicillin does not contain mold but is only a product made by the Penicillium mold?

. . . that some kinds of bacteria "eat" asphalt, detergent, jet fuel, metal, paint, paper, and wood?

. . . that bacteria in our stomachs help us digest some kinds of food?

. . . that rapidly frozen tissues, such as skin, blood, or eye corneas, can be preserved indefinitely until they are needed by those with an injury or disease?

. . . that supercold liquid nitrogen, which is kept at about –200°C, is used in surgery to destroy unwanted body cells, such as tumors and fungus growths?

QUIZ

Ask the students to write the correct New Word for each sentence below. Some words will be used more than once.

1. Mold and bacteria cause this. *(spoiling)*
2. It cools your body. *(evaporation)*
3. Workers use it to make candy and ice cream. *(refrigeration)*
4. It is a change in the state of a material. *(evaporation)*
5. Ice or cold water has long been used for this. *(refrigeration)*

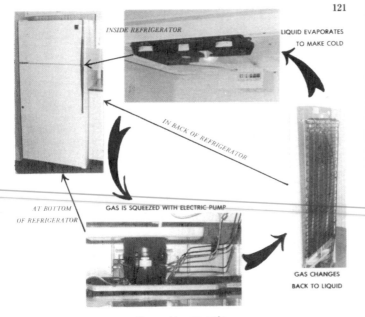

INSIDE REFRIGERATOR

LIQUID EVAPORATES
TO MAKE COLD

IN BACK OF REFRIGERATOR

AT BOTTOM
OF REFRIGERATOR

GAS IS SQUEEZED WITH ELECTRIC PUMP

GAS CHANGES
BACK TO LIQUID

How a refrigerator works

This helps to change the gas back into a liquid. Then it is ready to evaporate again in the refrigerator to do more cooling. Round and round, the special liquid goes. First, it evaporates to cool food; then it is changed back into a liquid to be used over.

Just as God knew that we needed heat, so He knew that we needed cooling. He planned that evaporation would cool our bodies. He gave men good minds to learn about evaporation so that they could make refrigerators.

Many people have used their minds to learn about evaporation. They know how to keep food from spoiling by freezing or cooling it. They have sent fresh food to faraway places in refrigerated trucks, railway cars, and ships.

But many people do not use their minds in the best way of all. They forget to thank God. They forget that He is the giver of every gift, even the gift of cooling by evaporation. Have we remembered to thank God today?

Answers for "Test Your Reading"

1. Food spoils when it becomes too *warm.*
2. Mold and other living things grow slowly in *cold (cool)* food.
3. When a liquid *evaporates,* it causes cooling.
4. Doctors use *refrigeration* to keep medicines and blood cool.
5. Long ago, people cooled their food with *ice* or *cold water.* (2)
6. The sweat evaporates from our bodies, and this evaporation cools us. (2)
7. Both a refrigerator and sweating produce cooling by evaporation. (2)
8. The liquid in a refrigerator evaporates much faster than sweat. (2)
9. The gas is changed back into a liquid again. (2)

(Total: 14 points)

Comments on "Extra Activities"

1. Molds grow the fastest when they have moisture, darkness, and moderate warmth. The moist bread in the covered container in the warm cupboard provides the most ideal environment for mold to grow. Mold does not grow well on dried or chilled food.

———————————— **Test Your Reading** ————————————

Copy and finish each sentence below.

1. Food spoils when it becomes too ——.
2. Mold and other living things grow slowly in —— food.
3. When a liquid ——, it causes cooling.
4. Doctors use —— to keep medicines and blood cool.
5. Long ago, people cooled their food with —— or ——.

Use good sentences to answer these questions.

6. How does sweating help to cool us?
7. In what way does a refrigerator work like sweating?
8. How does the liquid in a refrigerator evaporate differently than sweat?
9. After the special liquid in a refrigerator has evaporated, what change happens to the gas?

Extra Activities

Do these activities as your teacher directs.

1. You can learn how and where molds like to live. Ask your mother for some stale bread that is becoming moldy. If you have none, leave a slice of fresh bread uncovered for a few hours. Then break the bread into bite-sized pieces. Sprinkle half of the pieces with water, and put them into three small jars. Put the lid on each jar. Put one jar into the refrigerator, one on a sunny windowsill, and one in a warm cupboard. Also, put some dry, uncovered bread beside each of the jars.

   Wait for a few days. Then look at all the pieces of bread.

   In which place did the mold grow the fastest? Do molds like light or darkness? Do they like to be warm or cool? Do they like moist or dry bread? If you want to keep molds from growing, how and where will you keep your food?

   Materials needed:
   • *moldy bread*
   • *water*
   • *3 jars with lids*

2. Today you may finish your heat tour. Make a large sign that says "Stop 5," and hang it up. Underneath it, put one dish of water and one dish of rubbing alcohol. Label these dishes *Water* and *Alcohol.*

On an index card, write:

> **FEEL THE COOLING**
>
> Dip the fingers of one hand into the water. Dip the fingers of your other hand into the rubbing alcohol.
> Wave your fingers back and forth. Then answer the questions below.
>
> **Test 5**
>
> 1. Do your fingers feel warmer or cooler?
> 2. Which liquid makes you cooler, alcohol or water?
> 3. Were the liquids evaporating or condensing when they cooled your fingers?
> 4. What activity causes cooling in a freezer?
> Turn to the back of this card and check your answers.

On the back of the card, write:

> **ANSWER KEY—Test 5**
>
> 1. cooler
> 2. alcohol
> 3. evaporating
> 4. evaporation
> Count how many right answers you have. Write the number on your paper above Test 5.
> Now add all your correct answers from Test 1 through Test
> 5. How many did you have correct?
> *22-25 correct:* Very good! You must have studied heat before.
> *18-21 correct:* Good. You know many things about heat.
> *17 or less correct:* Fair. You can enjoy learning more about heat.

Arrange all your displays neatly and in the correct order. Now invite your family and friends to take your heat tour.

Materials needed:
- *poster board*
- *2 small dishes*
- *water*
- *rubbing alcohol*
- *masking tape*
- *large index card*

2. If the black paper for Stop 2 has faded somewhat, put up a fresh paper before your guests arrive.

Answer Key

Match

1. e
2. a
3. i
4. b
5. g
6. d
7. c
8. f
9. h

Fill

10. temperature
11. degree
12. solar energy
13. absorb
14. expand
15. contract
16. spoiling
17. evaporation

Choose

18. b
19. a

Lesson 6

Do You Remember What You Learned?

Match each word on the right to the best sentence beginning.

1. The temperature at which water freezes is its
2. The temperature at which water boils is its
3. We measure temperature with a
4. Heat moves through solids by
5. Heat travels through space by
6. Heat circles up and around in liquids and gases by
7. Copper is a good
8. Paper is a good
9. Food can be kept fresh longer by

   a. boiling point.
   b. conduction.
   c. conductor.
   d. convection.
   e. freezing point.
   f. insulator.
   g. radiation.
   h. refrigeration.
   i. thermometer.

Fill the blanks with words from the box.

absorb	evaporation	solar energy
contract	expand	spoiling
degree	refrigeration	temperature

10. The —— of water tells how warm it is.
11. The unit of measure on a thermometer scale is a ——.
12. The sun's light and heat is called ——.
13. Dark and dull roofs —— much heat from sunlight.
14. Most materials —— when they are heated.
15. In the winter, buildings and bridges —— because of the cold.
16. Mold causes ——.
17. Both your body and a refrigerator use —— to cause cooling.

Choose the best ending for each sentence.

18. Sunlight changes to heat when
   (a) it touches something shiny.
   (b) the earth absorbs it.
   (c) it reaches the atmosphere.
19. Two liquids used in thermometers are
   (a) alcohol and mercury.
   (b) water and ammonia.
   (c) petroleum and mercury.

Lesson 6

As you review this unit with the class, emphasize the major concepts, and help the students understand facts they may have forgotten. After this, you may want to review orally the questions from earlier lessons.

Your students would likely enjoy a question chain for additional drilling. Assign for the next class. You ask the first question, and call on a student to answer it. If his answer is correct, he asks the next question and calls on a classmate to answer it, and so on.

Establish guidelines such as these:

(1) Raise your hand if you think you know the answer.
(2) Try to call on everyone at least once.
(3) Accept an answer that is different from the book's wording if it has the same meaning.

20. A thermometer works because of
    (a) condensation and evaporation.
    (b) expansion and contraction.
    (c) conduction and convection.
21. In freezing temperatures, tiny living things
    (a) grow quickly.
    (b) grow slowly.
    (c) cannot grow.
22. Freezing water
    (a) contracts.
    (b) expands.
    (c) condenses.

Decide whether each sentence is true, and write yes or no.

23. The sun gets most of its heat from the earth.
24. Both steam and air expand and contract.
25. Solar energy can heat homes.
26. Heat always moves from something warm to something cooler.
27. Heat moves quickly through an insulator.
28. The special liquid in a refrigerator evaporates very slowly.
29. Long ago, people used cold water to cool their food.

Write the answers.

30. Tell how a round thermometer works.
31-32. David and Jason are part of a group that is touring a museum. They are watching a glass blower shape a pitcher. The glass blower tells the group that the temperature of the glass is about 800°C. He must hurry so that the glass does not cool and harden too quickly. David says that the glass blower should dip the pitcher into boiling water to keep it hot. But Jason says that boiling water would make the pitcher cooler. Who is right? Explain why.
33-34. Name two problems caused by expansion and contraction.
35-42. Copy the chart below, and fill in the correct temperatures.

	Celsius	Fahrenheit
boiling point of water		
body temperature		
room temperature		
freezing point of water		

20. b
21. c
22. b

Decide

23. no
24. yes
25. yes
26. yes
27. no
28. no
29. yes

Write

30. A round thermometer works because a metal spring inside expands when it is heated and contracts when it is cooled.

31-32. Jason is right.
     The boiling water would cool the hot glass because heat always moves from a hot object to a cooler object. Boiling water is 100°C, which is much cooler than the 800°C glass. *(2 points)*

33-34. (Any two) Glass breaks, water pipes burst, and roads become rutted because of expansion and contraction.

35-42.

	Celsius	Fahrenheit
boiling point of water	100°	212°
body temperature	37°	98°
room temperature	20°	68°
freezing point of water	0°	32°

(8 points)

(Total: 42 points)

Unit Five
God Cares for Man

"So Noah knew that the waters were abated from off the earth" (Genesis 8:11).

Noah and his family knew that God cared for them. When they thought of God's care, they probably thought of the strong ark that had kept them safe during the Flood. Or maybe they thought of the food and clothing God had provided for them.

You know that God cares for you. Does God's care make you think of His watching over you at night? Do you think of the father and mother He gave you? Do you think of the Bible He gave us?

All these things show you that God cares for you. In this unit, you will learn about one very special way that God protects you. You will study about your own wonderful body.

Think of all the cuts and bumps you have had since you were a baby. They have healed so well that you hardly ever think about them. If your body could not heal itself, today it might have cuts and black-and-blue spots all over it.

You are usually well because your body can fight sickness. But if God had not made your body this way, you would probably be sick all the time. You would have the flu, a cold, mumps, and many other illnesses all at once. Of course, you could not live very long if you were that sick.

In this unit, you can learn how to care for your body. You can do your part to stay healthy. Then you will show God that you are thankful for your body. We are glad that He takes care of us.

126

Unit Five

God Cares for Man

For Your Inspiration

Better Than Gold

Better than grandeur, better than gold,
Than rank and titles a thousandfold,
Is a healthy body and a mind at ease,
And simple pleasures that always please.
A heart that can feel for another's woe,
And share his joys with a genial glow,
With sympathies large enough to enfold
All men as brothers, is better than gold.

Better than gold is a conscience clear,
Though toiling for bread in an humble sphere,
Doubly blessed with content and health,
Untried by the lusts and cares of wealth.
Lowly living and lofty thought
Adorn and ennoble a poor man's cot;
For mind and morals in nature's plan
Are the genuine tests of an earnest man.

Better than gold is a peaceful home
Where all the fireside characters come,
The shrine of love, the heaven of life,
Hallowed by mother, or sister, or wife.
However humble the home may be,
Or tried with sorrow by heaven's decree,
The blessings that never were bought or sold,
And center there, are better than gold.

—*Abram J. Ryan*
1838–1886

Skin, Hair, and Nails
Protect Our Bodies

New Words

dermis (dėr′ mis), the inner layer of skin that holds blood vessels, glands, fat, and nerves.

epidermis (ep′ i • dėr′ mis), the tough, outer layer of skin.

gland (gland), a part of the body that makes a special liquid.

hair follicle (hār fol′ i • kəl), a small, rounded pocket in the skin from which a hair grows.

nail (nāl), a thin, hard covering on the end of a finger or toe.

Reading Together

When you tear your sleeve, your mother needs to mend it. But what if you cut your skin? Does your mother sew it shut? Of course not. Your clothes cannot mend themselves, but your skin can. This way of healing was God's idea. He made your skin able to do this wonderful thing.

Your skin is soft and stretchy, yet it is also tough and strong. Your skin can take much rubbing and scratching before it tears.

When you think of your skin, you think of the outside thick layer. This is called the *epidermis*. The epidermis is made of twelve to fifteen thin layers. Each new layer grows under

How is a shirt like the skin?
How is it different?

127

Lesson 1

CONCEPTS TO TEACH

- God gave us skin that can heal itself.
- The outer layer of skin, called the epidermis, is tough and strong; it protects us from scratches and rubbing.
- The blood vessels in the dermis provide blood to keep the skin alive.
- The oil glands provide oil that keeps the skin soft and waterproof.
- The sweat glands produce water that cools us by evaporation.
- The fat in the dermis layer protects us from bruises.
- The nerve endings in the dermis give us the sense of touch.
- Hair protects the head from bumps and bright sunlight; it also slows the loss of body heat.
- Hair and nails grow only at the base and soon die.
- The oil of the scalp helps to keep the hair strong and healthy.
- Combing and brushing help to distribute the oil.
- Nails protect the ends of the fingers and toes.
- Since the hair and nails have no feeling, they provide ideal protection from bumps and bruises. This also explains why it does not hurt to cut them.

all the others and pushes them up. Each layer is pushed up by newer layers until it reaches the outside of your skin. There it stays for a few months until it is slowly rubbed off.

You are always losing bits of skin. Your clothes rub it off. You wash it off while taking a bath. When you hoe in the garden, sometimes one place in your hand is rubbed very hard. A blister is raised in the sore skin. After the blister heals, a patch of dead skin comes off.

Reading on Your Own

Your skin is made of two main layers. The epidermis is one of these layers. Under this tough epidermis is the soft *dermis*. If you cut your skin so that it bleeds, you have cut into the dermis. The blood comes from many tiny blood vessels in the dermis. Blood is needed to keep your skin alive.

A *gland* is a very special part of your body. It makes a liquid that helps your body stay healthy. Your body has many different glands because it needs many different kinds of liquids.

One kind of gland in the dermis gives off oil. The oil helps to seal out water. It also keeps your skin soft. When your skin becomes rough and chapped, your skin does not have enough oil on it.

Did you know that you are always sweating? You sweat because special glands in your skin are giving off water. The sweat glands send the sweat to the top of your skin, where it evaporates. As you know from the last unit, this evaporation cools your body. You do not notice that you are sweating unless you feel very warm. Then your sweat glands give off water faster than it can evaporate.

There is also a layer of fat in the dermis. The fat protects you from bumps and bruises.

Besides blood, glands, and fat, the dermis also has very tiny nerve endings. These nerve endings tell you how things feel. When you rub this paper, you know that it is smooth, not rough. You know how warm it is. You know these things because your nerve endings are sending messages to your brain.

Why do you need hair? Your hair helps to keep your head warm. It is a good insulator because it holds many little spaces of air.

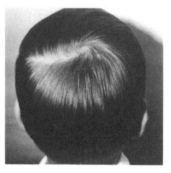

What does your hair do for you?

HELPS FOR THE TEACHER

Introducing the Lesson

Read this poem to introduce the theme of this unit.

My Body Is God's Temple

My body is God's temple;
  I'm building every day,
In home and church and schoolroom,
  By studies, work, and play.
I know if I build wisely,
  Refusing all that's wrong,
My temple will grow lovely,
  For God both pure and strong.
        —*Elizabeth A. Showalter*

Reprinted by permission of Herald Press, Scottdale, Pennsylvania.

There can be two applications of the word temple. One applies to third graders, and one does not. To the born-again Christian, his body is literally the temple of God, the Holy Ghost. But for third graders, you will need to limit the use of *temple* to the dwelling place of their soul.

You may also sing this as a song. The music and two more verses are found in *The Christian Hymnary*, hymn 701.

As you study this unit, help the students develop a healthy respect for their bodies. Your own neat, clean appearance and appropriate conduct will teach much. Avoid an overemphasis on God's judgment for misusing the body. Emphasize the joy and privilege of using our finite bodies to glorify such a powerful, loving God.

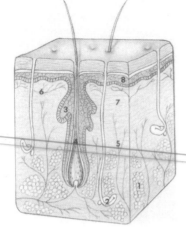
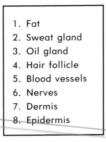

1. Fat
2. Sweat gland
3. Oil gland
4. Hair follicle
5. Blood vessels
6. Nerves
7. Dermis
8. Epidermis

The parts of the skin

Hair has no feeling in it. For this reason, it does not hurt to get a haircut. Hair makes a good cushion for your head. Your hair protects your head from being hurt.

Your hair also protects your head from bright sunlight. Your head might often be sunburned if you had no hair on it.

Only the root of a hair is alive. This living part is in a tiny pocket in the dermis. This pocket is called a *hair follicle*. New hair is always being made in the follicle. This new growth keeps pushing the older part of the hair out.

In the dermis, the oil glands are busily working for your hair. The oil they make keeps your hair strong and soft. You can help spread the oil by combing or brushing your hair every day.

Your fingernails grow in the same way as your hair. The part at the root of the *nail* is alive, but it dies when it is pushed outward by the newer part growing below it.

You know that it does not hurt to clip your fingernails. Because they are dead, you feel no pain. Your tough fingernails shield your tender fingertips from knocks and scrapes. Your toenails do the same thing for your toes.

In making your skin, hair, and nails the way He did, God wisely provided for your health, comfort, and protection.

Extra Information

Did you know—

. . . that the average person daily loses about 40 to 100 of the 100,000 hairs on his scalp?

. . . that your nails are made of hardened skin cells?

. . . that the crescent-shaped spot at the base of your nails is an area of small skin cells that carry less blood?

. . . that the flatter your hair shafts, the curlier your hair is? Thus, a straight hair is like a miniature garden hose, while a very curly hair resembles a tiny tape measure.

. . . that a hair on your scalp may grow five years before it falls out, but eyelashes only five months?

Experiment With Touch

Have a child discover that the skin on his fingertip is much more sensitive than the skin on his arm. Blindfold a child. Hold two pins close together, and touch his arm lightly with both pins at once. Keep moving the pins farther apart and asking him whether he feels one or two pins. When he feels two pins, that will show how far apart the nerve endings are. (At first, the two pins will feel like one because the two areas of skin connect to the same nerve ending.)

Now try the same thing on the child's fingertip. On his fingertip, he will be able to feel the two pins when they are very close together because of the abundance of nerve endings there.

Materials needed:

• *blindfold*

• *2 pins*

Answers for "Test Your Reading"

1. b
2. f
3. g
4. a
5. e
6. d
7. f
8. c
9. d
10. Skin can heal itself when it is cut.   (2)
11. A hair follicle is a small pocket from which a hair grows (or a tiny pocket that holds the living part of a hair).   (2)
12. Combing or brushing spreads oil through our hair.   (2)
13. Hair and nails grow at the root and push outward.   (2)
14. It does not hurt, because they are dead.   (2)

(Total: 19 points)

Comments on "Extra Activities"

1. The following are some of the differences you might observe between the skin of a baby and the skin of an old person.

Baby's skin	*Old person's skin*
soft	rough
smooth	wrinkled
tight	loose
moist	dry
light–colored	dark
perfect	blemishes, scaly, scratched
very fine short hair	longer, coarse hair

2. Encourage the students that it is important to learn how to give a report to other people. It is courteous to give clear and careful explanations.

    You may need to help the students find books or encyclopedia articles to study. Better yet, find some ahead of time, and place them together on a shelf. This may help some students decide which subject they want and may also save you from being swamped after class with requests for reading material.

Test Your Reading

Match each part of the body to the work it does. Use some answers twice.

1. Protects from rubbing or scratches
2. Keeps skin soft and seals out water
3. Gives off water to cool us
4. Keeps skin alive
5. Helps us feel things
6. Keeps head warm
7. Keeps hair strong and soft
8. Protects from bumps and bruises
9. Protects head from being hurt

a. blood
b. epidermis
c. fat
d. hair
e. nerve ending
f. oil
g. sweat gland

Use good sentences to answer the questions below.

10. What can our skin do that our clothes cannot do?
11. What is a hair follicle?
12. How is combing or brushing helpful to our hair?
13. How are hair and nails alike in the way they grow?
14. Why does it not hurt to clip our fingernails?

Extra Activities

Do these activities as your teacher directs.

1. Use a magnifying glass to look at the skin on your hand and arm. If you can, compare your skin with a baby's skin and an old person's skin. How does skin change as a person grows older? *Materials needed:*
   • *magnifying glass*
2. Do you know how to give a report to people? This unit project can give you some practice in giving reports. For this lesson, choose a subject you would like to talk about. Choose one of the subjects below. Each of them will be studied sometime in this unit.

My Wonderful Skin   Thank God for Hair
My Dead Nails   How to Fight Germs
Eating the Right Foods   Why Work?
Stand Tall!   Why Sleep?
Read about your subject in an encyclopedia or library book. Your teacher or parents may help you find good reading material.

QUIZ

Write the New Words on the chalkboard. Ask the students to write the correct New Word for each sentence below. Remind them to use correct spelling.

1. It makes a special liquid for your body. *(gland)*
2. It protects your finger or toe.   *(nail)*
3. This outer covering protects you from scratches. *(epidermis)*
4. It holds blood, glands, fat, and nerves. *(dermis)*
5. It holds the root of a hair.   *(hair follicle)*

Cleanliness Helps Keep
Our Bodies Healthy

New Words

disease (də • zēz′), sickness.

germ (jėrm), a tiny living thing that causes sickness.

stewardship (stōō′ ərd • ship), the work of taking care of things
that belong to someone else.

Reading Together

Do you know why you get sick? Often a sickness or *disease* is caused by tiny living things called *germs*.

Right now many germs are around you. They float in the air. They stick to your hair, skin, and clothes. But you cannot see them because they are so small.

Even with so many germs around you, you are usually healthy. Your body has at least five ways to fight germs.

First of all, your skin acts like a wall. It stops many germs from entering your body. But if your skin is cut, the germs can get inside. This is why you should wash any torn or cut skin. You should also put salve or a first-aid liquid on the cut to kill the germs.

When germs get into your eyes, your tears wash them away. Tears can also kill some of the germs.

Using a handkerchief protects others from our germs.

You breathe air that has germs in it. This is how many germs enter your body. But the linings of your nose and throat are just right for trapping these germs. The linings are made of a sticky material that holds the germs until you cough or sneeze them out. Since coughing and sneezing send many germs into the air, it is important to use a handkerchief.

Even if you wash your food carefully, it still has some germs on it. You eat these germs with your food. But most of them cannot live long in

131

Lesson 2

CONCEPTS TO TEACH

- Many diseases are caused by germs.
- The body has many defenses against germs: skin, tears, nose and throat linings, stomach liquids, and blood.
- Eating good food, drinking plenty of fresh water, and getting plenty of rest keep the body strong enough to fight germs.
- To avoid spreading germs, the mouth should be covered while sneezing and coughing; separate towels and drinking glasses should be used.
- Washing the skin and clothes helps to get rid of germs.
- Hands should especially be washed after using the rest room and before preparing or eating food.
- Nails should be trimmed and cleaned regularly to remove the germs that collect under them.
- Teeth should be brushed regularly to destroy germs that cause tooth decay.

HELPS FOR THE TEACHER

Introducing the Lesson

Read Leviticus 15:1–5, 13 to show how important cleanliness is to God. God told the Israelites how to control germs centuries before man knew they existed.

your stomach. In your stomach are very strong liquids that kill the germs.

What if your skin, tears, nose and throat linings, and stomach liquids cannot get rid of the germs? Then your blood will fight them. In your blood are many little workers that are trained to destroy germs. When a germ gets into your blood, these workers catch the germ and kill it.

Your body does its best to fight germs. But sometimes your body cannot get rid of them all. Then you become sick.

Now what can you do? You can help your body by getting plenty of rest, eating good food, and drinking plenty of water. This is important anytime, but even more so when you are sick.

A cold, the flu, measles, and many other diseases caused by germs can spread from you to someone else. What should you do if you have such a disease? You should always cover your mouth when you cough or sneeze. You should also use your own towel and drinking glass. This helps to keep germs from spreading.

Reading on Your Own

Since you do not enjoy being sick, you should know what you can do to stay well. One thing you can do is to take a bath regularly. You should always wash your hands before you touch food and after you use the rest room. Use plenty of soap and water to wash the germs away.

Your mother washes your clothes when they become dirty. But clothes also need to be washed because of germs that stick to them. The soapy water washes germs away or kills them.

Many germs are caught under your fingernails. You should not bite your nails, for the germs will enter your mouth. Instead, you should keep your fingernails and toenails clean and neatly trimmed.

Many germs can stick to your hair because it has oil on it. For this reason, you should wash your hair regularly. The shampoo and water clean the hair and get rid of many germs.

How do we use these to stay clean?

Can teeth be sick? Many people have disease in their teeth. Germs cause the disease by eating little holes in the teeth. The holes are called cavities. The cavities keep getting larger unless a dentist fills them.

How can you keep the germs off your teeth? You should brush your teeth after meals and at bedtime. The brushing scrubs away many germs

---

Extra Information

Did you know—

. . . that viruses that attack bacteria, called phages, have successfully overcome intestinal diseases in experiments with calves and pigs and show great promise for combating human infections?

. . . that ancient Romans cleaned themselves with sand and skin scrapers instead of soap?

. . . that the common cold is caused by more than one hundred different viruses?

. . . that the majority of test monkeys that were vaccinated before they ate plenty of sweets did not develop tooth decay? Dentists are hoping for similar success with humans within 10 or 15 years.

QUIZ

Ask the class to supply the correct New Word for each sentence below. Some will be used twice.

1. You have this when you care for something that belongs to another person. *(stewardship)*
2. This word means a living thing that makes people sick. *(germ)*
3. This word means any kind of sickness. *(disease)*
4. This word makes you think of caring for your body, which belongs to God. *(stewardship)*
5. This thing is too tiny to see. *(germ)*

and helps the teeth stay hard and smooth.

Staying clean and caring for your body helps to keep you well and comfortable. You are more pleasant to be near when you wear clean clothes and keep your hair and teeth clean. As you take good care of your body and keep clean and neat, you honor God, who made you.

God made our bodies, and they belong to Him. But God gave our bodies to us as a wonderful gift to enjoy. He wants us to take care of them. We want to use good *stewardship* by taking care of our bodies.

Test Your Reading

Copy each sentence below, and fill in the missing words from the words in the box.

blood	food	nails	stomach
brush	germs	skin	tears
clean	good	wash	torn
cough	linings	sleep	towel

1. Tiny living things that cause disease are called ——.
2. Five parts of our bodies that fight or kill germs are ——, ——, nose and throat ——, —— liquids, and ——.
3. Rules for Good Health
   a. Wash —— or cut skin, and put salve on it.
   b. Eat enough —— food.
   c. Get plenty of ——.
   d. Cover your mouth before you —— or sneeze.
   e. Use your own —— and drinking glass.
   f. Wash your hands before you touch —— and after you use the rest room.
   g. Wear —— clothes.
   h. Keep your —— trimmed.
   i. —— your hair regularly.
   j. —— your teeth every day.

Think about your lesson today. Then use a good sentence to answer this question.

4. Why does a doctor cover most of his body, including his mouth, nose, and hair, when he operates on a sick person?

Answers for "Test Your Reading"

1. Tiny living things that cause disease are called *germs*.
2. Five parts of our bodies that fight or kill germs are *skin, tears,* nose and throat *linings, stomach* liquids, and *blood*. (5)
3. a. Wash *torn* or cut skin, and put salve on it.
   b. Eat enough *good* food.
   c. Get plenty of *sleep*.
   d. Cover your mouth before you *cough* or sneeze.
   e. Use your own *towel* and drinking glass.
   f. Wash your hands before you touch *food* and after you use the rest room.
   g. Wear *clean* clothes.
   h. Keep your *nails* trimmed.
   i. *Wash* your hair regularly.
   j. *Brush* your teeth every day. (10)
4. A doctor covers himself so that germs will not spread from him to the sick person. (2)

(Total: 18 points)

Comments on "Extra Activities"

1. This poster may be hung in a hallway or rest room, where it will be seen often.

2. Perhaps the whole class could sing for an invalid or elderly person. Of course, it would not be wise to visit someone with a communicable disease. Tell the children to speak cheerfully but quietly and to listen with interest when the invalid speaks.

3. Your students may have difficulty in understanding the purpose of a list. Explain that often a subject is too large to say everything that could be said. Illustrate with the sample in their text: "Eating the Right Foods." Besides the things listed, the following could have been included:

   5. Keeping food free of germs
   6. Foods that are not best
   7. Sickness linked with eating
   8. Baking with whole wheat
   9. How to lose weight

   Use this illustration (*a*) to show that a list helps us focus on a few main ideas and (*b*) to show that there is no right or wrong list as long as each idea fits the main topic. Instead of concentrating on making a perfect list, each student should think much about his subject. The more he has read about his subject, the easier it should be to jot down some main ideas.

   After the lists are written, check to make sure they include main ideas, not specific details. Each main idea should stimulate questions, such as these:

   (1) What is this like?
   (2) Why or how does this happen?
   (3) How do I do this?
   (4) How do I know this is true?

   The answers to these questions will provide the specific details that will make up the bulk of each student's oral report.

How are these two things alike? See Proverbs 17:22.

Extra Activities

Do these activities as your teacher directs.

1. Make a poster about staying well. Write this title on it: "How to Stay Healthy." Write the ten rules from the exercise on page 133. Draw pictures for some of the rules.
   Materials needed:
   • *large sheet of poster board*
   • *crayons, markers, or poster paints*

2. Do you know someone who is sick? Ask your parents to take you to visit him. Try to cheer him with a nice card or flowers. He may also enjoy having you sing for him.

3. Have you studied your subject for a report to the class? Now make a list of things you want to say. Your list might look something like this:

   Eating the Right Foods
   1. God cares about our eating
   2. Groups of food
   3. Why we should not eat too much
   4. Foods that are good for us

   Show your list to your teacher. Ask him how you can make it even better.

God Provides a Good Diet

New Words

balanced diet (bal′ ənst dī′ ət), eating some foods from each food
     group.
Calorie (kal′ ər • ē), a measure of the amount of energy in food.
fat (fat), oily material found in foods such as butter or cream.
food groups (fōod grōops), classes of foods that are alike.
protein (prō′ tēn), a material that builds our bodies and is found
     in meat and eggs.
starch (stärch), a white material in grain and potatoes.
sugar (shoog′ ər), a sweet material in fruit and candy.

Reading Together

     Does your mother let you eat
whatever you want? No, she probably does not. Sometimes she might
ask you to eat a food that you do not
like. Why does she do this?
     Your mother wants you to be well
and strong. She knows that when
you eat well, you are likely to feel
well. She gives you different kinds of
food because your body needs them.

God created many different foods for us to eat.

135

Lesson 3

CONCEPTS TO TEACH

- There are four groups of food: milk, meat,
bread/cereal, and fruit/vegetable.
- A good diet includes some food from each of the
four food groups every meal.
- The body needs protein to build itself.
- The body needs fiber for good digestion.
- Every day the body needs a certain amount of
food for energy.
- The amount of energy in food is measured in
Calories. (One Calorie, with a capital C, is equal
to 1,000 calories. One calorie is the amount of
heat needed to raise 1 gram of water 1° Celsius.)
- Sugars, starches, and fats are energy foods.
- The energy food that we do not need is stored in
the body as fat.
- The body needs some fat to be healthy and to
have energy available during times of sickness.

- Good stewardship of the body includes eating
good food; a diet of snack food is poor
stewardship.
- As good stewards, we must eat moderately.
- Too much sugar, salt, or fat is not good for the
body.

Food has been classified into four *food groups*. They are the milk group, the bread and cereal group, the fruit and vegetable group, and the meat group. Look at the picture of the four food groups to find foods that belong in each group.

It is good for you to eat foods from each food group every meal. For breakfast, you might eat an orange, two slices of toast, an egg, and a glass of milk. Your lunch and supper may be different from your breakfast, yet you should again eat some food from each food group. When you eat foods from all four groups, you have a *balanced diet*. You are eating enough of each kind of food.

Foods from the milk and meat groups give you protein. Getting protein is very important because nearly all of your body is made of *protein*. What happens when you eat cheese or meat? Your body uses the protein to make new skin, fingernails, and other parts of your body. These replace the old parts that are worn out.

Whole wheat, apples, and celery have much fiber in them. You need fiber to digest your food well. When you eat, your food goes to your stomach. Then it moves along a long, soft tube. As it goes, the proteins and other needed materials are carried away by the blood. Finally, only fiber and other waste materials are left. Fiber helps move the waste materials through your body.

Reading on Your Own

Bread, cereal, potatoes, and beans are made mostly of *starch*. Starch is a white material in food. It has no taste of its own. A chocolate cake has much starch in it from the flour. But it also has *sugar* to make it sweet. Besides this, it has *fat* such as butter or oil.

Sugar, starch, and fat are all foods that give you energy and strength. You always need energy, whether you jump, walk, read, or sleep. So your body is always burning energy foods. This burning uses oxygen as a fire does, but God made your body to be able to burn the food without flames.

The harder you make your body work, the faster it burns food. For example, your food burns much faster when you run than when you write. Running takes much more energy than writing does.

The amount of energy a food gives us is measured in *Calories*. Every day a child your age needs about 2,400 Calories of energy. This might seem like much energy, but each Calorie is only a small amount of energy. For example, a teaspoon of sugar has 16 Calories. A hamburger sandwich has about 245 Calories, and a glass of milk has about 150 Calories.

The sugar, starch, and fat you eat may soon be burned to give you energy. But if the fat is not needed right away, it is stored under your

HELPS FOR THE TEACHER

Introducing the Lesson

Use your lunch to illustrate the four food groups. Point out that God has given us food that is well suited to the needs of our bodies. Failing to eat a balanced diet may increase the chances of suffering from poor digestion or a deficiency disease.

Some food must be changed before it is appetizing or safe to eat. Flour must be ground and baked, meat must be cooked, and milk must be made sanitary. But sometimes in processing food, it is made less healthful. The less sugar, salt, and fat that is added to food, the better it is for our bodies.

Materials needed:
• *your (well-balanced) lunch*

Extra Information

Did you know—

. . . that Eskimos eat raw fish and seal meat, and some Africans eat monkeys, snakes, caterpillars, and ants?

. . . that excessive salt intake can lead to high blood pressure, blood poisoning, and heart and kidney disease?

. . . that the food we eat is made of many complex chemicals? For example, an egg contains chemicals such as ovalbumin, conalbumin, mucin, amino acids, lipovitellin, butyric acid, and zeaxanthide.

THE FRUIT AND VEGETABLE GROUP   THE BREAD AND CEREAL GROUP

THE MEAT GROUP   THE MILK GROUP

THE FOUR FOOD GROUPS

skin. Any extra sugar or starch cannot be stored just as it is. Instead, it is changed to fat and also stored until your body needs it.

Your body needs some extra fat to protect you from bumps. The fat also gives your body a smooth shape. It gives you energy when you feel too sick to eat.

You need some fat but not too much. Too much fat comes from eating much more food than your body uses. It may come from eating too many snacks.

Candy, soft drinks, potato chips, and other snacks often have much sugar, salt, or fat. They have many Calories of energy, but very little fiber, protein, or other things your body needs. Besides this, eating too much sugar, salt, or fat makes it hard for your body to work right.

It is not wrong to eat foods that we like. But it is wrong to eat so much that we harm our bodies. It is wrong to eat so many snacks that we cheat our bodies out of a balanced diet. This is being a poor steward of the bodies God gave us.

How can we be good stewards of our bodies in our eating? We should eat enough good food to stay healthy. We should also stop eating when we have enough. We should eat a variety of foods from each food group. This helps us feel well and strong enough to do our work and to help other people.

Bulletin Board Idea

Ask the students to bring labels and magazine pictures of many different foods. Have them classify the foods according to the four food groups. Make this title for the bulletin board: *We Need Food From Four Food Groups.* Also make smaller titles that say: "Milk Group", "Meat Group", "Fruit and Vegetable Group", and "Bread and Cereal Group". Perhaps the students could help you arrange the pictures and labels attractively on the bulletin board.

QUIZ

Ask the class to choose a New Word to fit each sentence below.

1. Your body uses this to replace worn-out parts. *(protein)*
2. This is stored under your skin. *(fat)*
3. This white food has no taste by itself. *(starch)*
4. Most people like this sweet food. *(sugar)*
5. This is used to measure energy in food. *(Calorie)*
6. This means eating enough of each kind of food. *(balanced diet)*

Answers for "Test Your Reading"

1. yes
2. no
3. yes
4. yes
5. yes
6. fruit and vegetable
7. meat
8. milk
9. bread and cereal
10. b
11. c   *(Total: 11 points)*

————————————— Test Your Reading —————————————

Write yes *if the sentence is true. Write* no *if it is not true.*

1. It is wise to eat many different foods.
2. Fiber helps build our bodies.
3. Our bodies burn sugar, starch, and fat.
4. Our bodies burn food faster when we jump than when we read.
5. A sick person needs stored fat for energy.

Which of the four food groups is missing in each lunch?

6. ham sandwich, milk, popcorn
7. orange juice, jelly sandwich, cheese, peaches
8. lemonade, lettuce and bologna sandwich, pretzels, cake
9. orange, celery, fried bacon, ice cream

Choose the best answer.

10. The energy of food is measured in
    (a) degrees.   (b) Calories.   (c) pounds.
11. How can we be the best stewards of our bodies?
    (a) To eat no fat, sugar, or salt.
    (b) To eat mostly meat and fruit.
    (c) To eat just enough to be healthy.

Extra Activities

Do these activities as your teacher directs.

1. Keep a record of your meals for a week. Then check whether each meal had food from all four groups. If so, write *balanced* for that meal. If not, write *not balanced* and also the missing food group.

   At the end of the week, show your record to your family. Ask your mother whether you may plan a balanced meal for the family.

2. Look at some cereal boxes or other food boxes and bags. Find the amount of Calories in each serving. Also look for the amount of fat, protein, and sugar. Ask your parents to help you, if necessary.
   Materials needed: • food boxes that have nutrition information

3. Finish getting your list ready for your report. Then practice giving your report a few times to yourself and to your family. Try to remember these rules:
   a. Know your subject very well.
   b. Speak loudly and clearly.
   c. Look more at the people than at your list.
   d. Smile, but do not giggle.

Exercise and Good Posture Help Our Bodies

New Words

emotions (i • mō′ shənz), our feelings and thoughts.

exercise (ek′ sər • sīz), working or using our bodies.

muscle (mus′ əl), a part of the body that helps us move.

posture (pos′ chər), a way of holding the body.

Reading Together

A worker was shaping a clay pot on a wheel. He kept pushing the wheel with his foot to keep it spinning.

A man who was watching said, "That leg you use all the time must become very tired."

"No, my friend," the worker said. "It's the leg that does nothing that gets so tired."

This little story teaches us something important. Work is good for our bodies. God planned that we should work in order to stay healthy and strong.

We even sleep better after we have worked hard. The Bible says, "The sleep of a labouring man is sweet" (Ecclesiastes 5:12).

If we would no longer work or *exercise* our bodies, they would become weak. The *muscles* in our arms could not lift as much or push as

Which leg of the potter will get more tired? Why?

139

Lesson 4

CONCEPTS TO TEACH

- Work is a noble provision given by God for our emotional and physical welfare.
- We sleep better after we have worked hard.
- Our muscles will become stronger with exercise; they become weaker from a lack of exercise.
- Short times of exercise (recess) throughout the school day help us to study better.
- Laziness and too much rest are not good for us.
- Work helps to make healthy emotions.
- A lack of proper sleep weakens our body and makes it more liable to become sick.
- Children need more sleep than adults.
- Poor posture makes it hard for us to breathe properly and to digest our food properly.
- Poor posture may lead to back problems.
- Good posture is a habit that should be cultivated in youth if we wish to have good posture in adult life.
- A cheerful attitude helps us to have good posture.
- Good muscles help us to have good posture.
- We need to learn proper ways to stand, sit, walk, and lift.

hard. Our leg muscles could no longer help us run as fast.

It seems strange that using our muscles makes them stronger. Using our shoes and clothes makes them wear out. But our muscles are alive. Because of the way God made them, they can grow larger and stronger when they work hard.

Happy emotions

When we study at school, our minds are working hard, but our bodies are not working. Every so often, our bodies need some exercise. This is why we have recess. At recess time, we exercise our bodies and rest our minds. Then we can think clearly again.

Work is also good for our *emotions*. Our emotions are the way we feel about ourselves and the things that happen to us. They also include how we feel about God and others.

Someone with healthy emotions usually feels happy. When he has problems, he cheerfully tries to solve them. He feels good because he can work to help his family and other people.

Being lazy is hard on the emotions. A lazy person grumbles about his problems. He does not like to work. He feels that others do not need him or love him. A lazy person may be unhappy because he does not like himself.

Diligent work

HELPS FOR THE TEACHER

Introducing the Lesson

Begin class by having the students do an exercise from "Suggestions for Exercise." Ask them to notice how exercise makes them feel warmer and causes faster breathing and heartbeat.

Also demonstrate good and poor posture while standing, sitting, walking, and lifting a heavy object. Here again, your previous example is much more important than your present words. You will be able to teach this lesson more effectively if you consistently exemplify good posture.

Commend some students that usually have good posture. After this, be sure to notice and encourage others who are trying to improve their posture.

Extra Information

Did you know—

. . . that your body contains about 650 muscles?

. . . that some men who went without sleep for 11 days became fearful and irrational?

. . . that because muscles are much denser than fat, a physically fit person may wear clothes that are several sizes smaller than an unconditioned person who weighs exactly the same?

. . . that it is impossible to remove fat from only one trouble spot of the body? For example, doing dozens of sit-ups daily for a leaner stomach will certainly strengthen the stomach muscle, but any fat that is lost comes from all over the body.

. . . that repeated fasting and crash dieting actually encourage the body to hoard fat more than ever as a natural defense against starvation?

Enough sleep

Your body cannot digest food very well. Poor posture is also hard on your back. Sometimes older people have back problems because they did not practice good posture when they were young.

It is very important to learn good posture while you are young. Then you are likely to have good posture all your life. You are more likely to feel strong and healthy.

Reading on Your Own

God gave us the day for working and the night for sleeping. We need enough sleep to stay healthy. If we do not get enough sleep, we may become sick. Losing sleep makes our bodies become weak. They cannot fight germs as well.

How much sleep is enough sleep? Right now you need about ten hours of sleep each night. As you grow older, you will need less sleep.

We need enough sleep but not too much. Too much sleep is a sign of laziness. The Bible says, "He that gathereth in summer is a wise son: but he that sleepeth in harvest is a son that causeth shame." There is a time to sleep and a time to work. We need both to be healthy.

Is good *posture* important? Does the way you hold your body matter? Does walking right and sitting right make any difference?

Yes, it does. If you have poor posture, you cannot breathe well.

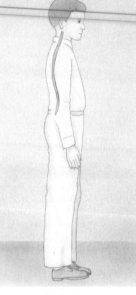

Good posture

Suggestions for Exercise

Use these exercises to supplement your recess activities or to provide a welcome break in a long class period.

1. *Toe Touch (for abdominal muscles and agility):* Stand straight, and stretch arms above head. Touch toes by bending at the waist, not the knees. Repeat at least 15 times. (For the sake of modesty, have students stand *beside* each other instead of *behind* each other.)

2. *Jumping Jack (for general fitness):* Stand with legs spread apart, arms stretched above head, and palms together. Lower arms in a wide arc while bringing knees together in a single jump. Then raise arms through a wide arc while jumping to spread legs apart. Repeat rapidly at least 15 times.

3. *Posture Helper:* Press back against wall. Have arms outstretched at sides, knees slightly bent, and feet turned outward. Then stretch tall while raising arms in a smooth arc and keeping back pressed against wall. Repeat at least 15 times.

4. *Leg Builder:* Stand straight against a wall with hands on hips. Lower body to an imaginary chair, keeping back pressed against wall. Count slowly to three; then rise. Repeat smoothly at least 15 times.

Keep in mind that your choice of games and activities at recess is very important. By providing a variety of recess games and activities, you can help to develop healthy students in your school.

How can you have good posture? First of all, think of your emotions. Are you usually cheerful? Do you like to work? A cheerful, busy person is much more likely to have good posture.

Besides this, you also need strong muscles to carry and move your body. To have strong muscles, you need to exercise them often. Do you like to work hard? Do you like to run and jump every day? If you do, it is easier for you to have good posture.

poor   good
Walking posture

You may be cheerful and get exercise, but still have poor posture. If so, you may need to study good posture. You may need to learn the right way to stand, sit, walk, and lift things.

If you really want to have good posture, you can. Study the pictures on this page carefully. Try to practice good posture all the time. Ask your family and friends to remind you if you forget.

poor   good
Sitting posture

There are many rules for good posture, but here are the main ideas.

1. Keep your head high, as though a string were pulling the top of it.
2. Keep your stomach pulled in, not sagging out.
3. Relax: do not be stiff and strained.
4. When you lift something heavy, let your strong leg muscles do most of the work.

God created us to walk upright with good posture. He does not want us to stoop or crawl like an animal. If we are thankful to God for our bodies, we will want to show it by having good posture. We are good stewards of our bodies when we have good posture.

poor   good
Lifting posture

QUIZ

Write the New Words on the chalkboard. Ask the class to spell them correctly when they choose one for each sentence below.

1. This means the way you hold your body when you stand or move. *(posture)*
2. This means your feelings and thoughts. *(emotions)*
3. This means putting your body to work. *(exercise)*
4. It helps your body to work and exercise. *(muscle)*

────────── **Test Your Reading** ──────────

Copy each sentence below, and fill in the missing words.
1. Work helps our bodies stay —— and helps us —— well.
2. When we work our muscles hard, they become ——.
3. Recess gives our minds —— so that we can think clearly again.
4. If we have good ——, we will usually be happy and will cheer-fully try to solve our problems.
5. If we lose too much sleep, we may become ——.

Use good sentences to answer these questions.
6. What three problems are caused by poor posture?
7. What three things can help us have good posture?
8. What are four basic rules for good posture?

Look at the picture below. Write each number, and tell whether the person has good or poor posture.

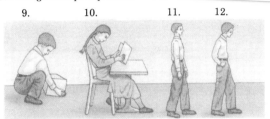

    9.   10.   11.   12.

Extra Activities

Do these activities as your teacher directs.
1. Test your posture. Tie a scissors onto a long string. Ask someone to hold the other end. Then stand just as you usually do, and have the other person hold the string beside your ear. The string should hang freely, not touching your body. If you have good posture, the string will line up with your body. The scissors will hang beside your heel, not your toes.
   Materials needed:
   • *long string*
   • *scissors*
2. Give your unit project report to the class when your teacher calls on you.

Answers for "Test Your Reading"

1. Work helps our bodies stay *healthy (or strong)* and helps us *sleep* well.   (2)
2. When we work our muscles hard, they become *stronger (or larger)*.
3. Recess gives our minds *rest* so that we can think clearly again.
4. If we have good *emotions*, we will usually be happy and will cheer-fully try to solve our problems.
5. If we lose too much sleep, we may become *sick*.
6. Poor posture keeps us from breathing well and from digesting our food well. It can cause back problems.   (4)
7. Healthy emotions, strong muscles, and studying good posture can help us have good posture.   (4)
8. Keep your head high, as though a string were pulling the top of it.
   Keep your stomach pulled in, not sagging out.
   Relax: do not be stiff and strained.
   When you lift something heavy, let your strong leg muscles do most of the work. (5)
9. good posture
10. poor posture
11. good posture
12. poor posture   *(Total: 23 points)*

Comments on "Extra Activities"

2. If you choose to grade the students on their oral reports, try to do so unobtrusively. This helps them relax and do their best. Require the rest of the class to listen respectfully to the student who is speaking.

ANSWER KEY

Match

1. a
2. c
3. b
4. g
5. f
6. i
7. h
8. e
9. d

Fill

10. glands
11. hair follicles
12. nails
13. stewardship
14. balanced diet
15. protein
16. Calories
17. emotions
18–19. muscles, posture

Write

20. root
21. cooler
22. stomach liquids
23. skin
24. day
25. sick
26. more
27. poor

Lesson 5

Do You Remember What You Learned?

Match each word on the right to its meaning on the left.

1. Inner layer of living skin	a. dermis
2. Tough, outer layer of skin	b. disease
3. Sickness	c. epidermis
4. Tiny living things that cause sickness	d. exercise
5. Classes of foods that are alike	e. fat
6. Sweet material in fruit	f. food groups
7. White material in bread	g. germs
8. Oily material in meat	h. starch
9. Making our bodies work or play	i. sugar

Fill each blank with a word from the box.

balanced diet	hair follicles	posture
Calories	muscles	protein
emotions	nails	stewardship
glands		

10. The —— in our bodies make water, oil, and other liquids.
11. Hair grows from little pockets called —— ——.
12. Our —— protect the ends of our fingers and toes.
13. We should use good —— in taking care of our bodies.
14. Foods from the four food groups give us a —— ——.
15. We need —— to build our bodies.
16. Running uses more —— of energy than walking does.
17. A happy, busy person has healthy ——.
18–19. Strong —— help us have good ——.

Write the best word for each sentence.

20. Hair and nails grow at the (root, end).
21. When sweat evaporates, we become (warmer, cooler).
22. Our (stomach liquids, nerve endings) kill germs that we eat with our food.
23. Our (skin, blood) stops germs from entering our bodies.
24. God provided the (day, night) for working.
25. A person who loses too much sleep can easily become (lazy, sick).
26. Children need (more, less) sleep than older people.
27. A boy with poor posture is likely to have (good, poor) posture when he is old.

144

Lesson 5

Review the unit theme and the main concepts for each lesson. Remind the students to follow the steps in "How to Study for a Test" on page 5 of the textbook (page 11 of this manual).

Decide whether each sentence is true, and write yes *or* no.

28. Our tough epidermis protects us from scratches and rubbing.
29. God made our skin able to heal itself.
30. Fat protects us from bumps and gives us energy.
31. Hair helps cool our heads.
32. Oil helps to keep our hair strong and smooth.
33. Combing and brushing is good for our hair.
34. Eating too much food is good stewardship of our bodies.
35. Exercising our bodies can help our minds think better.

Choose the best ending for each sentence.

36. Oil helps to
    (a) cool us when we are hot.
    (b) keep our skin soft.   (c) keep our skin alive.
37. When we touch something, we use our
    (a) hair follicles.   (b) nerve endings.   (c) blood vessels.
38. Three parts of the body that fight germs are
    (a) hair, nails, and skin.
    (b) blood, tears, and skin.   (c) hair, teeth, and stomach.
39. Fiber helps us
    (a) digest our food.
    (b) make new skin.   (c) have energy to work.
40. When we make our muscles work hard,
    (a) they become weaker.
    (b) they stay the same.   (c) they become stronger.
41. Poor posture
    (a) causes healthy emotions.
    (b) causes extra fat.   (c) causes back problems.

Use good sentences to give the answers.

42–43. What two things should we do to keep our germs from spreading to others?
44–47. How should we keep our teeth, skin, hair, and nails clean?
48–49. Give two ways that working helps our bodies.
50–52. What three things can help us have good posture?
53–55. Give three rules for good posture.

Draw a picture for each exercise.

56–59. Draw food for each of the four food groups. Label each picture with the correct food group.
60–61. Draw two people with good posture: one standing and one sitting.

Decide

28. yes
29. yes
30. yes
31. no
32. yes
33. yes
34. no
35. yes

Choose

36. b
37. b
38. b
39. a
40. c
41. c

Use

42–43. Cover our mouths before we cough or sneeze.
Use only our own towel and drinking glass. (Other answers may be acceptable.)

(3 points)

44–47. Brush our teeth every day.
Take a bath regularly (or wash our hands with soap and water).
Wash our hair regularly.
Keep our fingernails trimmed.

(5 points)

48–49. Working keeps our bodies strong and healthy.
Working helps us sleep well.

(3 points)

50–52. Having healthy emotions or being cheerful can help us.
Having strong muscles or getting enough exercise can help us.
Learning about good posture can help us.

(4 points)

53–55. (Any three) Keep your head high.
Keep your stomach pulled in.
Relax.
Let your leg muscles do most of the lifting.

(4 points)

Draw

56–61. (Answers may vary.)

(Total: 66 points)

Unit Six
God Cares for the Animals

"There went in two and two unto Noah into the ark . . ." (Genesis 7:9).

Do you have a soft kitten to cuddle? Do you have a lively puppy to chase? Or do you have a bouncy pony to ride?

Maybe you live on a farm. You may sell rabbits. Your family may milk cows. You may raise pigs, sheep, or horses.

Whether you have many or few animals, you know that they need special care. They need good food and clean water. They need a place to stay.

But not all animals are pets or farm animals. Not all animals are tame. Who takes care of all the wild animals? God does. He takes care of the frogs, snakes, foxes, deer, and all the other animals.

Look at the picture above. It shows how God took care of the animals at the time of the Flood. He sent them into the ark that Noah had built. There they were safe from the deep waters where they would have drowned.

The same God is still caring for the animals today. In Unit Six, you will study about some kinds of animals. You will learn how God is caring for them.

146

Unit Six

God Cares for the Animals

For Your Inspiration

Psalm 8

O LORD our Lord,
  how excellent is thy name in all the earth!
  who hast set thy glory above the heavens.

Out of the mouth of babes and sucklings
  hast thou ordained strength because of thine enemies,
    that thou mightest still the enemy and the avenger.

When I consider thy heavens, the work of thy fingers,
  the moon and the stars, which thou hast ordained;
What is man, that thou art mindful of him?
  and the son of man, that thou visitest him?

For thou hast made him a little lower than the angels,
  and hast crowned him with glory and honor.
Thou madest him to have dominion over the works
                              of thy hands;
  thou hast put all things under his feet:

All sheep and oxen, yea,
  and the beasts of the field;
The fowl of the air, and the fish of the sea,
  and whatsoever passeth through the paths of the seas.

O LORD our Lord,
  how excellent is thy name in all the earth!

Animals Saved From the Flood

New Words

characteristics (kar′ ik • tə • ris′ tiks), the kind of body an animal has and the way its body works.

classification (klas′ ə • fə • kā′ shən), putting things into groups.

cold-blooded (kōld′ blud′ id), having a body that cannot heat or cool itself.

skeleton (skel′ ə • tən), all the bones in an animal's body.

warm-blooded (wôrm′ blud′ id), having a body that keeps itself warm.

Reading Together

What if God had not saved animals during the Flood? What if He had only saved Noah and his family? Just think! You could never visit a zoo. You would not have pets or farm animals.

Besides, you could eat no meat, eggs, cheese, or ice cream. You would have nothing made of leather or wool because all of these things come from animals.

God knew that man would need animals. So He carefully planned a way to save them from the Flood. First, God told Noah how to build the ark. This ark was to be a dry home for the animals during the Flood. God also told Noah how much food to store in the ark for the animals.

Finally, everything was ready. But where were the animals? God did not ask Noah to chase them into the ark. So Noah waited. Then the animals came; they crawled and flew and hopped and thumped. Animals and more animals were everywhere! Only God knew how to tell them all to come into the ark.

147

Lesson 1

CONCEPTS TO TEACH

- God provided a way to have animals after the Flood by saving at least two of each kind in the ark.
- The food that the animals would need to stay alive was stored in the ark by Noah.
- In talking to Noah about the animals, God used group or class names: fowl (birds), cattle, and creeping things.
- Classification helps us study the thousands of different kinds of animals in a concise and orderly way.
- Classification is based on the characteristics that are alike in animals.
- Some animals have no skeleton (jellyfish, earthworms), some have their skeleton on the outside (insects, starfish), and some have their skeleton on the inside (fish, frogs, birds, snakes, cattle).
- Among those that have a skeleton on the inside, some are cold-blooded (frogs, fish, snakes), and some are warm-blooded (birds, cattle).

What about the fish and the other water animals? They did not need the special protection of the ark. They were used to living in the water.

When God talked to Noah about the animals, He did not say each animal's name. He did not say, "Take five sheep, five cows, five chickens, and . . ." Neither did He say, "Take two ladybugs, two blackbirds, two foxes, two tigers . . ." God would have had to say thousands of names!

Instead, God said names for groups of animals. He used these group names: fowl (or birds), cattle and creeping things. When God used these group names, He was using *classification*. Classification is grouping things that are alike.

Reading on Your Own

You use classification often. When your mother tells you to clean up a room, what do you do? You do not put toys into the freezer. You put them into the toy box. You do not put your socks into the drawer with the spoons and forks. You put them with the rest of your clothes. You put each kind of thing together in a group. That is classification.

We need classification when we study animals. It would take us far too long to study each animal one by one. But we can study a whole group of animals in a short time. We can study animals in groups because God made their bodies in an orderly way.

How are animals put into groups? Are animals of the same size or shape or color grouped together? No, an animal is most often grouped by the *characteristics* of its body. In other words, it is grouped according to the kind of body it has.

Let's look at some important animal characteristics. First of all, many animals have a *skeleton*. A skeleton is made of all the hard parts of an animal's body. These hard parts hold the body together. They give each animal its own shape, which may be tall, or round, or flattened.

Animals with skeletons are put into one huge group. Dogs, ants, fish, birds, and snakes are animals with skeletons.

Which animals have no skeletons? Many water animals, such as snails and jellyfish, have no skeletons. Neither does our garden friend, the earthworm. These are only a few of the large group of animals without skeletons.

The animal group with skeletons has been divided into two smaller groups. Animals in the first group have their skeletons on the outside of their bodies. Ants, bugs, butterflies, and spiders belong to this group. When we see these animals, we can see their skeletons!

Fish, birds, snakes, and dogs belong to the second group. Their skeletons are made of bones inside their bodies. We cannot see their skeletons from the outside.

The animal group with inside skeletons can be divided into two smaller groups. One group has the

---

HELPS FOR THE TEACHER

Introducing the Lesson

Share this poem with your students.

How Great Is Noah's God!

How great is Noah's God!
   For long ago, He made
All kinds of living creatures that
   His skill and might displayed.

How great is Noah's God!
   He planned the ark to save
The animals and Noah's kin
   From out a watery grave.

How great is Noah's God!
   I'm glad that I can say:
The very God that Noah loved
   Is still my God today.

                    —*Naomi Lapp*

Emphasize the value of classification and the concept that this is done on the basis of similar characteristics.

Extra Information

Did you know—

. . . that almost a million kinds of animals have been classified? Of this number, about 800,000 kinds are insects, 21,000 kinds are fish, 8,600 kinds are birds, 6,000 kinds are reptiles, 4,000 kinds are mammals, and 3,000 kinds are amphibians.

. . . that every year, scientists find many new species of animals? Among the recent ones are pointy-nosed frogs and moth larvae with bright pink hair.

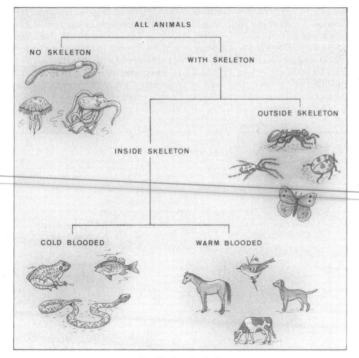

ALL ANIMALS

NO SKELETON

WITH SKELETON

OUTSIDE SKELETON

INSIDE SKELETON

COLD BLOODED

WARM BLOODED

Classification of animals

characteristic of being *cold-blooded*. Frogs, fish, and snakes are a part of this group.

What does it mean to be cold-blooded? A cold-blooded animal cannot make its own heat. Its body cannot control its own temperature. For this reason, its body temperature changes very easily. When a cold-blooded animal lies in the warm sunshine, its body becomes warm. When it lies in the cool shade, its body becomes cool.

Birds, dogs, and cows are some *warm-blooded* animals. A warm-blooded animal can control its body temperature. Its body temperature does not change very much. For

Reading Suggestion

Choose animal books from your school library. Keep them in a separate, easy-to-reach spot in your classroom. Encourage the students to read them in their spare time.

An Animal Game (*an indoor recess activity*)

Obtain three small things that come from animals, such as a seashell, a feather, a piece of fur, a horn, or something made of leather or wool. First, show the things to the students. Tell them that you will hide them in the classroom. Also, tell them that they will not need to move or uncover anything when they are searching.

As the students find the things, they should leave them in their hiding places. The winner is the first person who can quietly tell you the hiding places of all three things.

Materials needed:

• *3 animal parts or products*

example, a dog's body is about as warm on a cold winter night as it is on a warm summer day.

A warm-blooded animal stays warm because its body makes its own heat. Its body makes heat by "burning" the food it eats. This kind of burning does not use fire, yet it keeps the animal warm.

We could keep dividing the animals into smaller groups. But this is enough classification for now. You have learned some of the most important ways of grouping animals. You have learned that classification helps us study the animals more quickly and easily.

Answers for "Test Your Reading"

1. yes
2. yes
3. no
4. yes
5. yes
6. f, h
7. a, d
8. b
9. c, h
10. a, d, f   *(Total: 15 points)*

———————————— **Test Your Reading** ————————————

Read each sentence below. If it is true, write yes. *If it is not true, write* no.

1. We still have animals today because God saved each kind of animal during the Flood.
2. Noah took food into the ark for the animals.
3. Animals of the same color are usually grouped together.
4. God used animal classification names when He talked to Noah.
5. Classification helps us study many animals in a short time.

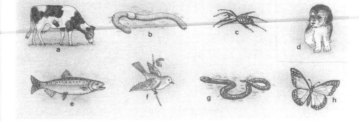

The questions below ask you to group animals. For each question, write the letter of each animal pictured above that fits into that group. The numbers after the questions tell how many letters you will need.

6. Which animals can fly? (2)
7. Which animals have four feet? (2)
8. Which animal has no skeleton? (1)
9. Which animals have outside skeletons? (2)
10. Which animals are warm-blooded? (3)

QUIZ

Write the New Words on the chalkboard. Ask the students to give the one they think of when you say the phrases below.

1. Orderly groups   *(classification)*
2. Body warmth stays the same   *(warm-blooded)*
3. Body warmth changes   *(cold-blooded)*
4. What an animal is like   *(characteristics)*
5. All of an animal's bones   *(skeleton)*

Extra Activities

Do these activities as your teacher directs.

1. Your lesson classified animals by the way they are made, but they can be grouped in other ways. Find "Animal" in the *World Book Encyclopedia*. Find the part that says, "Animal (Where Animals Live)." Notice how those animals are grouped by the places where they live. Then find "Animal (Ways of Life)" and "Animal (Bodies)." Look at the pictures. Can you think of some other ways of classifying animals?

2. Start a bone collection. Look in the fields or woods for bones of squirrels, rabbits, or other small animals. Ask your mother to save bones when she cooks meat.

    If the bones are not already clean and dry, you can clean them at home. Ask your mother for a saucepan. Fill it almost full of water. Ask your mother to help you boil the bones for about two hours. Remove all the meat that is left, and wash the bones well. Boil the bones again, but this time add some dish detergent to the water. When the bones are clean, let them dry in the sun or in a warm oven.

    Label the bones like this: "Wing of a Chicken" or "Leg of a Rabbit." Display your bone collection on a table or shelf.
    Materials needed: • *saucepan*
    • *various animal bones*   • *dish detergent*

3. You are not an animal, but you do have a skeleton. Feel the strong bones in your head, arms, and hands. Now stand up. Without your skeleton, you would flop down like a rag doll. Do you feel how your skeleton keeps you straight and tall?

4. For your unit project, how would you like to make your very own animal scrapbook? For today, cut two sheets of construction paper about 7 1/4" X 9". On one of the sheets, print "I Like Animals" in large, neat letters. This will be the front cover. You may wish to decorate it with animal stickers or animal pictures cut out of magazines. At the bottom, write your name neatly.

    Then cut seven or more sheets of plain white paper about 7" X 8 1/2" to make pages for your scrapbook. Keep these pages and the covers in a folder until the end of the unit.
    Materials needed:
    • *construction paper*   • *scissors*   • *black marking pen*
    • *ruler*   • *folder*   • *white typewriter paper*

Comments on "Extra Activities"

Because the third activity requires no materials and very little time, it is ideal for a class time activity.

Lesson 2

God Made the Amphibians

New Words

amphibian (am · fib′ ē · ən), a cold-blooded animal that changes from a water animal to an animal that can live on land.

frog (frog), a small amphibian with strong hind legs for jumping.

gill (gil), a body part with which water animals get oxygen from the water.

lung (lung), a body part with which land animals get oxygen from the air.

salamander (sal′ ə · man′ dər), an amphibian with short legs and a tail.

toad (tōd), an amphibian much like a frog but with shorter legs and rougher skin.

Reading Together

It is a lovely summer evening. You and your family are relaxing outside. Out in the woods, you hear a friendly, drumming sound. "Ga-LUMM, GaLUMM, GaLUMM . . ." What do you hear?

You are outside picking strawberries. You reach under a leaf, but something moves right under your hand. There sits a small, warty creature. Then he hops away. What is it?

Did you guess *frogs* and a *toad*? You were right! Frogs and toads are part of the group of animals called *amphibians.*

An amphibian is an unusual animal. It lives part of its life in the water and part of it on the land. This is possible because its body goes through a great change as it grows up.

A baby amphibian is a water animal. It looks much like a tiny fish. Its long, flat tail helps it to swim. A baby amphibian uses *gills* to get dissolved oxygen from the water.

As the amphibian grows older, it becomes a land animal. *Lungs* form in its body. The lungs get oxygen from the air. Then the amphibian can live out of the water.

152

Lesson 2

CONCEPTS TO TEACH

- Amphibians live part of their life in the water and part on the land.
- Young amphibians use gills to take oxygen from the water.
- Older amphibians use lungs to take oxygen from the air.
- Amphibians have webbed, soft-toed feet without claws.
- Amphibians are cold-blooded.
- Amphibians have thin, moist, loose skin.
- Amphibians have smooth skin; it is not covered with scales like fish, or feathers like birds, or hair like cattle.
- Amphibians are helpful to man because of the insects they eat.

HELPS FOR THE TEACHER

Introducing the Lesson

The very best introduction to this lesson would be to show a live amphibian. If you have a frog, you could use the suggestions in Activity 2. However, if this is not possible for you, do the following activity.

Slip a plastic bag over one hand and spread the fingers of both hands apart. Tell the class to pretend that your hands are frog's feet. Which one would make the best foot to swim with? Which one would move more water? Invite their guesses.

Put a hand into each container, submerging only your fingers and thumbs. Make slow, rowing motions with your fingers. (If you use the palms of your hands, it is harder to notice the contrast.) Be sure to use the same amount of force and speed for each hand. Ask your students to tell which hand moves more water.

Invite a few students to try the same thing. Ask whether they can feel the difference.

Every amphibian's body changes as it grows. But different kinds of amphibians change in different ways. One kind never grows legs. Another kind grows legs but loses its tail. Frogs and toads are in this group.

A third kind of amphibian also grows legs but keeps its tail. The *salamander* is such an amphibian.

Salamanders, frogs, and toads have soft feet. They have no claws on their toes. Their feet are webbed like a duck's feet. Webbed feet help them to swim better. Some amphibians also have pads on their feet for climbing.

Reading on Your Own

How big are amphibians? Frogs, toads, and most amphibians are small. But a few amphibians are large. One kind of salamander may grow five feet long. If it could stand on its tail, it would be taller than you are.

All amphibians are cold-blooded. Do you remember what that means? It means that they cannot make their own body heat. Amphibians are about as warm or as cool as the water or air around them.

Many amphibians like to live in cool, damp, shaded places. Some salamanders like to be cooler than other amphibians. They can even live inside a block of ice!

Why do amphibians like to be cool and wet? An amphibian uses its skin to take in water and oxygen. The amphibian lies on wet ground or in

Bullfrog

the water. The water soaks in right through its skin. Do you see now why an amphibian keeps its skin moist? If its skin would become too dry, it would die of thirst.

All amphibians have thin, loose skin. They have no hair like cattle, or feathers like birds. Neither is their skin covered with scales like fish. For this reason, we say that they have smooth skin. Smooth skin has no hair, feathers, or scales on it.

Many amphibians are helpful to us. For example, toads eat insects that eat our garden plants and field crops. Large amphibians also eat other kinds of animals. One such example is a large bullfrog. It will eat young turtles, snakes, and mice.

Did you know that God used amphibians to show His power? The Bible tells about it in Exodus 8. God wanted Moses to bring the Israelites out of Egypt into Canaan. But Pharaoh, the ruler of Egypt, would not let them leave Egypt to serve God. He

Explain that God gave a frog legs and feet so that it could move on land. (A fish needs no legs or feet.) God made a frog's feet webbed (like the hand with the bag) because He also planned for it to swim in water. For every animal, God made its body match the way He planned for it to live.

Materials needed:
• *live amphibian*
• *plastic sandwich bag*
• *2 large, wide containers*

Extra Information

Did you know—

. . . that though many amphibians have a short life span, one Giant Salamander lived more than 51 years?

. . . that amphibians are considered smarter than fish? After only one lesson, a toad remembers that a bumblebee's taste is not worth its sting!

. . . that some Goliath frogs weigh as much as a human baby? One weighed 7 3/4 pounds and measured 30 centimeters long.

. . . that one jumping frog covered nearly 10 feet in a single leap? In three consecutive jumps, this two-inch frog traveled more than 32 feet.

QUIZ

Ask the students to say the New Words that fit these phrases.

1. Body part that land animals use to breathe *(lung)*
2. Body part that water animals use to breathe *(gill)*
3. Animal that lives both in water and on land *(amphibian)*
4. Amphibian that does not lose its tail *(salamander)*
5. Amphibian that is a very good jumper *(frog)*
6. Amphibian whose smooth skin is bumpy *(toad)*

Answers for "Test Your Reading"

1. water, land
2. gills
3. lungs
4. salamander
5. b
6. b
7. c
8. a
9. a
10. a
11. c
12. b   *(Total: 13 points)*

Comments on "Extra Activities"

1. Be sure that your students follow directions, especially in getting plenty of pond water and few eggs. Freshly hatched tadpoles will eat microscopic life that is present in the pond water. If you choose to put your tadpoles in an aquarium, they will also eat the green algae that commonly grows on the sides.

   The complete metamorphosis of a frog or toad may take a few months. Because of this, you could show the different stages with a few older tadpoles and an adult. Look for these in a shallow pond or swamp. If possible, include one frog or toad whose back legs are already formed. A kitchen strainer will help you scoop up tadpoles more easily.

   Older tadpoles need a rock or board on which they can crawl out of the water. They breathe air from the water's surface as soon as their lungs are formed. Feed older tadpoles bits of meat, lettuce, and fish food. Be careful not to pollute the water with too much food. Change the tadpoles' water every week. Replace it with more pond water (*not* chlorinated water).

   If you take good care of them, the tadpoles may continue to develop into adulthood. The care of adult frogs and toads is described in Activity 2.

   • *kitchen strainer*
   • *rocks*
   • *board*
   • *raw meat*
   • *lettuce*
   • *fish food*

wanted the Israelites to keep on working for him. God told Moses to ask his brother Aaron to stretch his hand over the waters. Aaron did. All at once, many, many frogs came out of the rivers.

The frogs hopped into ovens. They jumped into people's beds. They even leaped onto the people.

What a problem the frogs were! Pharaoh asked Moses to pray that God would take the frogs away. He promised to let the Israelites go free.

When Moses prayed, God made all the frogs die. God had sent the frogs to show Pharaoh that He is very powerful. He wanted Pharaoh to know that He is the only true God.

——————— Test Your Reading ———————

Fill each blank with a word from your lesson.

1. Amphibians live in —— when they are young and can live on —— when they are older.
2. A young amphibian uses —— to get oxygen from the water.
3. Amphibians grow —— to get oxygen from the air.
4. One kind of grown amphibian with both a tail and legs is called a ——.

Read each sentence below. Is it true of all, some, or no amphibians? Write the letter of the best answer.

5. They lose their tails.
6. They have legs and webbed feet.
7. They have claws.
8. They are cold-blooded.
9. They keep their skin moist to soak up water.
10. They have thin, loose skin.
11. They have hair, feathers, or scales on their skin.
12. They were sent to Pharaoh to show the power of God.

a. all amphibians
b. some amphibians
c. no amphibians

Extra Activities

Do these activities as your teacher directs.

1. You can raise baby frogs or toads. Look for eggs in the shallow water of a pond or swamp. Frog eggs are often found floating in clumps near the top of the water. Strings of toad eggs are wrapped around water plants deeper in the water. Use a big jar to scoop up some eggs and plenty of pond water. Take only a few, or the growing frogs or toads will be crowded. Be sure you get some water plants too.

2. The two best times to find amphibians are after a heavy rain or at night. Look on the banks of streams or ponds or under rocks and fallen logs. A strong flashlight will make amphibians easy to see and capture at night. Keep them in a jar with wet leaves until they reach the classroom.

   Follow the suggestions below to teach concepts about frogs and other amphibians.

   —Feel the frog's cool skin. (*Frogs are cold-blooded.*)
   —Slowly move your finger toward the frog's eye until it closes its eye. (*Frogs have thin, clear eyelids.*)
   —Find nostril vents, and notice throat movements. (*Frogs breathe air.*)
   —Compare the frog's front and back legs. Watch the frog swim. (*The back legs of a frog are larger and stronger for swimming than the front legs are.*)
   —Watch the frog float in water. (*The protruding eyes of a frog can see above the water*

Bring the jar to your classroom. If you wish, you may put the eggs into a larger aquarium. Do not place the jar or aquarium where it is very warm and sunny. In a week or two, you should see tiny baby amphibians! Ask your teacher how to care for them.
Materials needed:
- *wide-mouthed gallon jar*   • *aquarium (optional)*

2. Catch a frog or a toad or both. Bring them to school in a jar with a lid. Also bring some living insects in another covered jar. (Punch several holes in the lids to let in air.) Feed the insects to the frog (or toad). As you do, watch the frog's tongue. Can you see what happens?

   Look at the frog's eyes, skin, and legs. Can you tell how it breathes? Put the frog into a bucket of water, and watch its strong legs as it swims.

   If you have both a frog and a toad, can you tell how they are alike? How are they different? Ask your teacher about making a nice home for your amphibians. When you have finished observing them, you should return them to their natural home.
   Materials needed:
   - *2 jars with lids*
   - *bucket*

3. If you do not have a live frog or toad, you can still learn about them. Answer the questions in Activity 2 by reading and looking at pictures. Find "Frog" and "Toad" in the *World Book Encyclopedia* or in a nature book.

4. For your unit project, draw the salamander below. Keep it in your folder.

surface while the rest of the frog is submerged.)
—Put both live and dead insects into the frog's jar. *(Frogs eat only live food. Their long, sticky tongues are fastened to the front of their mouths. Because of this, the frogs can catch prey that is a distance away without moving their bodies.)*
—Compare a frog with a toad. *(Frogs and toads look very similar. They both have soft feet without claws. A frog's skin is more slippery than a toad's skin. A frog has longer legs and can jump farther than a toad. Frogs are usually not as broad and dark as toads. Frogs are likely to live in the water, while most toads live on land.)*

An adult frog or toad will do well in a terrarium. You will need to have a pool of water in it. Some charcoal can be added to absorb gases that would make the terrarium smell sour. Keep your terrarium in a cool, shaded place.

Once a day, feed your amphibian live food, such as insects or spiders. It may also eat bits of raw meat or earthworms if they are dangled from a string. (The poor eyesight of amphibians may account for the fact that they only eat things that are moving.)

In this or any other activity with live animals, be sure that students treat them kindly. Appoint responsible students to feed and care for them. Should any captive animal become sick, ask advice from a veterinarian or a local pet shop owner. In any case, if the animal is not cared for properly, or if the students are losing interest in it, return it to the wild.

CAUTION: If you handle toads, be sure to wash your hands afterward. A toad's poison is irritating to eyes and broken skin.
- *strong flashlight*   • insects
- *jar*   • spiders
- *wet leaves*   • raw meat
- *screen to cover terrarium* • earthworms
- *charcoal*   • string

glass cover

Tape any sharp edges or sand with sandpaper.

plants

sunken bowl of water

hiding place under rocks

soil and moss

Lesson 3

The Life of a Toad

New Words

life cycle (līf sī′ kəl), the stages of growth in the life of an animal.

metamorphosis (met′ ə • môr′ fə • sis), the great change in some animals from one kind of body to a very different body.

tadpole (tad′ pōl′), a young frog or toad.

Reading Together

A toad begins his life in a cool, quiet pond. Along with many other little toad eggs, he is wrapped in something like clear jelly. Strings of the jelly and eggs are wrapped around plants in the water.

It is springtime. The sun warms the water and the eggs. The warmth helps the toad eggs hatch.

The toad is now a baby toad, or a *tadpole*. His little tail is growing longer. But he is still smaller than your fingernail. You can hardly tell his head from his body.

At first, the tadpole has no eyes or mouth. He holds onto plants with a sticky body part. Then like a tiny fish, he swims around in the water. He uses his gills to get oxygen from the water.

Soon eyes and a mouth grow on the tadpole's head. He can see little plants and animals to eat.

The next weeks and months bring more changes to the tadpole's body.

He grows bigger and bigger. First, his back legs grow, and then his front legs grow. Lungs grow inside him.

At the same time, the tadpole is losing his gills. Soon he will not need them to get oxygen from the water. His tail keeps getting shorter. Soon he will not need it to help him swim. The little toad is getting ready to leave the water, just as God planned that toads should.

Reading on Your Own

One warm, rainy night the toad hops out of the water. He is ready to live on land. His legs and lungs have grown stronger. His gills and tail are gone. The toad wants to find a good home where there are plenty of juicy insects to eat.

The toad travels for a few nights. During the day, he hides under rocks and bushes. He does not travel during the day unless it is raining. The warm sun would dry out his skin.

Soon the toad comes into a garden. Sure enough, he finds plenty of

Lesson 3

CONCEPTS TO TEACH

- God has marvelously provided for the welfare of toads and all amphibians.
- Young toads and frogs are called tadpoles.
- Toads have long, sticky tongues for catching insects.
- A toad's warts protect it from enemies.
- An animal's life cycle is its stages of growth that are repeated in each generation of its kind.
- A metamorphosis is a great bodily change.
- God planned that toads and all animals can be food for other animals.

HELPS FOR THE TEACHER

Introducing the Lesson

Stimulate interest in today's lesson by reading the following poem expressively.

My Friend Hopper

I have a toad named Hopper,
　Who's funny as can be,
For I like cake and ice cream,
　But he eats bugs and fleas.

I like to play in sunshine,
　But Hopper hides away.
He's wide awake past midnight,
　Then sleeps throughout the day.

Our God made toads so different
　From me, it's plain to see.
I'm glad that God made Hopper;
　I'm glad that He made me.

—Naomi Lapp

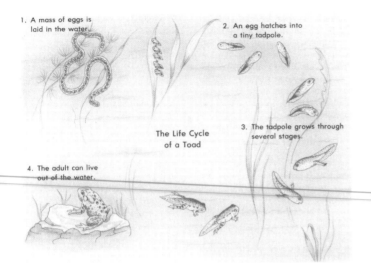

1. A mass of eggs is laid in the water.

2. An egg hatches into a tiny tadpole.

3. The tadpole grows through several stages.

The Life Cycle of a Toad

4. The adult can live out of the water.

insects to eat. His long, sticky tongue zips out and *snap*! The toad has a fly for breakfast.

A family lives in a house near the garden. They do not even know that the toad is there. They do not see how he helps them. He eats many insects that like to eat the beans and corn in the garden.

One day a big, hungry dog comes sniffing at the toad. The dog tries to eat him. But the toad's warty skin makes a poison. How it burns and stings the dog's mouth! Quickly the dog drops the toad.

After two years, the toad is an old toad. He still lives in the garden.

Sometimes he visits the pond where he was a tadpole.

One day a big, hungry black-snake finds the toad. It grabs him and eats him. The toad's poison does not bother blacksnakes.

The toad's story tells about his life. The stories of the toad's mother, father, and grandfather would sound like his story. This is because they all have the same *life cycle*.

In the life cycle of any kind of animal, the same things happen again and again. For example, all toads hatch from eggs. Their bodies make great changes as they grow. They are full-grown within a few

Extra Information

Did you know—

. . . that tadpoles are also called polliwogs?

. . . that the poison of the large Colorado River toad is potent enough to kill a dog?

. . . that toads have an amazing homing instinct? They will return to their home breeding area after being carried a mile away.

. . . that one Marine toad, the largest in the world, measured over nine inches long and weighed almost three pounds?

Discussion Suggestion

This lesson teaches God's plan for animals to kill other animals for food. Because of this, your students may raise questions about human death or murder. If so, use the Bible to teach your students these truths:

1. Man is created in God's image *(Genesis 1:27)*.
2. Man has a soul; animals do not *(Ecclesiastes 12:7; 1 Corinthians 15:39)*.
3. Man was created on a higher level than the animals *(Psalm 8:5-8)*.
4. We treat a person's death with far more respect than an animal's death *(Ecclesiastes 3:21)*.
5. It is wrong for men to kill each other *(Matthew 5:21)*.

months. The grown mother toads lay eggs that hatch into more tadpoles. The tadpoles grow up to be mothers and fathers of more toads. And so this life cycle keeps going on and on.

During a toad's life cycle, its body goes through a great change called a *metamorphosis*. The toad changes from a water animal to a land animal. Some other kinds of animals also have a metamorphosis. But your body does not go through a metamorphosis. Although it does change as it grows, the changes are not as great as in animals that have a metamorphosis.

God made toads so that they like to eat insects. If nothing ate the insects, they would become too plentiful. They might eat all our garden plants and field crops.

God also made snakes so that they like to eat toads. If nothing ate the toads, they would also become too plentiful. This is part of God's plan. Some animals are eaten by other animals.

Some people believe strange things about toads. They believe that they will get warts if they touch toads. But no one has ever proved this to be true. As you have learned, a toad's warts have a poison inside. Many animals do not like the poison. God gave the toad warts to protect it from its enemies.

Some people also used to believe that toads rained from the sky. They thought this because they saw many toads after a rain. Now, think of the toad's story. Think about his skin. What do you think really happened?

Answers for "Test Your Reading"

1. third
2. fourth
3. second
4. c
5. a

Test Your Reading

The phrases below tell about a toad's life cycle. Use the words first, second, third, *and* fourth *to put the phrases in the right order. The first one is done for you.*

1. (——) Tadpole with legs
   (first) Toad eggs
2. (——) Toad with lungs
3. (——) Tadpole with gills and tail

Choose the best ending for each sentence. Write the letter on your paper.

4. A toad travels at night because
   (a) it is afraid of people during the day.
   (b) it can find more insects at night.
   (c) its skin stays more moist at night.
5. A toad's tongue is
   (a) sticky.   (b) dry.   (c) warty.

QUIZ

Write the words *life cycle, metamorphosis, tadpole,* and *toad* on the chalkboard. Ask the students to choose a word for each sentence below.

1. It is a great change in an animal's body. *(metamorphosis)*
2. This amphibian is fully grown. *(toad)*
3. This amphibian is still growing. *(tadpole)*
4. Each toad goes through the same stages of growth as all the toads before him. *(life cycle)*

6. A toad's warts
   (a) help keep its skin moist.
   (b) help protect it from enemies.
   (c) help it breathe.
7. We do not believe that
   (a) animals eat and are eaten.
   (b) touching a toad causes warts.
   (c) toads go through a metamorphosis.

Extra Activities

Do these activities as your teacher directs.

1. Would you like to see toads tonight? It is not hard to do if you live near a woods. First, ask someone older to go with you. You may need your boots and some insect repellent to keep the insects away. Be sure to take a good flashlight along. After dark, listen for the sounds of toads singing. Quietly follow the sounds until you find the toads. They sometimes sing even if a flashlight shines on them.
   Materials needed:
   • *flashlight*
   • *insect repellent*
   • *boots*
2. Use modeling clay to make models that show the life cycle of a toad. Use the pictures on page 157 to help you. Try to make all of the shapes. Display them on a table or shelf with this title, "Life Cycle of a Toad."
   Materials needed:
   • *Play-Doh or modeling clay*
3. For your unit project, draw the toad shown below. Keep it in your folder.

6. b
7. b   *(Total: 7 points)*

Comments on "Extra Activities"
   Most of the activities in Lesson 2 are still appropriate for this lesson.

Lesson 4

God Made the Reptiles

New Words

alligator (al′ ə • gā′ tər), a large reptile covered with bony plates.

crocodile (krok′ ə • dīl), a reptile much like an alligator but with a more pointed nose.

lizard (liz′ ərd), a small reptile with legs.

reptile (rep′ təl), one of a group of cold-blooded animals that are covered with scales or plates.

scale (skāl), one of the thin, flat pieces that cover snakes and lizards.

snake (snāk), a reptile without legs.

turtle (tėr′ təl), a reptile with a hard, rounded shell.

Reading Together

Look carefully at the two animals on this page. Only one is an amphibian. Which one is it?

Think of the characteristics of an amphibian. That will help you choose. Which animal has moist, smooth skin? Which one has soft feet without claws? Did you choose the animal on the left? Good! You may remember that this amphibian is a salamander.

The animal on the right is a *lizard.* Let's look at its characteristics. The lizard is covered with small, flat *scales*. The scales are smooth and dry, not slimy or wet. The lizard's feet have claws. Its eggs have tough, leathery shells. The lizard does not go through a metamorphosis like an amphibian. It breathes with lungs all of its life.

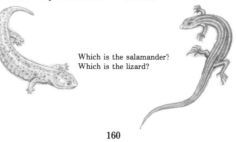

Which is the salamander?
Which is the lizard?

160

Lesson 4

CONCEPTS TO TEACH

- Reptiles are cold–blooded.
- Reptiles are covered with scales or horny plates.
- Reptiles with legs have claws on their feet.
- Reptiles lay eggs with leathery shells.
- Turtles have hard shells on their backs for protection.
- Lizards, snakes, alligators, and crocodiles are other members of the reptile family.

HELPS FOR THE TEACHER

Introducing the Lesson

Read these verses selected from Job 41. Tell your class that this is God speaking. He is describing a large water animal called a leviathan in verse 1.

Bible scholars believe that this may refer to the crocodile, one of the reptiles studied in this lesson. You can use this description to introduce the lesson. At the end of the lesson, you can use it again to see if the students can give the characteristics mentioned that are true for the crocodile.

None is so fierce that dare stir him up:
   who then is able to stand before me? . . .
Who can open the doors of his face?
   his teeth are terrible round about.
His scales are his pride,
   shut up together as with a close seal.
One is so near to another,
   that no air can come between them.
They are joined one to another,
   they stick together,
   that they cannot be sundered. . . .
He maketh the deep to boil like a pot:
   he maketh the sea like a pot of ointment. . . .
Upon earth there is not his like,
   who is made without fear.

Job 41:10, 14–17, 31, 33

Because of all these characteristics, the lizard is placed in the *reptile* group. Look at the picture on this page. All the animals you see here are reptiles.

God gave the lizard the characteristics of the reptile group. But He also gave many lizards a special characteristic. If a big, hungry *snake* grabs a lizard's tail, the tail breaks off! The long tail does not lie still but keeps wiggling and twisting. While the snake is watching the tail, the lizard flees to safety. After a while, the lizard grows a new tail. Of all the reptiles, lizards are the only ones that can "drop" their tails and grow new ones.

Lizards and snakes are very much alike. Both are reptiles. Both are covered with smooth, dry scales. Many kinds of lizards and snakes live on land. Both eat the same kinds of food, such as insects, frogs, and mice.

How can we tell lizards and snakes apart? Snakes do not have legs, as most lizards do. Neither can snakes blink their eyes or "drop" their tails, as most lizards can.

Reading on Your Own

A *turtle* is another special reptile. On its back and underside, it has a round shell made of hard plates. The shell keeps the turtle safe. Whenever a turtle thinks something will hurt it, it pulls its head and legs inside its shell. With its shell shut tightly, the turtle looks like a rock. Most animals cannot bite through the hard shell.

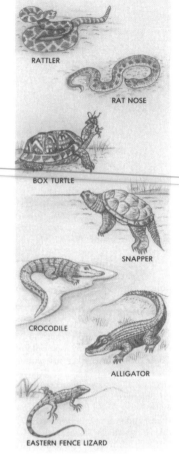

RATTLER

RAT NOSE

BOX TURTLE

SNAPPER

CROCODILE

ALLIGATOR

EASTERN FENCE LIZARD

Examples of reptiles

Extra Information

Did you know—

. . . that a man uses 40 times more energy than an inactive reptile of similar dimensions? Man and warm-blooded animals use much energy simply to maintain their body temperature.

. . . that a basilisk, a kind of lizard, can "walk on water"? It runs so fast that the water surface provides enough resistance to support its weight.

. . . that chameleons, lizards that are famous for their ability to change colors, have another amazing feature? Their sticky tongues can shoot out as far as their total body length.

. . . that long ago, alligators were very plentiful in Florida? Early explorers said that one river was so full of alligators that, except for their hostile nature, a man could have walked across the river on their backs. Today the alligator is a threatened species and is protected by law.

. . . that turtles live longer than any other vertebrates? One tortoise lived 152 years in captivity before it was accidentally killed.

crocodile's nose is more pointed. And the crocodile has a pair of teeth that stick out even when its mouth is closed. A crocodile "smiles" more than an alligator. But do not get too friendly with one. Look at those sharp, pointed teeth. A crocodile may have one hundred teeth on each jaw!

Crocodiles and alligators are the largest kinds of reptiles. Some of them grow as long as a pickup truck. Crocodiles and alligators are much bigger than most lizards, snakes, and turtles. The biggest crocodiles weigh as much as a small car.

What do alligators and crocodiles eat? Small alligators and crocodiles eat turtles, snakes, fish, and birds. The biggest ones eat larger animals, such as raccoons and small bears.

Today you have learned about lizards, snakes, turtles, alligators, and crocodiles. Let's review some of the characteristics of reptiles.
1. They are cold-blooded.
2. They breathe with lungs all their life.
3. They are covered with scales, plates, or a shell.
4. If they have feet, the toes have claws.
5. If they lay eggs, the shells are tough and leathery.

Each of these reptiles does the work God planned for it. Each one is good because God made it. "And God made . . . every thing that creepeth upon the earth after his kind: and God saw that it was good."

Some turtles live on land, but others live in the water. They eat plants, worms, insects, and other small animals. Turtles have no teeth, but they do have strong, bony jaws. A snapping turtle's jaws are hard and sharp enough to bite off your finger!

But most turtles are not as fierce as the snapping turtle. They are quiet, gentle animals. You need not be afraid to pick up the common box turtle or the painted turtle.

Alligators and *crocodiles* look like very large lizards. Their bodies are covered with hard, bony plates. These plates are thicker and tougher than the scales on lizards and snakes. Because alligators and crocodiles are cold-blooded, they like to live in warm areas. Both live in freshwater rivers and swamps, but some crocodiles live near the sea in salty water.

Alligators and crocodiles look very much alike. But look closer. The

Test Your Reading

In the word groups below, one word does not belong. Write that word on your paper.
1. alligator   salamander   lizard   crocodile
2. shell   jaws   legs   snake
3. metamorphosis   plates   claws   scales

Use good sentences to give the answers.
4. What happens after a lizard loses its tail?
5. Explain how a turtle uses its shell to protect itself.
6. Tell three ways crocodiles differ from alligators.
7. Name five characteristics of a reptile.

Extra Activities

Do these activities as your teacher directs.
1. On a warm day, try to find a small turtle or lizard. Look near shallow water and under rocks, leaves, and bushes. If you catch one, look at its shell or scales. Feel its dry, thick skin. Watch how it eats and moves. Can it blink its eyes? Can you see any ears? You may enjoy keeping your reptile in the classroom for a short time. Ask your teacher how to care for it. After you have finished observing it, be sure to return it to its natural home.
2. In the *World Book Encyclopedia*, find "Alligator," and study the pictures carefully. Do the same for "Crocodile," "Lizard," "Turtle," and "Snake." Now find "Animal" in the *World Book Encyclopedia*. Find the big, colored pictures of the animals. Can you pick out all the reptiles in those pictures? Tell whether they belong to the lizard, turtle, snake, or crocodile group.
3. For your unit project, draw the turtle shown below. Keep it in your folder.

Answers for "Test Your Reading"
1. salamander
2. snake
3. metamorphosis
4. A new tail will grow (or while its enemy is watching the wiggling tail, the lizard flees to safety).   (2)
5. When a turtle is in danger, it draws its head and legs inside its shell and closes the shell.   (2)
6. A crocodile's nose is more pointed than an alligator's.

   A crocodile has a pair of teeth that stick out when its mouth is closed; an alligator does not have these.

   A crocodile "smiles" more than an alligator.   (4)
7. Reptiles are cold-blooded.
   Reptiles breathe with lungs all their life.
   Reptiles have scales, plates, or a shell.
   Reptile feet have claws.
   Reptile eggs have tough, leathery shells.   (6)

   (Total: 17 points)

Comments on "Extra Activities"
1. Whatever your reptile, point out these three things:
   a. It is cold-blooded.
   b. It has dry, scaly skin.
   c. Its feet have claws.

   If you have a turtle, notice that it has no teeth. But it does have jaws with sharp, horny edges. Tap its head lightly. Show the students how it draws into its shell. Turn it upside-down, and watch how it rights itself again.

   If you have a lizard, look for its ears. Slowly move your finger toward its eye to watch it blink. Try various light and temperature conditions to see whether it will change colors. Using a metal tongs, grasp the end of its tail firmly to see whether it "drops" its tail.

   The terrarium described in Lesson 2 of this unit will make a good home for either reptile. Put your reptile's home in a place that provides both sunlight and shade.

   For the lizard, you may use a wire cover

that is weighted down. Also include small plants. Sprinkle them daily with water for the lizard to lap.

Be sure the pool of water is large enough for the turtle to swim freely. Make a slope of soil topped with gravel next to the pool so that the turtle can easily climb in and out of the water.

Once a day, feed your reptile. Lizards eat live insects and spiders. To feed a turtle, put it into a deep glass bowl full of water. Drop bits of raw meat or lettuce into the water. Wait 15 minutes for the turtle to finish eating; then return it to its home. (This avoids polluting the turtle's pool.)

Change your reptile's water at least twice a week. The turtle's gravel should be washed off frequently.

- *metal tongs*
- *terrarium from Lesson 2*
- *wire cover*
- *small plants*
- *water*
- *gravel*
- *insects*
- *spiders*
- *deep glass bowl*
- *raw meat*
- *lettuce*

Lesson 5

The Life of a Garter Snake

New Words

fang (fang), a long, hollow tooth of a poisonous snake.

molt (mōlt), to shed an old skin for a new one.

serpentine movement (sėr′ pən • tēn mōōv′ mənt), the twisting of a snake as it travels.

venom (ven′ əm), a poison that snakes use to kill other animals.

Reading Together

A little garter snake is born near a stream in the woods. He does not hatch from an egg, as many snakes do. The garter snake and his twenty brothers and sisters are born alive. They are born with lungs for breathing.

At first, the garter snake is only six inches long. He looks like a striped brown and yellow shoelace. Even though the garter snake is so little, he can already take care of himself. He finds tiny insects to eat.

The garter snake has no legs. How does he go anywhere? God gave the garter snake and many other snakes *serpentine movement.* The snake twists his body in S shapes. Each curve pushes against a root, a stone, or something else on the ground. In this way, the garter snake "swims" on land! Does it sound hard to do? You could not do it, because you are too stiff. But the snake's

Garter snake showing serpentine movement

skeleton is made of many short bones. He can twist and turn every which way. The garter snake's serpentine movements look smooth and easy.

Although the garter snake keeps growing larger, his body does not change greatly otherwise. He does not have a metamorphosis. In about two years, the garter snake is as big as his mother. Then he is a little longer than your arm.

Like all snakes, the garter snake is cold-blooded. He does not have to eat as often as warm-blooded animals

164

Lesson 5

CONCEPTS TO TEACH

- Snakes travel with a serpentine movement.
- Cold-blooded animals can do without food longer than warm-blooded animals.
- Many snakes swallow their food alive.
- The senses of feeling and smelling are very important to snakes.
- Shedding old skin is called molting.
- Snakes help man by eating pests.
- Harmless snakes should not be killed.
- Poisonous snakes use fangs and venom to kill animals.

HELPS FOR THE TEACHER

Introducing the Lesson

Tell the Bible story of the Garden of Eden in Genesis 3. Point out that Eve probably believed that snakes were good or even beautiful. If she had thought they were ugly and repulsive, Satan would hardly have chosen to appear as a snake. He may not have been successful in deceiving her.

Teach that snakes are a part of God's creation. And God had said that all His creation was good. But Satan used the likeness of a snake to trick Eve. Afterwards, the Bible frequently connects snakes with sin and Satan, as in Numbers 21:6, Proverbs 23:32, Matthew 23:33, and Revelation 20:2.

While there is a natural enmity that God made between man and snakes, teach the fact that snakes are basically helpful to us.

do, because his body does not make its own heat. In fact, the garter snake can live for many months without eating. But the garter snake eats often if he can find plenty of food, such as insects, fish, frogs, and salamanders.

The garter snake does not kill an animal before he eats it. He swallows it alive. The garter snake can eat an animal that is larger than its head. He simply stretches his jaws very wide and swallows.

Reading on Your Own

You have five senses in your body: seeing, hearing, feeling, smelling, and tasting. Which are the most important to you? You would probably say that seeing is first, followed by hearing.

To a snake such as the garter snake, feeling and smelling are most important because he cannot see very well. Feeling and smelling help him know where he is going. To feel and smell, the snake keeps flicking his forked tongue out. When his tongue is out, it is picking up very tiny bits of things ahead of him. When the snake's tongue is in, it is smelling the bits. They might smell like pine needles, a frog, a raccoon, or a person.

If the garter snake smells pine needles or frogs, he keeps going ahead. But when he smells a raccoon or a person, he stops. Quietly the snake slips away to a safer place.

Sometimes the garter snake smells a person and also feels the ground shaking harder and harder. That means that the person is coming right toward him! Then the snake flees for his life. He does not want to be stepped on or killed. Snakes cannot hear sounds, but they can feel the ground vibrate.

You have learned that you are always losing bits of your skin. Your body also keeps making new skin all the time. You hardly even find it out.

The garter snake loses his skin too. But he loses his skin all at once. This is called *molting*. When the garter snake is ready to molt, he finds a rough, scratchy tree or rock. He scrapes his head against it. Soon his dry skin starts slipping off. The skin turns inside out as it comes off. The garter snake keeps rubbing until he is free from his old skin. His new skin is all ready for him. It was underneath the old skin. The snake looks bright and clean again in his new skin.

Although God made thousands of different kinds of snakes, many of them are like the garter snake. All of them have scales and breathe with lungs. They are very good at smelling and feeling. They molt every few months. They move with serpentine movements.

Most snakes are helpful to us. They are very good at catching mice and rats that eat our grain. Snakes are better mouse catchers than cats. They can squeeze into very small holes where cats cannot enter. We should not kill these snakes.

Extra Information

Did you know—

. . . that 92 percent of snakes are harmless to man?

. . . that snakes and other reptiles are largest and most plentiful in the tropics, smaller and fewer in temperate zones, and very scarce in Arctic regions?

. . . that the deep hollows or pits on copperheads and other pit vipers are very sensitive to heat? These pits help the snakes locate warm-blooded prey.

. . . that a rattlesnake will not rattle at a king snake? King snakes eat rattlers and are immune to their venom.

. . . that you are more likely to be struck by lightning than to be bitten by a poisonous snake?

. . . that hungry rats have been fed large amounts of fresh rattlesnake venom without suffering ill effects? However, if the same venom had been injected into their bloodstream, it would have killed dozens of them.

God gave **fangs** to a few kinds of snakes. These fangs are two extra long teeth at the front of the snake's mouth. Usually, the fangs are hollow inside.

When the snake wants to kill an animal for food, the fangs fill with **venom.** The venom is a poison. As the snake bites the animal, the venom goes through the fangs and into the animal's bloodstream. The animal becomes very sick. Soon it stops struggling, and the snake eats it.

Most people try to stay away from these poisonous snakes. But sometimes a poisonous snake does bite a person. The person becomes very sick. He must quickly go to a doctor.

However, a poisonous snake does not hunt people as it hunts animals. Like the garter snake, it is afraid of people. It bites if people happen to step on it. It bites if it is caught and cannot get away. A mother snake might bite because she thinks people will hurt her babies.

God made no mistake when He made snakes, even poisonous ones. Snakes and all the other reptiles do an important work. They are an interesting part of God's creation.

Answers for "Test Your Reading"

1. a
2. c
3. c
4. b
5. c
6. a
7. c
8. c
9. b
10. serpentine movement
11. molt
12. fang, venom   *(Total: 13 points)*

—————— Test Your Reading ——————

Read each sentence below. Is it true of garter snakes, of poisonous snakes, or of most snakes? Write the letter of the best answer.

1. They are born alive.
2. They have scales.
3. They always breathe with lungs.
4. Their bite makes people sick.
5. They are helpful to us.
6. They have yellow and brown stripes.
7. They are very good at feeling and smelling.
8. They are cold-blooded.
9. They use venom to kill animals.

a. garter snakes
b. poisonous snakes
c. most or all snakes

Fill each blank with one of your New Words.

10. A garter snake uses ——— ——— to go from place to place.
11. To ——— is to shed skin.
12. When a poisonous snake bites, each ——— has ——— inside it.

QUIZ

Ask the students to give the correct New Word when you say the phrases below.

1. Snake's way of traveling   *(serpentine movement)*
2. Long, hollow tooth   *(fang)*
3. Snake's poison   *(venom)*
4. To scrape off a layer of old skin   *(molt)*

Extra Activities

Do these activities as your teacher directs.

1. In the United States, there are only four kinds of poisonous snakes: the rattlesnake, the copperhead, the water moccasin or cottonmouth, and the coral snake. Find pictures of these snakes in a nature book or in the *World Book Encyclopedia* article "Snake."

   Coral snakes live across the southern part of the United States. Copperheads and water moccasins are found in the Southeast. Rattlesnakes are mostly found in the Southwest, but they can be found from Canada to South America.

   Do any of these poisonous snakes live in your area? You can tell them apart from other snakes by studying their pictures and by learning their characteristics. Here are some of their characteristics:

   Coral snake: small, rounded head, red and yellow bands beside each other.

   Copperhead: red-orange or copper color, head wider than neck, no rattle on its tail, a little hollow or pit below and in front of each eye.

   Water moccasin: dark color, head wider than neck, inside of mouth looks white, pits near eyes.

   Rattlesnake: head wider than neck, pits near eyes, makes dry, buzzing sound with rattles on tail (rattles are hard, horny pieces joined together loosely), always lifts tail to rattle.

2. Here is an interesting test about snakes. Answer yes or no.
   a. Are snakes slimy?
   b. Can a snake's tongue sting you?
   c. Does a milk snake drink milk?
   d. If you would pull a poisonous snake's fangs, would it make a good pet?
   e. Does a mother snake swallow her baby snakes when they are in danger?
   f. Can a racer snake go faster than a man?
   g. Can some snakes jump into the air?
   h. Can some snakes put their tails into their mouths and roll like a hoop?
   i. Can a whip snake whip a man?
   j. Can some snakes throw themselves like a knife?

The answers to this test are given on the next page following Activity 4.

Comments on "Extra Activities"

1. This activity is especially appropriate if poisonous snakes live in your area. No doubt, students will be eager to tell about a time when they saw a snake. Encourage exact descriptions of snakes, but discourage any wild snake stories.

2. Discuss these facts and misconceptions. This should help to dispel some of the wild, irrational fears that some students have about snakes.

3. Read the story of the apostle Paul's snakebite in Acts 28:1–16. Even though no one treated his snakebite, Paul did not become sick. Why not? Read Luke 10:19 for a good clue.
4. For your unit project, draw the garter snake that is shown below. Keep it in your folder.

Answers to the test about snakes (Activity 2)

The answers are all no. Many people have wrong ideas about snakes. Now read these facts about the first six questions.

   a. Snakes are dry and smooth.

   b. A snake's tongue is used for feeling and smelling, not stinging.

   c. A milk snake eats mice and rats, not milk.

   d. If a poisonous snake's fangs were pulled, the snake would grow new ones. It is not safe for a pet.

   e. No mother snake has ever been known to swallow her young snakes. But some snakes do eat other kinds of snakes as food.

   f. The fastest racer snakes travel less than 4 miles per hour. Most snakes could not keep up with a man at a fast walk (4 miles per hour), much less a man at full speed (10 to 15 miles per hour).

God Made the Mammals

New Words

fur (fėr), thick hair that covers many mammals.

mammal (mam′ əl), an animal that has hair and feeds milk to its young.

mammary gland (mam′ ə • rē gland), a part inside a mammal's body that makes milk.

marine (mə • rēn′), of or in the sea.

rodent (rōd′ ənt), a mammal with large front teeth for gnawing.

Reading Together

Let's think of some animals in the Bible. Do you remember the donkey that talked to Balaam? Do you remember the sheep that David tended or the lions in the story of Daniel?

These animals are *mammals*. The Bible says more about mammals than about any other group of animals.

What are mammals like? Mammals may be spotted or striped, skinny or fat, slow or swift, black, white, brown, or yellow. Some mammals are as small as a grasshopper, but the largest ones are as long as a house!

Though mammals come in many sizes, shapes, and colors, they all have some body characteristics that are alike. All mammals have skeletons inside their bodies. They are born with lungs for breathing.

All mammals are warm-blooded. Their bodies make their own warmth by burning food. Because of the wonderful way in which God made their bodies, their body temperature stays nearly the same all the time.

Mammals have two special characteristics that belong only to them. Only mammals have hair on their bodies. On many mammals, the hair grows so thickly that it is called *fur*. Dogs, cats, rabbits, and bears are mammals with fur.

What is the second characteristic belonging only to mammals? Only mammals feed milk to their babies. This milk is made inside the mother's body by the *mammary glands*. In fact, the word mammal itself comes from the word *mammary*.

169

Lesson 6

CONCEPTS TO TEACH

- Mammals are warm–blooded and breathe with lungs.
- Mammals have hair.
- A thick covering of hair is called fur.
- Mammals get their name from the mammary glands that produce milk to feed their young.
- Mammals are divided into many groups according to similar characteristics:

egg-laying mammals: platypus, anteater

pouched mammals: kangaroo, koala bear, opossum

insect-eating mammals: mole, shrew

flying mammals: bat

marine mammals: whale, dolphin, porpoise

flesh-eating mammals: dog, wolf, fox, cat, lion, tiger, bear

gnawing mammals (rodents): mouse, rat, chipmunk, squirrel, beaver, muskrat

hoofed mammals: horse, zebra, pig, cow, sheep, goat, camel, giraffe, deer

trunk-bearing mammals: elephant

handed mammals: ape, monkey

Reading on Your Own

Mammals are a large group of animals. In order to study them more easily, we will divide them into smaller groups. We will divide them into groups that have like characteristics.

The first group is the unusual egg-laying mammals. Most mammals are born alive, but mammals in this group hatch from eggs. Only two animals belong to this group: the spiny anteater and the platypus. The spiny anteater lives up to its name. It eats plenty of ants with its long, sticky tongue. The platypus is also called a duckbill because it has a flat bill like a duck.

Mammals that lay eggs

In the next group of mammals, the mothers care for their babies in a special way. These mothers carry their babies in pockets or pouches. A pouch made of skin is fastened right onto the mother's stomach. She keeps her babies warm and feeds them milk in the pouch. Kangaroos, koalas, and opossums are mammals with pouches.

Mammals that have pouches

Another group of mammals eats bugs, flies, and other insects. Moles and shrews are in this group. As you can guess, these mammals are quite small.

One of the smallest mammals is a bat about an inch long. However, bats are better known for another reason; they are the only mammals that can fly. They even fly in the dark! Their wings make them look like birds. But they are classed as mammals for two reasons: they have fur instead of feathers, and they feed milk to their young.

Mammals that eat insects

HELPS FOR THE TEACHER

Introducing the Lesson

Have the students turn back to page 146, the unit introduction. Ask them to name the kinds of animals they see in the picture. Write them on the chalkboard. Ask if they see any reptiles or amphibians.

Inform the students that all the animals you have listed belong to the same group—mammals. Then turn to Lesson 6. Together, look at the pictures on pages 170-172, to notice how the big group of mammals is divided into many smaller groups. This will reemphasize the value of classification, for a big subject is easier to study in small pieces.

Mention that although this is the last large animal group in this unit, there are more groups that we will not take time to study: protozoa, sponges, coelenterates, worms, spiny-skinned animals, mollusks, arthropods, fish, and birds.

Extra Information

Did you know—

. . . that a tablespoon could easily hold 20 newborn opossums? All marsupials (pouched mammals) are born small and undeveloped.

. . . that the largest mammal ever measured was a blue whale over 110 feet long?

. . . that a rodent's teeth grow continuously until old age? A rodent must keep gnawing to wear away its teeth. Otherwise, its teeth would grow too long, prop the rodent's mouth open permanently, and eventually cause death by starvation.

Rodents are mammals that have large front teeth. Some rodents use their large front teeth to chew on sticks, trees, and even walls! Mice, rats, squirrels, beavers, and muskrats are all rodents.

Mammals with large front teeth

You probably know the meat-eating mammals very well. A bear is one kind of meat eater. Dogs, wolves, and foxes (the dog family) are also meat-eating animals. Other meat-eaters are cats, lions, and tigers (the cat family).

Mammals that eat meat

Many tame farm animals are mammals with hoofs. They are cows, pigs, sheep, and goats. Other hoofed mammals, such as deer, zebras, camels, and giraffes, are wild. Most of the mammals with hoofs eat plants instead of meat.

Mammals with hoofs

Some mammals have trunks. They are the elephants. Of all the animals that live on land, elephants are the largest.

A mammal with a trunk

The *marine* mammals live in the ocean. The word marine means "of the ocean." Of all the marine mammals, such as dolphins, porpoises, and whales, the whales are the largest. In fact, whales are the largest of all animals. The biggest whale would have room for at least five elephants on its back.

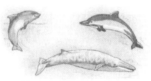

Mammals that live in the ocean

Suggestion for Storytime

Choose some students for storytellers. Ask them to tell a Bible story of a mammal. Give some basic rules for speaking to a group of people:

1. Know your story well.
2. Speak loudly and clearly.
3. Do not giggle.

Bible Mammal Game

The object of this game is to find the Bible reference and mammal as quickly as possible. First, write a reference on the chalkboard. Ask your students to keep their Bibles closed until you say "Go." As soon as they find the correct verse and mammal, they should raise their hand.

When a number of hands have been raised, choose one student to name the mammal. Give many or all of the students the opportunity to name a mammal, not always the first one to raise his hand.

1. Genesis 18:7   *(calf)*
2. 1 Samuel 6:4   *(mice)*
3. 1 Kings 10:22   *(apes)*
4. 2 Kings 2:24   *(bears)*
5. Nehemiah 4:3   *(fox)*
6. Job 39:19   *(horse)*
7. Proverbs 26:17   *(dog)*
8. Isaiah 31:4   *(lion*
9. Luke 15:15   *(swine)*
10. John 10:12   *(sheep or wolf)*

In the last group are apes and monkeys. They can use their fingers to pick things up. Monkeys use their tails for balancing and for swinging from branch to branch. Apes and monkeys also have better minds than most animals do.

Mammals that use fingers

God created many different kinds of animals. Each one is made in its own special way. Each one is interesting to study and shows what a great Creator God is. God cares for each animal from the least to the greatest.

"O Lord, how manifold are thy works! in wisdom hast thou made them all: the earth is full of thy riches. . . . These wait all upon thee; that thou mayest give them their meat in due season."

Answers for "Test Your Reading"

1. no
2. no
3. yes
4. yes
5. yes
6. b
7. c
8. b
9. a

(Total: 9 points)

Test Your Reading

Write yes *if the sentence is true; write* no *if it is not true.*

1. A mammal's skeleton is on the outside of its body.
2. Mammals are cold-blooded.
3. Hair or fur grows on mammals.
4. All baby mammals drink milk.
5. A few baby mammals hatch from eggs.

Choose the best ending for each sentence. Write the letter on your paper.

6. The name *mammal* comes from the word
   (a) *marine.*   (b) *mammary.*   (c) *mammoth.*
7. The marine mammals
   (a) breathe with gills.
   (b) eat mostly insects.
   (c) live in the ocean.
8. Rodents
   (a) carry their babies in a pouch.
   (b) have long front teeth.
   (c) are the largest animals.
9. Mammals are grouped
   (a) by their characteristics.
   (b) by their color.
   (c) by the way they breathe.

QUIZ

Ask the students to supply the correct New Word when you say the phrases below.

1. Hairy, warm–blooded animal   *(mammal)*
2. Thick hair   *(fur)*
3. Of the sea   *(marine)*
4. Mammal with large teeth for gnawing   *(rodent)*
5. It makes milk   *(mammary gland)*

Extra Activities

Do these activities as your teacher directs.

1. If you live on or near a farm, you can study mammals, such as cats, dogs, rabbits, pigs, horses, and cows.

   Ask an older person to help you look at some mammals' teeth. Look at the teeth of plant eaters (cows or horses) and the teeth of meat eaters (dogs or cats). How are the teeth different? Would it work for a meat eater to have a plant eater's teeth? Why not?

   Feel the warm bodies of some mammals. Feel their hair or fur. What is one reason for the hair or fur? How is a baby pig's hair different from a kitten's fur?

   Look at the way their eyes, ears, noses, legs, and tails are different from each other.

2. Look in your school library. You will probably find books about mammals. Read some of them. Remember, your teacher may not always have time to answer your questions, but a book is always ready to teach you.

3. Use modeling clay to make one of the mammals in this lesson. Find a picture of the mammal in this lesson or in an encyclopedia. Try to make your mammal look just like the mammal in the picture.
   Materials needed:
   • Play-Doh

4. For your unit project, draw the giraffe pictured here. Keep it in your folder.

Comments on "Extra Activities"

1. Meat eaters, or carnivores, have sharp, pointed teeth for tearing meat. Plant eaters, or herbivores, have short, flat teeth for grinding plants.

   Of course, hair or fur helps keep animals warm. Other less obvious functions of hair are for protection and sensation. A coat of fur acts as a shield against injuries, and whiskers are very sensitive to touch. By using its whiskers, or tactile hairs, a cat can find its way through cramped and dark places.

   Encourage comparisons, such as "A pig's hair is stiffer than a kitten's fur" or "A kitten's ears are more pointed than a pig's."

2. As mentioned earlier in this unit, it would be very helpful to group the books about mammals in a visible and accessible spot. Keep encouraging the students to read.

3. Some appropriate mammals to make are a mouse, a sitting dog or cat, a rabbit, a kangaroo, a bear, an elephant, or a whale. Discourage the students from attempting mammals with too many long, thin body parts, such as a horse, cow, deer, or giraffe.

Lesson 7

The Life of a Chipmunk

New Words

balance of nature (bal′ əns ov nā′ chər), having about the same
amount of animals from year to year.

burrow (bėr′ ō), an animal's underground home.

chipmunk (chip′ mungk), a small, striped rodent.

environment (en • vī′ rən • mənt), everything around a living thing.

habitat (hab ′ ə • tat), the special kind of place where an animal
usually lives.

Reading Together

A baby *chipmunk* is born in a
cozy *burrow* in the ground. It is
springtime, but the chipmunk does
not know it. He and his two sisters
cannot see or hear. Because they
have no fur yet, they look like tiny
pink mice.

Mother Chipmunk takes good
care of her babies. She keeps them
warm on their bed of grass and oak
leaves. Like all mammals, she feeds
them milk when they are hungry.

In a few weeks, the chipmunk can
hear and smell. He can hear his
sisters squeaking. He can smell the
nutty, earthy smell of the burrow.
His eyes are open now, but he still
cannot see anything. The burrow is
too dark.

The chipmunk keeps growing bigger and stronger. Soon he looks very

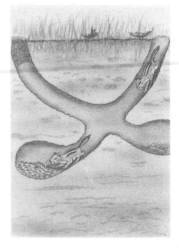

Chipmunks live in underground burrows.

174

Lesson 7

CONCEPTS TO TEACH

- An animal's environment is the world around it.
- A chipmunk's underground nest is called a burrow.
- A chipmunk's burrow protects it from enemies.
- A chipmunk, being a rodent, has strong teeth for gnawing through the shells of nuts.
- The balance of nature results in about the same number of animals of each kind surviving every year.
- God planned the balance of nature for two reasons:
  (1) to provide food for all the animals.
  (2) to keep the animals from becoming too plentiful.
- An animal's habitat is its natural living area.

Note: You may need to explain the difference between *habitat* and *environment*. Tell the students that both animals and people live in an environ-

ment. Pause to name things in your immediate environment, such as walls, desks, other people, air, water, and trees. Notice that an environment is continually subject to change.

Then discuss *habitat*. Notice that it applies only to animals. *Habitat* is an animal's natural homeland. It refers to a general kind of place in nature. On the chalkboard, list some animals and their habitats.

Animal	*Habitat*
toad	woodland
alligator	river or swamp
tiger	grassland
whale	ocean

Finally, give this example: If a chipmunk were captured and put into a cage, his environment would be changed. But his habitat would not change. His natural homeland would still be the woods.

A chipmunk

much like his mother. His thick fur is brown with black and white stripes down his back.

One fine morning, the young chipmunk is ready to explore his *environment*. His environment is the world around him. He creeps up through the long tunnel of the burrow. At the top, he pokes his head outside.

Oh, the light is so bright! The little chipmunk sniffs the fresh air. He watches a worm wiggle through the grass. Nearby, he sees his mother stuffing acorns into her cheek pouches.

Then a great, black shadow moves toward the chipmunk. What is it? Mother Chipmunk has seen it too. "Chit-chit-chit!" she shrills.

The little chipmunk whisks back into the burrow. Mother Chipmunk dives in after him. She chatters and scolds. She is saying, "Don't you know that a hawk will eat you?"

Reading on Your Own

In a few months, the chipmunk is full-grown. He is old enough to dig his own burrow. He digs with his strong front feet. At the same time, he kicks back the soil with his hind feet. He uses his nose and forehead to push the extra soil.

The chipmunk is very neat and tidy. He scatters the extra soil over the ground. He does not leave piles of dirt around his burrow. He does not want snakes, cats, or weasels to find his burrow.

The chipmunk also keeps himself neat and clean. Often his small paws wash his face. Every day he washes his coat of fur all over.

Although the chipmunk cannot see well, he has a very good sense of smell. With one sniff, he knows whether a mushroom is the kind he likes. By smelling, he finds seeds, nuts, and berries to eat.

HELPS FOR THE TEACHER

Introducing the Lesson

Give this illustration to the students: Imagine that you have drawn a beautiful picture. You took a long time to draw the daisies, butterflies, pine trees, and mountains just right. You did your very best. Then you left your finished picture on your desk.

Soon your friend notices the picture. He grabs it and shouts, "Look what I found! This pretty picture is mine; I'm going to hang it up in my room." Would that be right?

Pause for the students to answer. Then ask them to listen carefully as you read this verse: "For every beast of the forest is mine, and the cattle upon a thousand hills."

Explain that a chipmunk is a "beast [animal] of the forest." Since God has made all the animals, we would be cheating Him if we studied them without giving Him glory. Encourage the students to frequently pause and think of God as they study a chipmunk today.

Extra Information

Did you know—

. . . that although a few chipmunks may carry rabies, chipmunks are not generally considered harmful to man?

. . . that a chipmunk may dig a 30-foot tunnel with three or more entrances?

. . . that chipmunks sometimes eat insects, bird eggs, and young birds?

When the chipmunk eats a nut, he does not gobble. He holds it in his front paws and takes small bites. His sharp front teeth are just right for nibbling like this because he is a rodent.

The chipmunk's cheeks are like dry, stretchy bags. He stuffs them full of seeds and nuts. Then he carries them back to his burrow and unloads them. Back and forth he scurries. His pile of nuts grows larger and larger. He will need them in the wintertime when food is much harder to find.

The chipmunk must always watch for enemies. Big birds, snakes, foxes, and other animals are always ready for a chipmunk dinner. Often the chipmunk must scamper to his burrow. Sometimes he climbs a tree. If he needs to, he can even swim.

The chipmunk lives to be two years old. One day he is not quite fast enough. A sly weasel catches him.

God planned that weasels would eat chipmunks. If no animals ever ate them, most of them would live long lives. Each year, many baby chipmunks would be born, but only a few old chipmunks would die. In time, there would be too many chipmunks. There would not be enough food for all the chipmunks.

Of course, chipmunks are not the only animals that have enemies. Toads, garter snakes, and many other animals have enemies too. Every year about the same number of animals are eaten by their enemies. Every year about the same number of animals stay alive. This is called the *balance of nature*.

God planned this balance of nature so that no kind of animal becomes too plentiful. He also planned it so that each kind of animal has enough food. Large animals eat smaller animals. Smaller animals eat the smallest animals. The smallest animals eat plants. Of course, many larger animals also eat plants.

We can see God's wisdom in planning the balance of nature. We can also see His wisdom in providing a

Compare this habitat with the one on the next page.

QUIZ

Ask the students to supply the correct New Word when you say the phrases below.

1. Small, striped rodent   *(chipmunk)*
2. Chipmunk's underground home   *(burrow)*
3. Everything around an animal   *(environment)*
4. An animal's natural home area   *(habitat)*

habitat to fit each animal. An animal's habitat is the special kind of place where it lives.

The woods is a good habitat for the chipmunk, the garter snake, and the toad. Grasslands are a good habitat for lions and giraffes. The ocean is a good habitat for whales and some turtles.

Now, imagine a whale in the woods or a lion in the ocean! That would never work. Each animal can live best in the habitat God planned for it.

Test Your Reading

Choose a word from the word box to finish each sentence.

balance of nature	habitat
burrow	mammal
environment	rodent

1. Because chipmunks have fur and feed milk to their young, they are in the —— group.
2. A chipmunk's underground home is his ——; there he also hides from his enemies.
3. Each plant, animal, and material around a chipmunk is a part of its ——.
4. Because a chipmunk has long front teeth for gnawing, it is called a ——.
5. A chipmunk's —— is the woods.
6. To keep the —— —— ——, some animals are eaten by other animals.

Use good sentences to give the answers.

7. Name four things that chipmunks eat.
8. How does a chipmunk carry food to its burrow?
9. Name two reasons why God planned the balance of nature.

Answers for "Test Your Reading"

1. mammal
2. burrow
3. environment
4. rodent
5. habitat
6. balance of nature
7. Chipmunks eat mushrooms, seeds, nuts, and berries.   (5)
8. Chipmunks carry food in their large cheek pouches.   (2)
9. God planned the balance of nature to provide food for all the animals and to keep the animals from becoming too plentiful.   (3)

(Total: 16 points)

182   *Unit 6*

Comments on "Extra Activities"

1. If a state park or wild animal reserve is nearby, the students may see more animals there than in a small woods. Emphasize the need for slow, quiet movements.

Extra Activities

Do these activities as your teacher directs.

1. Do you have a woods near your home? Go on a "Wild Animal Hunt." You will only watch the animals, not kill them. Ask someone older to go with you, and take along some food.

   Walk very quietly into the woods. Scatter the food near old tree stumps, streams, or wherever you think animals may be living. Crouch down and wait quietly. If you are patient, you may see chipmunks or other wild animals come to get the food.

   Then tell or write about any animals that you see.

   Materials needed:
   - *nuts*   • *meat scraps*
   - *bread*   • *fruit*

2. Ask your parents whether you could visit a zoo soon. If you go, be sure to notice the amphibians, reptiles, and mammals. Look for the characteristics that are alike in each group.

3. Make flash cards of the animals you have studied so far to drill the animal groups. For example, write *toad* on one side of a card. On the other side, write its classification, *amphibian*. Do the same for a frog, a salamander, and some reptiles and mammals.

   You may also make some flash cards with a characteristic on one side and the classification on the other. For example, write *has hair* on one side and *mammal* on the other side.

   Ask someone to show the flash cards to you until you can say them very quickly.

   Materials needed:
   - *thin white cardboard*

4. For your unit project, draw the chipmunk shown below. Keep it in your folder.

God Protects the Animals in Cold Weather

New Words

hibernation (hī′ bər • nā shən), spending the winter in a deep sleep.

instinct (in′ stingkt), the things an animal does without learning them.

migration (mī • grā′ shən), a trip to a warmer place for the winter.

Reading Together

Wintertime is fun. You can build a big snowman. You can go sledding. When you are cold, you can come inside to a cozy, warm house. Your mother may give you cookies and a hot drink.

For the animals, winter is not all fun. Food is hard to find because the plants do not grow. The animals have no fire to warm them.

Yet God takes care of the animals during the winter. Extra thick fur grows on bears, foxes, and many other animals. The fur keeps them warm, just as a blanket keeps you warm.

God knew that winters are cold. He knew that the animals cannot easily find food. So God planned that many animals go into *hibernation* during the winter. Hibernation is a special, deep sleep.

Hibernation is an important way God protects animals.

During the chipmunk's life, God used hibernation to care for him. Remember how he stored his nuts in the fall? Later he crawled into his burrow and curled up. Then he fell into a deep sleep. His body became much cooler. His heart almost stopped beating, and he breathed very slowly.

179

Lesson 8

CONCEPTS TO TEACH

- Some mammals are protected from the cold by growing extra thick fur in the winter.
- Some animals are protected from the cold by building underground homes and hibernating.
- Some animals escape the cold by migrating.
- These methods of protection from the cold are instincts that were designed for the animals at Creation and show the wisdom of God.
- Instincts are ways that animals act without learning them.

HELPS FOR THE TEACHER

Introducing the Lesson

Let a sense of wonder fill your voice as you read this poem. Afterward, ask the students to identify the *who*.

Deer Mouse

Who tells the little deer mouse
when summer goes away
that she should fix a cozy place,
a comfy place, to stay,
and fill her cupboard shelves with seeds
from berries, weeds, and hay?

Who tells the little deer mouse
before the year is old
that she should wear a warmer coat
to shield her from the cold?
I'm glad that *Someone* tells her
and she does as she is told.

—*Aileen Fisher*

Sometimes the chipmunk woke up to eat some nuts. But most of the winter, he took long naps. His burrow sheltered him from the cold wind and snow.

Besides chipmunks, many other mammals hibernate in the winter. Bats, mice, ground hogs, skunks, raccoons, and bears hibernate. But most of these mammals do not store food in their nests as a chipmunk does. They store food right in their bodies.

In the fall, these animals eat until they become very fat. Then during the long, cold winter, their bodies use the stored fat. When the animals wake up in the spring, they are much thinner. Of course, they are also very hungry!

Do cold-blooded animals hibernate? The toad and the garter snake do. In the fall, the toad digs a hole in the mud under a stream. The garter snake finds a certain place in some rocks. There, he and many other garter snakes gather every fall to hibernate. When it grows cold, they all fall asleep.

Like the chipmunk, the garter snake and the toad also become very cool. Their heart beats very slowly. They breathe very little. But unlike the chipmunk and other mammals, the garter snake and the toad do not wake up from time to time. They sleep until the spring sun warms their body.

How does the chipmunk know that he must gather nuts for the winter? Does the toad know that he will freeze to death unless he hibernates deep in the ground? How does the garter snake know when it is time to go to the rocky place to hibernate?

Each of these animals has an *instinct* that tells it how and when to do these things. They somehow know what to do without ever learning it. God gave each kind of animal certain instincts when He created it.

Reading on Your Own

For some mammals, fish, butterflies, and birds, God did not plan hibernation in the winter. Instead,

Nest building is an instinct given by God. Could you build a robin's nest like this? Why not?

Extra Information

Did you know—

. . . that a chemical called hibernating–inducing trigger is produced in the blood of hibernating mammals? Mammals will even hibernate out of season when this chemical is injected into their blood.

. . . that the increase or decrease of daylight hours stimulates special hormones in some birds, which then triggers migration at the right time of year?

. . . that some birds show signs of migratory behavior even in a laboratory where lighting, temperature, and feeding conditions are kept constant?

. . . that when migrating starlings were transported far away from their normal flight path, the young birds became disoriented, while the parents found their way to their usual winter homes?

. . . that a salmon, which is born in a river and migrates out to sea, may travel thousands of miles back to the river where it was born, which it identifies by its odor?

He planned that they take a trip to a warmer place. Taking such a trip is called *migration*. In the warmer place, these animals can find more food.

Could you find a place hundreds of miles away without a map? A robin does just that. In the summertime, he is busy feeding his babies, his mate, and himself. But by the fall, the young robins can take care of themselves. Then the robin knows that it is time to go south. He knows it by the instinct that God gave him.

Great crowds of robins gather together. Away they fly! How do they know where to go? Do they know by the way the wind blows, by the amount of sunshine, or by looking at the land beneath them? Only God knows the answers to these questions. He gave the instincts that tell them when, where, and how to go.

After a few weeks, the robins come to their winter home. This home is the very same place where they had come last fall. There the robins eat and rest.

In the spring, away they go! They fly right back to the place where they had lived the summer before. This place might be your backyard.

Arctic terns travel farther than any other migrating animals. Every fall these amazing birds migrate almost halfway around the earth. Every spring they find their way back again, traveling 22,000 miles in all.

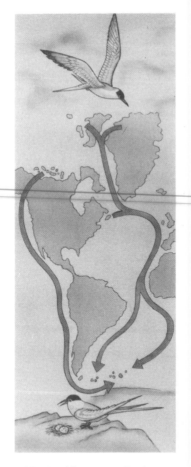

Migration of the arctic tern. How does it know where to fly?

Activity on Migration

Using bird books or encyclopedias, find migratory routes for some birds, butterflies, or fish. Then use a globe or large map to trace the migrators' journeys from summer homes to winter homes, and back again.

Materials needed:

- *bird books*
- *globe*

QUIZ

For each sentence below, ask the students whether it tells about hibernation or migration.

1. Animals have an instinct to travel. *(migration)*
2. Animals have an instinct to go to sleep. *(hibernation)*
3. Animals store much food in their bodies. *(hibernation)*
4. Animals find their way without a map. *(migration)*
5. Animals breathe very slowly. *(hibernation)*

Long ago, God talked to Job about migration. He asked Job, "Doth the hawk fly by thy wisdom, and stretch her wings toward the south?" Of course, Job knew that he could not teach a hawk how to migrate.

Today we still do not know all about migration or hibernation. How it happens is God's secret. We can only marvel at the greatness of God.

"God thundereth marvellously with his voice; great things doeth he, which we cannot comprehend. For he saith to the snow, Be thou on the earth. . . . Then the beasts go into dens, and remain in their places."

Goshawk

Answers for "Test Your Reading"

1. yes
2. yes
3. no
4. yes
5. c
6. d
7. a
8. e
9. b   *(Total: 9 points)*

─────────── **Test Your Reading** ───────────

If the sentence is true, write yes. *If it is not true, write* no.

1. Amphibians and reptiles hibernate in the winter.
2. Some mammals hibernate, and others migrate.
3. In the fall, animals migrate to colder lands.
4. Migration and hibernation make us marvel at God's greatness.

Choose a word to finish each sentence below. Write the correct letter on your paper.

5. In the winter, many mammals have extra thick ——.
6. A deep winter sleep is called ——.
7. An animal's journey to its winter home is a ——.
8. Hibernation and migration protect animals from the ——.
9. Animals hibernate and migrate by ——.

a. migration
b. instinct
c. fur
d. hibernation
e. cold

Extra Activities

Do these activities as your teacher directs.

1. Watch for the first robins, blackbirds, bluebirds, or barn swallows to return from the South. Also, look for signs of animals coming out of hibernation. Watch for ground hogs, beavers, skunks, and raccoons or their tracks.

2. Do you still have a frog or some other cold-blooded animal in your classroom? Ask your teacher how to make it go into a quick "winter hibernation" and how to wake it up again in the "spring." This will not hurt the animal.

   Materials needed:
   • *cold-blooded animal*

3. For your unit project, draw the robin shown below. This will be the last picture in your scrapbook unless you want to add more on your own.

   Punch holes at the left side of each cover and drawing. Assemble the pages in order, and pull yarn through the holes. Tie the yarn. Your scrapbook is finished!

   Materials needed:
   • *paper punch*
   • *yarn*

Comments on "Extra Activities"

2. First, pretend it is autumn. Invite the students to feel the animal's skin. Notice its temperature and its response to touch. Try feeding it an insect, larva, or small worm. Notice its general alertness and rate of movement.

   Then place the animal into a large jar. Punch holes in the lid of the jar, and screw it on. Put the jar into a bucket or dishpan. Put a small amount of ice into the bucket, and tell the students that winter is coming. The animal is becoming colder.

   Gradually add more ice to reduce the temperature slowly inside the containers. Meanwhile, review the behavior of a cold-blooded animal in hibernation, as discussed in the lesson. Unscrew the lid periodically, and notice the skin temperature of the animal and its response to stimuli. See if it will eat.

   When your winter has lasted long enough to make the animal noticeably sluggish and inactive, take the jar out of the bucket. Tell the students that spring has come. Take the animal out of the jar, and notice how its alertness and activity increase as its temperature rises.

   • *live insects or small worms*
   • *wide-mouthed jar with lid*
   • *hammer and nail to punch holes*
   • *bucket or dishpan*
   • *ice cubes (about a half gallon)*

ANSWER KEY

Match

1. f
2. d
3. h
4. g
5. a
6. i
7. b
8. e
9. c

Fill

10. characteristics
11. warm-blooded
12. cold-blooded
13. amphibian
14. salamander
15. frogs
16. lizard
17. crocodile
18. marine

Lesson 9

Do You Remember What You Learned?

Match each word on the right to its meaning on the left.

1. Animal's bones   a. fangs
2. Great changes in an animal's body   b. fur
3. Reptile with a shell   c. habitat
4. Reptile without legs   d. metamorphosis
5. Snake's long teeth   e. rodent
6. Snake's poison   f. skeleton
7. Thick hair   g. snake
8. Mammal with large front teeth   h. turtle
9. Place where an animal lives   i. venom

Fill each blank with a word from the box.

amphibian	crocodile	marine
characteristics	frogs	salamander
cold-blooded	lizard	warm-blooded

10. Each animal has its own special ———.
11. A ——— animal's body burns food to keep it warm.
12. A ——— animal's body cannot make its own heat.
13. An ——— lives first in the water and then on land.
14. A ——— is an amphibian that keeps its tail throughout life.
15. God used ——— to show Pharaoh His power.
16. A ——— is a reptile covered with scales.
17. A ——— is a large reptile covered with bony plates.
18. Whales and other ——— mammals live in the ocean.

184

Lesson 9

As in other reviews, drill the vocabulary words and key concepts, as given in "Concepts to Teach." Be alert to student weaknesses, and repeat quizzes or other activities if necessary. Ask the students to follow the steps given in "How to Study for a Test," listed on page 5 of the textbook (page 11 of this manual).

Label the pictures of a toad's life cycle. Use words from the word box below.

full-grown toad	toad eggs
older tadpole	young tadpole

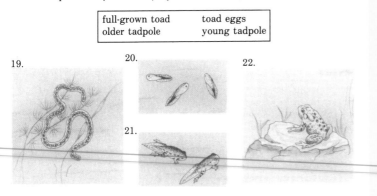

19.   20.   22.

21.

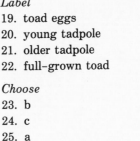

Label

19. toad eggs
20. young tadpole
21. older tadpole
22. full-grown toad

Choose

23. b
24. c
25. a
26. c
27. b

Choose the best ending for each sentence. Write the letter on your paper.

23. Today we still have animals because
    (a) each animal eats other animals.
    (b) two of each kind were saved during the Flood.
    (c) we put them into classification groups.
24. All animals have first been divided into two large groups, as follows:
    (a) warm-blooded animals or cold-blooded animals.
    (b) animals with inside skeletons or with outside skeletons.
    (c) animals with skeletons or without skeletons.
25. Both gills and lungs
    (a) are used to get oxygen.
    (b) are found in warm-blooded animals.
    (c) are used by reptiles.
26. A metamorphosis happens to
    (a) reptiles.
    (b) mammals.
    (c) amphibians.
27. An alligator is most nearly like a
    (a) salamander.
    (b) lizard.
    (c) turtle.

28. a
29. c
30. b

Decide

31. yes
32. yes
33. yes
34. no
35. yes
36. yes
37. yes

Group

38. M
39. R
40. M
41. A
42. R
43. A
44. M
45. A
46. R
47. M

Use

48. Classification helps us study many animals in a short time.

    (2 points)

49. A turtle draws its head and legs inside its shell to protect itself from an enemy.   *(2 points)*

50. Hibernation is a deep sleep during the winter.
    Migration is a trip to another area.   *(3 points)*

    (Total: 54 points)

28. When a snake is molting, it is
    (a) shedding its skin.
    (b) laying eggs.
    (c) moving with S shapes.
29. A chipmunk is
    (a) an amphibian.
    (b) a reptile.
    (c) a mammal.
30. An animal's environment is
    (a) the place where it was born.
    (b) everything around it.
    (c) its winter home.

Decide whether each sentence is true. Write yes *or* no.

31. Noah stored enough food for the animals in the ark.
32. Animals with like characteristics are grouped together.
33. Mammals got their name because of the mammary glands that they have.
34. Young salamanders drink milk.
35. The balance of nature keeps animals from becoming too plentiful.
36. Migrating butterflies find their way by instinct.
37. Migration and hibernation protect animals during the winter.

Group each kind of animal. Write A *if the sentence tells about amphibians. Write* R *for reptiles and* M *for mammals.*

38. They are warm-blooded.
39. They have scales and claws.
40. They feed milk to their young.
41. They breathe with gills when they are young.
42. One kind travels by serpentine movement.
43. They have smooth, moist skin.
44. They have hair or fur.
45. They have soft, webbed feet.
46. They lay eggs with leathery shells.
47. Most of their young do not hatch from eggs.

Use good sentences to give the answers.

48. How is classification helpful to us?
49. Explain how a turtle uses its shell.
50. Explain what hibernation and migration are.

Animals are a gift from God. Many of them make nice pets.

Unit Seven

God Told Man to Care for His Creation

"Be fruitful, and multiply, and replenish the earth" (Genesis 9:1).

After the Flood, God said to Noah, "I give all the animals to you. I will make them afraid of you." Today the animals still have that instinct to be afraid of man. The fierce tiger, the strong elephant, and the huge whale are all under the rule of man. If man wants to catch an animal, he can. Even though the animal can run much faster, hit much harder, or fly much higher, man can always find a way to conquer it. Man's mind is far above an animal's mind.

Besides this, God gave Noah the plants and all other materials to use. God said, "Just as I gave you the green plants, so have I given you all things." From Noah's time until today, man has been raising plants for food. He has used wood, stone, and metal to make tools and buildings. He has built machines to make his work easier and faster. He has used the animals to serve him.

What a great honor God gave to man—he can rule over the whole earth! But with this honor came solemn duties. Man must rule the earth wisely. He should honor God by the way he uses God's materials.

But today many people are careless. They waste materials, such as wood and petroleum. They kill animals just for fun. They are proud of their tall buildings, fast cars, and powerful machines. They forget that God gave them the useful materials and their keen minds. They do not honor and obey God. But we can decide to honor God. In this unit, you can learn right ways to use and care for God's creation.

188

Unit Seven

God Told Man to Care for His Creation

For Your Inspiration

Contour Furrows

Now this is art, a lusty, vigorous thing!
No pastel-tinted water coloring,
No formless, tortured carving out of wood,
No oil blobs, never to be understood,
Could equal this—as real as death and birth:
These curved plow-sweeps across the page of
earth,
These scalloped ribbonings of brown and green
Stair-stepping down to willow's golden sheen.

The artist paused, from the tractor seat
Surveys his work. Where sky and furrow meet,
His masterpiece is joined to heaven now—
The land his palette, and his brush a plow.

—*Ruth Delong Peterson*
Reprinted by permission of Farm Journal

Farming Provides for Many of Our Needs

New Words

crop farming (krop fär′ ming), raising fields of grain or other plants.
dairying (dār′ ē • ing), milking cows and selling milk.
livestock (lĭv′ stok′), cows, pigs, and other farm animals.
truck farming (truk fär′ ming), raising vegetables to sell.

Reading Together

Did you know that most children in America live in towns and cities? In fact, less than three out of a hundred Americans live on farms. Think of it! Some children hardly ever taste sweet corn fresh from the garden. They have never ridden on a wagon full of prickly, sweet-smelling hay. They cannot splash in a stream in the woods. Some children scarcely even know that eggs come from chickens and that milk comes from cows. To them, food always comes from a grocery store.

Children who live in the country know very well where food comes from. They help to plant and harvest vegetables. They may have daily chores, such as gathering eggs in the chicken house or feeding the calves. They are glad for the rain that makes the field crops and gardens grow.

On a farm, children help with the work.

189

Lesson 1

CONCEPTS TO TEACH

- A farm is a good place for a Christian family to live.
- God has planned that farming should help to supply our needs for food and clothing.
- A farmer is a steward of the land he uses and of the livestock he raises.
- A farmer must follow God's plan in order to have healthy crops and livestock.
- A lazy farmer cannot expect a good harvest.

HELPS FOR THE TEACHER

Introducing the Lesson

Take time for a brief overview of the unit. Then ask the class to name various farm products: cereal grains, fruit, vegetables, honey, and meat.

Ask some farmer's children to describe their farm chores. Help them appreciate their work by pointing out that they are helping to provide food or clothing for others.

You might also mention some Bible farmers. Cain, Noah, Gideon, and Elisha raised crops. Abel, Abraham, Isaac, Jacob, Job, and Amos had livestock.

What do we get from a dairy farm?

By working so closely with God's earth, the farm children can see how great and good God is. This helps them to learn to trust God. Farm children can also learn good work habits because their parents can work with them every day.

Some people choose to farm because they enjoy working with plants and animals. They like the way a family can work together to raise food for themselves and for families who live in cities too. A farm is a good place for a growing Christian family to live.

Reading on Your Own

God planned that farming would supply our need for food and clothing. Some of our food comes from farm animals. For example, we get meat from *livestock*, such as beef cattle and pigs. We get both eggs and meat from chickens. We get milk from cows. Milking cows and selling milk is called *dairying*. Many dairy farmers have herds of fifty or more cows.

What do we get from a crop farm?

Extra Information

Did you know—

... that large–scale irrigation projects were developed by the Babylonians and Egyptians as early as 3000 B.C.?

... that the Romans developed methods of crop rotation with wheat and legumes?

... that Holstein cows were produced by selective breeding as early as 100 B.C. in the Netherlands?

... that bees may travel 13,000 miles to make one pound of honey?

... that American farmers, who are less than 0.3 percent of the world's farmers, produce 25 percent of the world's beef, 50 percent of the world's corn, and 64 percent of the world's soybeans?

QUIZ

Ask the students to write the correct New Word for each sentence below. Remind them to use correct spelling.

1. It means raising vegetables to sell.   *(truck farming)*

2. It means milking cows and selling the milk.   *(dairying)*

3. It means farm animals.   *(livestock)*

4. It means raising fields of plants.   *(crop farming)*

We probably eat more food that comes from plants than from animals. Grain is a common food that comes from plants. The most important grain crops are wheat, corn, and rice. These grains are used to make food, such as bread, noodles, and breakfast cereal. Grain is also an important food for livestock. Many farmers raise large fields of grain. Raising grain or other crops is called *crop farming*.

Our tomatoes and lettuce may come from our own gardens. Or we can buy fresh vegetables from farmers who do *truck farming*. A truck farmer's fields look like large gardens. He sells most of his vegetables in towns and cities where people do not have gardens.

Farm animals give us two materials from which clothing is made: wool and leather. Wool for our sweaters and coats comes from sheep. Leather for our shoes comes from the skins of livestock, such as cattle, sheep, and pigs.

Cotton is another material used to make clothing. It comes from cotton plants, which farmers raise in large fields. At harvest time, the cotton is sent to factories where it is made into cloth. This cloth is used to make shirts and dresses for us to wear.

Every farmer should be a good steward. If his work is crop farming or truck farming, he must try to keep his crops free from weeds and disease. He tries to protect his soil from erosion. He must plow his fields and plant his crops so that the soil does not wash away.

A careless or lazy farmer cannot expect a good harvest. If he does not get rid of the weeds, his crops will grow poorly. If he harvests his crops too early or too late, they will be unripe or spoiled. Every farmer who wants a good harvest must learn to follow God's plan.

How can a farmer who has livestock be a good steward? He should give his livestock fresh water, a balanced diet, and clean shelter. He should

What do we get from a truck farm?

Answers for "Test Your Reading"

1. dairying
2. crop farming
3. truck farming
4. eggs, meat, milk
5. fruit, grain, vegetables
6. leather, wool
7. cotton

try to keep his livestock free from disease. He should treat his livestock kindly even if they cause him trouble. Such a farmer is following God's plan for his livestock. The Bible says, "Be thou diligent to know the state of thy flocks, and look well to thy herds."

Livestock

Test Your Reading

Write one of your New Words for each picture to show what kind of farming is being done.

1.   2.   3.

Write each word from the box under the correct heading below.

cotton	grain	milk
eggs	leather	vegetables
fruit	meat	wool

Food From Animals

4. _____ _____ _____

Food From Plants

5. _____ _____ _____

Clothing From Animals

6. _____ _____

Clothing From Plants

7. _____

Use good sentences to give the answers.

8. Name two good things about living on a farm.
9. Name two kinds of livestock.
10. How can a farmer be a good steward of his crops?
11. How can a farmer be a good steward of his soil?
12. Name four things a farmer should do for his livestock.

Extra Activities

Do these activities as your teacher directs.

1. If you live on a farm, invite your classmates to visit it. Show them your pets, livestock, garden, and crops. Explain how you help to care for them. If none of you lives on a farm, perhaps you could visit one on a field trip.
2. Make your own book for your unit project. Cut 2 sheets of construction paper about 8 1/4" X 10 3/4" for the covers. Use 15 sheets of notebook paper for the pages. Assemble the pages and covers together, and staple them along the left side. On the front cover, write neatly *How We Use God's Earth*, and number the pages.

   On the top line of page 1, write "I Like to Live on a Farm." At the top of page 2, write "My Little Garden (or Flower Garden)." On page 3, write "How We Get Wool (or Cotton)." On page 4, write "I Help Can (or Freeze) Food." On page 5, write "How to Care for Calves (or animal of your choice)."

   Then write an interesting paragraph on each page about the title at the top. Perhaps you would like to find or draw small pictures that tell about each paragraph. Add them to your book to make it attractive.

Materials needed:
- *construction paper*
- *ruler*
- *scissors*
- *notebook paper*
- *stapler*
- *black marking pen*
- *small pictures*

8. Any two. Living on a farm is good because the family can work together.

   They learn to trust God.

   The children can learn good work habits.

   The children can learn to care for plants and animals.   (3)

9. Cows and pigs (or chickens, horses, and so forth) are two kinds of livestock.   (3)

10. A farmer should try to keep his crops free from weeds and disease.   (2)

11. A farmer should protect his soil from erosion.   (2)

12. A farmer should give his livestock fresh water, a balanced diet, and clean shelter and should try to keep them free from disease.   (5)

(Total: 27 points)

Comments on "Extra Activities"

2. Have the students write short paragraphs or "stories," drawing from their own experiences. If they have not experienced a certain activity, help them anticipate what it would be like and write accordingly.

Machines Help Man Do Work

Lesson 2

CONCEPTS TO TEACH

- There are six simple machines: the lever, the wheel and axle, the pulley, the inclined plane, the screw, and the wedge.
- A lever has more force when the load is moved closer to the pivot point.
- The longer the inclined plane, the easier it is to move a load uphill.
- A screw is a spiral inclined plane.
- The sharper a wedge is, the easier it splits things.
- The larger the wheel, the easier it is to turn the axle.
- Machines make our work easier.

HELPS FOR THE TEACHER

Introducing the Lesson

Choose some of the practical problems below to illustrate how machines help us. Of course, it would be ideal if you could do all of them in class.

Lever: Use a short screwdriver and a long screwdriver to pry open a paint can. Show that the longer lever makes it easier to open the can.

Wheel and axle: Use a short wrench and a long wrench to loosen a tight nut on a bolt. Loosening a nut on a car tire would show a common need for a long wrench. Or you could use a screwdriver to tighten some screws in the students' desks. The handle is a wheel, and the shaft is an axle. (Of course, nuts and bolts are screws, but do not explain this yet unless the students ask about it.)

Pulley: Fasten a sturdy hook in the ceiling of the classroom or in the top of the doorframe, and hang a small pulley on the hook. Tell the class to pretend that the ceiling is a leaky roof on a tall building. On the roof, some workers are sealing the leaks with a thick, sticky liquid. They have asked you to bring them another bucket of the liquid. Then loop some heavy string over the pulley, tie the string to the handle of a small bucket, and raise the bucket. Explain that the pulley makes it easier to lift a heavy bucket because it is easier to pull down than to lift up.

Inclined plane: Use a short board and a long

New Words

inclined plane (in • klīnd' plān), any slanting surface on which a load can be moved upward.

lever (lev' ər), a long tool that moves freely on a pivot point.

machine (mə shēn'), any tool that makes work easier or faster.

pulley (pool' ē), a wheel used with a rope to raise a load.

screw (skr̅o̅o̅), an object like a nail with a thread or groove winding around it.

wedge (wej), a tool that tapers from a thick end to a thin edge.

wheel and axle (hwēl and ak' səl), a wheel or handle that turns another wheel or axle.

Reading Together

Look at Ben. He can lift his father, who weighs three times as much as Ben does! Of course, Ben could not do this all by himself. A *machine* is helping him.

You might think that a machine is something big, noisy, and costly. You may think that it is made of metal. But that is not true of all machines.

Ben's machine is only a stone and a board. But it is a real machine because it makes the force of his muscles seem greater. It helps him lift more than he could lift by himself.

Ben's machine is not made of many parts like a car or a sewing machine. It is only a simple machine.

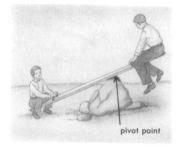

Using a lever

194

board to slide a heavy box of books up to a table. Show that the longer board makes it easier to push the box upward.

Screw: Suppose that Dan and Joe wanted to hike to the top of a mountain. The shorter trail was like this:

The longer trail was like this:

Which trail would be easier to climb?

Wedge: Drive a thin, pointed nail and a thick, blunt nail of equal length into a board. Count the number of strokes to show that the thinner nail is easier to drive. Of course, you must use the same amount of force for each stroke.

There are six different kinds of simple machines: the lever, inclined plane, screw, wedge, wheel and axle, and pulley.

Ben's simple machine is called a *lever*. Every lever is made of a long object that can move freely on a pivot point. Ben's pivot point is the stone.

See how far Ben is from the pivot point. See how near his father is. What if Ben and his father would change places? Could he still lift his father? No, of course not. The force of his muscles would seem to be much less. This teaches you something important about levers. The closer the load is to the pivot point, the easier it is to lift it.

Scissors are really two levers fastened together at the pivot point. For a scissors, the "load" is the paper or cloth you want to cut. You know that the closer the paper is to the pivot point of the scissors, the easier it is to cut it.

Using an inclined plane

Reading on Your Own

Look at Lucy. Her boards are another kind of simple machine: an *inclined plane*. See how the boards help her move the wagon up on the porch? Without these inclined planes, Lucy could hardly lift the wagon up on the porch.

Look at some other inclined planes on this page. Notice that each one makes it easier to push or pull a load upward. The longer the inclined plane is, the easier it is to move the load upward on it.

Extra Information

Did you know—

. . . that the laws of the lever and the pulley were known more than 200 years before Christ? Archimedes, a Greek inventor who discovered the laws, said, "Give me a place to stand on, and I will move the earth."

. . . that the Egyptian pyramids, which were built with the labor of thousands of workers, could have been built easily with several heavy-duty cranes?

. . . that many scientists recognize only two kinds of simple machines: the lever and the inclined plane? To them, the wheel and axle and the pulley are variations of the lever.

. . . that a certain inclined plane can decrease the force of a child's fall by increasing the distance he travels? (It is called a slide.)

Discussion Suggestion

Ask questions like these: If a thinner, sharper wedge needs less force, why aren't all wedges paper-thin? If a longer inclined plane takes less effort, why aren't all inclined planes a mile long?

Additional Demonstrations

Lever: Place a heavy box on a wheelbarrow, as close as possible to the handles. Tie it to the handles so that it cannot slide forward. Ask a student to push the wheelbarrow.

Then place the load close to the wheel, which is the pivot point. Have the same student push the wheelbarrow, noticing how much easier it is.

Materials needed:
- *heavy box*
- *wheelbarrow*
- *rope*

Materials needed:

Lever:
- *paint can with sticky lid*
- *long and short screwdrivers*

Wheel and axle:
- *nut on bolt*
- *long and short wrenches*
- *screwdriver*

Pulley:
- *sturdy hook*
- *small pulley*
- *heavy string*
- *small bucket*

Inclined plane:
- *box of books*
- *long and short boards*

Wedge:
- *hammer*
- *thin and thick nails of equal length*
- *board*

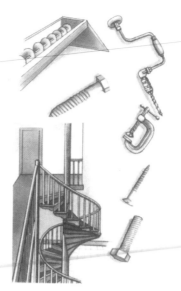

Where is the screw in each?

Splitting wood with a wedge

A *wedge* on its side looks like an inclined plane, but it is used for a different purpose. It can be used to cut or split things like wood. The thin, sharp edge of the wedge splits the wood apart when the wide end is hit with a big hammer.

Did your mother ever try to cut meat with a dull knife? It was hard work, wasn't it? The cutting edge of a knife is a wedge. You know that sharp knives cut the best. This is true of any wedge. The sharper the wedge, the more easily it cuts things.

Now look at these strange inclined planes! Instead of going straight upward, they go upward in circles. This kind of inclined plane is called a *screw*.

A winding stairway is a screw that does not turn. Instead, those who climb it do the turning. But smaller screws can be turned. Some large metal screws move grain through pipes. Smaller metal screws are often used to fasten things tightly. You have often seen these screws with grooves winding around them.

A wheel and axle we use every day

Let's think about two more simple machines: the wheel and axle and the pulley. Have you ever tried to open a door that has lost its knob? It was much harder to open because you no longer had a *wheel and axle*

Wheel and axle: Put masking tape around the middle of a broomstick. Then measure six and eighteen inches away from the middle on both sides. Tape all four places as shown. Call

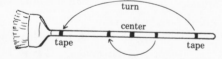

on two pupils of about equal size and strength. (Choose well-behaved students who will not make this demonstration a wrestling match.) One student should hold the broomstick at the inner marks and the other student at the outer marks. Each should try to turn the broomstick in a circle—one clockwise and the other counterclockwise. They should turn steadily and without jerking. Tell the class that this is a wheel and axle with only two spokes. You might liken it to the cross-

piece of a steering wheel. Ask the class to predict which student will have the greater force.

When it becomes clear that the student at the outer marks has the greater force, have them switch places and repeat the activity. This should clearly show the relationship between distance and force.

Materials needed:
- *broom*
- *masking tape*
- *tape measure*

Pulley: Have two students stand a few feet apart, facing each other. With arms outstretched, each one should grasp a broomstick with both hands and hold it horizontally. They should try to keep the broomsticks apart and parallel while a smaller student, standing between them, tries to pull the broomsticks together. (Make it clear that

to help you. The wheel is the big part of the knob; the axle is the little part that works the latch.

Why does a doorknob make it easier to open the door? You turn the big knob with only a little force. That makes the little axle turn with much force. This is how all wheel and axles work. Any knob or handle that you turn is a wheel and axle. It is always easier to make a large wheel turn a small axle than to turn the axle itself. The larger the wheel, the greater the force is at the axle.

In a wheel and axle, the wheel is fastened to the axle. But the wheel of a *pulley* can turn on its axle. A pulley has a rope that turns on the wheel. When you pull down on one side of the rope, the other side goes up. It is easier to pull down on the rope than to push the weight upward.

In this lesson, you have learned about six simple machines. These machines can be made in many shapes and sizes. But they all help us do work. All machines make work easier.

Using a pulley to do work

Test Your Reading

Fill each blank with a word from your lesson.
1. A machine that has only a few parts is called a ——— ———.
2. A long object that turns on a pivot point is called a ———.
3. A winding inclined plane called a ——— can fasten or move things.
4. A rope on a wheel makes a ——— that can raise or lower a load.
5. Machines make our work ———.

Answers for "Test Your Reading"
1. simple machine
2. lever
3. screw
4. pulley
5. easier

---

this must be done decently, as in any other science activity.) Of course, the smaller student will be unable to pull the broomsticks together.

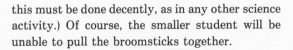

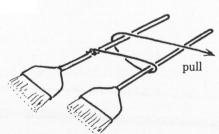

pull

Then tie a length of rope tightly to the middle of one broomstick. Loop the free end of the rope around the middle of the second broomstick and then around the middle of the first stick. Take care that the rope does not cross itself. Explain that the round broomsticks act somewhat like pulleys; adding a loop is like adding a pulley. Ask the smaller student to stand behind one of the broomstick-holders and to pull at the free end of the rope. It should be noticeably easier to pull the broomsticks together. If necessary, you may add another loop and proceed as before. By now, the class should understand that adding "pulleys" increases the rope-puller's force.

Explain that real pulleys, of course, have wheels. Adding real pulleys would have made the rope-puller's work even easier because the wheels would have greatly reduced the friction. Finally, ask the class to relate this demonstration to the many ropes and pulleys of giant cranes and earth-moving machines.

Materials needed:
• *2 brooms*
• *rope*

6. B—The sharper a wedge is, the more easily it cuts or splits things.

7. B—The longer an inclined plane is, the easier it is to move a load uphill.

8. A—The larger the wheel or handle, the greater the force is at the axle.   *(Total: 11 points)*

Which picture in each pair below shows work being done more easily? Write A or B to show which one you choose. After the A or B, copy a rule from the box that tells why that way is easier. The first one is done for you.

A   B

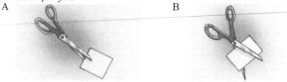

B—A lever's greatest force is near its pivot point.

6. A   B

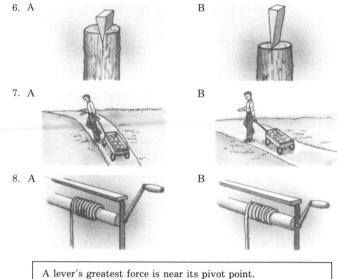

7. A   B

8. A   B

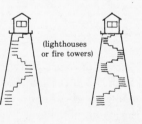

> A lever's greatest force is near its pivot point.
> The longer an inclined plane is, the easier it is to move a load uphill.
> The sharper a wedge is, the more easily it cuts or splits things.
> The larger the wheel or handle, the greater the force is at the axle.

Inclined plane and screw: Draw the following sketches on the chalkboard or on a large poster, and discuss them. They illustrate the relationship between the inclined plane and the screw and between effort and distance in general.

Shorter but Harder   *Longer but Easier*

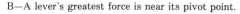

(lighthouses or fire towers)

(Real screws may also be used.)

Extra Activities

Do these activities as your teacher directs.

1. Use a seesaw to learn about levers. Ask a friend about your size to help you. First, try to balance evenly on the seesaw. Where must you sit in order to balance?

    Next ask a smaller person to climb on the seesaw while you sit on the one end. How close to the center must you move until he can lift you?

    Then ask your friend and the smaller person to sit together on one end of the seesaw while you lift them from the other end. Balance evenly as before.

    You may also try to lift and balance a stack of bricks and a bucket of water. You will notice that the closer the load is to the center of the seesaw, the easier it is to lift it.

    Materials needed:
    *   *seesaw*
    *   *friend your size*
    *   *friend smaller than you*
    *   *bricks*
    *   *bucket of water*

2. You can see that a screw is an inclined plane. Trace the inclined plane below, and cut it out. Tape the side to your pencil, and wind the paper around it. Now your inclined plane has become a screw!

    Materials needed:
    *   *white paper*   *   *pencil*
    *   *scissors*   *   *tape*

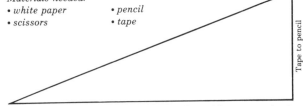

3. Continue your unit project by adding these titles to your book on pages 6, 7, and 8.

    "I Used Ten Machines Today"
    "Three Machines in a Pencil Sharpener"
    "Simple Machines of the Bible"

    Then write interesting paragraphs, and include small pictures, as in the last lesson.

Wedge: Break or cut off the tip of a pin or needle. Use it and a good pin or needle to pierce some closely woven cloth. Ask the students to explain the results.

Materials needed:

*   *2 pins*
*   *cloth*

Comments on "Extra Activities"

3. For the first topic, the student could name ten everyday objects that are simple machines. (The pictures in the textbook should be helpful.) The student could also write what kind of simple machine each object is and whether the machine is used to increase force or speed.

    For the second essay, the student should tell that a pencil sharpener is actually three simple machines in one: the handle is a wheel and axle, the revolving cutters are screws, and the cutting edges are wedges. He could also discuss these simple machines in general. Some alternate suggestions instead of a pencil sharpener are: a scissors (the cutting edges are wedges; the whole is a pair of levers) or a screwdriver (a lever when prying off a lid, a wheel and axle when turning a screw).

    For the third topic, the student may give examples of simple machines in the Bible, such as: a lever (shovels and tongs in 1 Kings 7:40, 49), a wheel and axle (potter's wheel in Jeremiah 18:3, an inclined plane (hill in 1 Kings 16:24; stairs in 2 Kings 9:13), a screw (winding stairs in 1 Kings 6:8), and a wedge (ax in 2 Kings 6:5). The student may also add details of how these simple machines were used.

QUIZ

Give examples of various objects or situations. Then call on students to identify the simple machine in each.

Lesson 3

Wind and Water Can Do Work

New Words

sail (sāl), a large piece of cloth made to catch the wind.

turbine (tėr′ bən), a wheel that is turned by moving water or air.

water wheel (wô′ tər hwēl), a wheel with cups or blades that is turned by falling water.

windmill (wind′ mil′), a machine with blades on a wheel that is turned by the wind.

Reading Together

Did you ever ride on a moving stairway? It carries you higher and higher. You do not have to do a thing until you step off at the top.

When you ride a moving stairway, a motor that uses electric energy carries you up. But when you climb a stairway, you use your own energy. Your muscles do the work of moving you up the steps. Either way, the work of moving upward takes energy. Work always takes some kind of energy.

The energy of the wind can do useful work. Long ago, the wind pushed heavy ships across the ocean. The *sails* on the ships caught the wind. If the wind blew hard, the ships moved quickly over the water. If the wind blew gently, the ships moved slowly. If the wind did not blow, the ships hardly moved at all.

Years ago, men used the wind to move them across the ocean.

200

Lesson 3

CONCEPTS TO TEACH

- Before work can be done, there must be a source of energy.
- Muscles supply the energy for the work the body does.
- A sail or windmill can put the wind's energy to work.
- Falling water has energy.
- The greater the fall of water, the more energy it has.
- Water wheels and turbines use the energy of moving water.
- Dams are built across rivers to make the water fall farther.
- Wind and water power do not pollute the environment and will never be used up.

HELPS FOR THE TEACHER

Introducing the Lesson

Use a disposable plastic cup and a drinking straw to make a model water wheel as shown. Turn it with a stream of water from a faucet or from a pitcher held over a bucket.

As your water wheel turns, explain that this is how huge turbines work. Show pictures of an old-fashioned water wheel and of a modern turbine.

cut off

To minimize the wobble of your turbine on the straw, make a double hub. Cut a second cup very low and slit its sides so you can wedge it upside down inside the bottom of your turbine cup.

Today some sailboats still use only the wind's energy. But most large ships burn fuel oil. They travel at full speed without the wind.

Some ships use both fuel energy and the wind's energy. They have engines that burn fuel, and they have sails that catch the wind's energy. The wind helps to save both fuel and money.

What other work does the wind do? In some places, it pumps water from deep in the ground. The wind spins the blades of a tall *windmill*. The energy of the spinning blades runs a pump that pumps the water.

The wheel of a windmill is a *turbine*. The turbine of a windmill has slanted blades that are pushed by the moving air.

Wind is used to pump water.

Water wheels use energy from water to run machines.

Reading on Your Own

Let's pretend you are taking a walk through the woods. You are walking under a big, twisted hickory tree. Then you feel a tap and a BUMP! Two big hickory nuts bounce off your head. You pick up the nuts and rub your sore head. How strange—the nuts are the same size. Why did one nut hit so much harder than the other one?

Both hickory nuts weigh the same. But one nut fell from the top branches of the tree, and the other nut fell from the lower branches. The one that fell farther hit you harder. The farther the hickory nut fell, the more energy it had. The same is true for any other falling object. Gravity pulls down on all materials. The farther any object falls, the more energy it has.

Long ago, men knew that falling objects have energy. They knew that falling water could provide much useful energy. So they built large, wooden *water wheels* with paddles or buckets to catch the water. They

Materials needed:
- *disposable plastic cup*
- *drinking straw*
- *scissors*
- *pictures of wooden water wheels and modern turbines*

Extra Information
Did you know—

. . . that water wheels were used in Greece more than a hundred years before Christ?

. . . that in the Netherlands, thousands of windmills were built to drain the land? Some were also used to grind wheat, to saw wood, to make rope, and even to send messages.

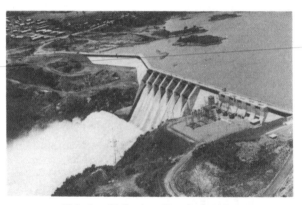

Water from this dam is used to make electricity.

placed a water wheel in a swiftly flowing stream or under a waterfall. The falling water would turn the wheel, which would then run a machine. The machine would saw wood, grind wheat into flour, or do some other work.

The water wheels of today are not straight paddles or buckets. They are slanted like the blades of a windmill. Of course, a water turbine is made heavier and stronger than a wind turbine because moving water pushes harder than moving air.

Today the energy from falling water is used mostly to make electricity. A large waterfall, such as Niagara Falls, can provide much electricity. But there are not many large waterfalls that are suitable. In most of the rivers, the water does not fall very far at once.

For this reason, dams have been built across many rivers. A dam makes the water fall farther at one place. Then it has much energy to spin huge turbines. The spinning turbines produce much electricity.

Yet only a small part of our country's electricity comes from water power. Most of the electricity comes from burning coal, petroleum, or other fuel.

Burning these fuels makes the air and water dirty. Besides, these fuels are being used up very fast. Someday, they may be gone.

However, we can never use up all the wind and water. They can supply useful energy again and again. Day after day, the wind keeps on blowing. The rivers keep on flowing over dams and waterfalls. Neither wind nor

QUIZ

Ask the students to give the correct New Word for each sentence below.

1. It can pump water with the wind's energy. *(windmill)*
2. It helps a boat use the wind's energy. *(sail)*
3. It helps change the energy of moving water or air to electricity. *(turbine)*
4. It is powered by falling water. *(water wheel)*

water power makes the earth dirty or smelly.

If energy from the wind and moving water is clean and free, why don't we use it to make all our electricity? It is true that the energy itself is free. But it costs much money to build dams and machines that change the energy to electricity. In many places, it has been cheaper to get electricity from fuels.

The energy from muscles, the wind, moving water, and fuel is a great gift from God. We need it to do our work. We should not waste this energy or use it in any way that is harmful to God's creation. Instead, we must always use energy wisely to do good work.

Test Your Reading

Write yes *or* no *for each sentence below.*

1. Some work can be done without energy.
2. We do work with our muscle energy.
3. Sailboats and windmills get their energy from the pull of gravity.
4. The wind's energy is used to pump water.
5. Falling water can turn water wheels and turbines.
6. Someday we may use up all the water power.

Choose the best ending for each sentence below.

7. The energy of the wind
   (a) causes dirty air and water.
   (b) is used to save fuel and money.
   (c) is being used more than fuel energy.
8. The water of Niagara Falls has the most energy
   (a) at the top of the falls.
   (b) at the middle of the falls.
   (c) at the bottom of the falls.
9. At a waterfall or dam, the energy of falling water is usually changed to
   (a) heat energy.
   (b) fuel energy.
   (c) electric energy.
10. A dam causes water to have more energy because
    (a) the water falls farther.
    (b) the river has more water.
    (c) the water is cooler.

Answers for "Test Your Reading"

1. no
2. yes
3. no
4. yes
5. yes
6. no
7. b
8. c
9. c
10. a   *(Total: 10 points)*

Comments on "Extra Activities"

2. Use the pinwheel to spark a discussion about windmills and their use. Show pictures of an old-fashioned Dutch windmill and of a farm windmill.

   • *pictures of windmills*

3. For the first topic, the student could describe a dam and explain the purpose of dams in general. He could look up "Dam" in *The World Book Encyclopedia* to help him.

   The second topic would be easier to write if the child could see a windmill at work and ask questions about it. If this is not possible, he can study "Windmill" in *The World Book Encyclopedia*. He could explain what windmills have been used for and compare wind power with other sources of energy.

   For the topic "Sail On!" the student could describe sailing in the past and today. The articles "Sailing" and "Ship" in *The World Book Encyclopedia* would be helpful.

   For the last topic, the student could give details about Niagara Falls and the electricity it produces. It could go on to describe water power in general. Some articles to read in *The World Book Encyclopedia* are "Niagara Falls," "Turbine," and "Water Power."

Extra Activities

Do these activities as your teacher directs.

1. Visit a windmill, water wheel, or dam in your area. Ask someone to explain how it works.
2. Trace the pattern below onto a sheet of paper. Cut out the square of paper. Cut on the lines going toward the center. Look at the drawing to put it together. Then spin your pinwheel in the wind.

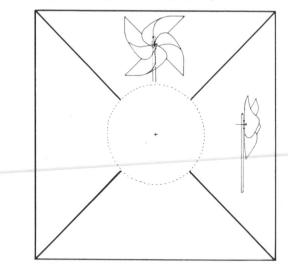

Materials needed:
   • *paper*   • *pin*
   • *scissors*   • *drinking straw*

3. For your unit project, add these titles to your book on pages 9–12.

   "Why Build a Dam?"
   "A Windmill Works Hard"
   "Sail On!"
   "The Power of Niagara Falls"

   Then complete the pages, as described in Lesson 1.

Man Is a Steward
of God's Creation

New Words

conservation (kon′ sər • vā′ shən), the wise use of the materials
and living things on the earth.

raw material (rô mə • tēr′ ē • əl), wood, stone, petroleum, or any
other material that can be used to make useful things.

steward (stōō′ ərd), a person who cares for things that belong to
someone else.

technology (tek • nol′ ə • jē), the knowledge and skills needed to do
a task.

Reading Together

Think of everything that belongs
to you: all your clothes, toys, books,
and pets. Do you have anything that
someone did not give you?

Perhaps you have been given a
bicycle. Your parents bought it for
you to use. How do you think they
would feel if you did not take care of
the bicycle? They would decide that
you do not really like it very much.
They were hoping that you would be
a good *steward* of the bicycle they
bought. But if you do not care for it,
they have the right to take it away
from you.

205

Lesson 4

CONCEPTS TO TEACH

- Everything we have belongs to God.
- Carelessness leads man to use his belongings wrongly.
- Conservation is the wise use of the materials God gave us.
- God wants us to use the materials of His creation to spread the Gospel to others.
- Raw materials of the earth are good, but man's use of them can be evil.
- Technology is the skills and knowledge needed to use materials to do work.
- It is not the size of a project but its purpose that determines whether it is right or wrong.
- Giving glory to God is a part of good stewardship.

HELPS FOR THE TEACHER

Introducing the Lesson

Read and discuss the parable of the rich fool in Luke 12:16–21. Notice that he, like many foolish people today, thought he had complete control over his earthly possessions. Discuss what he should have done instead to be a good steward.

Things your parents are stewards of

Your parents are also stewards of their belongings. In fact, everyone on earth is a steward. God owns everything we have. If He wants to, He can take it all away. The Bible asks, "What hast thou that thou didst not receive? now if thou didst receive it, why dost thou glory [feel proud], as if thou hadst not received it?"

Can you understand why God hates when people are proud? They may be proud of their nice clothes, fast cars, or large farms. They may feel that their things are theirs. Because they are not thankful to God for them, they may be careless. Careless people are poor stewards. A careless person may throw trash into a clean stream. He may kill fish and birds just for fun. He may fail to put out his campfire, which may then cause a roaring forest fire. Such a person is not thankful for God's gifts but wastes them.

A good steward is thankful for God's gifts. He tries to use them carefully. For example, a good steward guards clean air and water like a treasure. He does not waste energy from petroleum and other fuels. He tries to protect wild animals. By doing these things, a good steward is practicing *conservation*. Conservation is using God's creation wisely.

A good steward will only use God's gifts for good purposes. He will use them to provide food, shelter, and clothing for himself and others. For example, farmers raise crops and livestock to supply both food and clothing. Builders use wood and stone to build houses for shelter.

A good steward shares God's gifts with poor people. He is willing to provide food, shelter, and clothing for them. The Bible says, "He that hath pity upon the poor lendeth unto the Lord."

Another good purpose for using God's gifts is to spread His teachings. The Bible says, "Go ye into all the world, and preach the gospel to every creature." It is wise to spend our time and money to teach others about Jesus. Indeed, it is always good stewardship to obey God.

How are these tracts related to good stewardship?

Extra Information

Did you know—

. . . that 4,000 miles of streams and rivers in ten western states remain polluted because of unwise mining practices over 50 years ago?

. . . that erosion causes up to six billion dollars worth of damage a year to streams, fisheries, and water supplies?

. . . that in a recent year, Americans grew twice as much timber as they harvested?

. . . that the United States has less than 5 percent of the world's population but consumes over 25 percent of the energy used?

Discussion Suggestion

Discuss how to practice good stewardship at school. Here are some starters.

1. Keep trash off the playground.
2. Use pencils, paper, and erasers carefully.
3. Waste very little food at lunch time.
4. Use time wisely.
5. Use school property carefully.

Reading on Your Own

Sometime after the Flood, a group of people began to build a city with a tall tower. It was called Babel. These builders used *raw materials* that God had created. Some of their raw materials were clay and asphalt. This asphalt is called slime in the Bible. The builders baked the clay to make bricks. They melted the sticky asphalt and put it between the bricks. Then the asphalt would cool and become very hard. The bricks and asphalt made strong walls for their city and tower.

Brick making and building are kinds of *technology*. Technology is knowing how to make and do things. This knowledge helps man to use the right materials to do special work.

Using technology and raw materials was not wrong. Building something large was not wrong. After all, Noah had used the technology of shipbuilding to build the large ark. His raw materials were wood and asphalt. So why was God pleased with Noah and displeased with the builders of Babel?

Noah honored and obeyed God with his work. He wanted people to think of God when they saw the ark. But the builders of Babel were proud. They built the city and tower so that

Compare these two pictures. Why was the one good technology? Why was the one wrong technology?

QUIZ

Ask the students to write the correct New Word for each phrase below.

1. One who is a caretaker   *(steward)*
2. Something God made that man makes into useful things   *(raw material)*
3. Skills for doing special work   *(technology)*
4. Using materials wisely and carefully   *(conservation)*

other people would think they were great. Babel was not built to honor God at all.

So God decided to stop their building. He made the people speak different languages. Then the builders could not understand each other. The Tower of Babel was never finished.

Raw materials and technology are a part of God's world. They are also a part of science, for science is the study of God's world.

Today we can still use materials or technology in right or wrong ways. We can even study science in right or wrong ways. Do we study science so that people think we are great? Then our study of science is wrong. Do we study science to honor God, the Creator, and to learn how to care for His creation? Then our study of science is right. Studying science should always cause us to be thankful for God's protected world.

Answers for "Test Your Reading"

1. b
2. e
3. a
4. c
5. d
6. g
7. f
8. h
9. i
10. Our study of science is wrong if we study to make people think we are great.
11. Our study of science is right if we honor God (or learn to care for God's creation).

(Total: 11 points)

————————— **Test Your Reading** —————————

Match each sentence beginning to the right ending.

1. Everything we have
2. A steward
3. Being careless
4. Using God's gifts wisely
5. Having skills to do work

a. is being a poor steward.
b. belongs to God.
c. is a part of conservation.
d. is a part of technology.
e. takes care of things that belong to someone else.

Match each sentence beginning to the right ending.

6. Both Noah's ark and the Tower of Babel were built by
7. God was pleased with Noah and the ark because Noah was
8. God was displeased with Babel and its builders because they were
9. A right purpose for using God's gifts is

f. honoring and obeying God.
g. using technology.
h. wanting honor for themselves.
i. providing food, shelter, and clothing.

Copy and finish each sentence below.

10. Our study of science is wrong if we ——.
11. Our study of science is right if we ——.

Extra Activities

Do these activities as your teacher directs.

1. Make a poster about conservation. At the top of a large sheet of poster board, write "Let's Protect God's Creation." On one half, draw a picture showing wastefulness or carelessness. You could draw a stream full of trash, a field with erosion in it, or a fire spreading in a forest. (For more ideas, find "Conservation" and "Environmental Pollution" in the *World Book Encyclopedia.*) On the other half, draw a picture showing conservation. You could draw a clean river and woods, a field with strip-cropping in it, or a child feeding the wild birds. Hang your poster on the wall of your classroom or hallway.

   Materials needed:
   • *large sheet of posterboard*
   • *crayons, markers, or poster paints*

2. To finish your unit project, add these titles to your book on pages 13–15.

   "How I Can Share God's Gifts"
   "God Owns My Pets (or Money, Toys)"
   "Let's Protect the Wild Animals (or Birds, Forest)"

   Complete the pages, as described in Lesson 1.

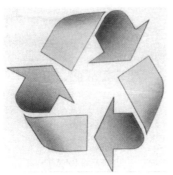

What is this sign? Where have you seen it? What does it mean? How is this sign related to good stewardship? Try to find an example of this sign to bring to school.

Comments on "Extra Activities"

2. The student who writes on the first topic could describe some gifts from God, such as time, talents, and possessions. Then he could describe times when he or his family shared in the past and how he would like to share in the future.

   For the second topic, the student should discuss God's ownership of our possessions and describe how to be good stewards.

   For the third topic, the student should choose one aspect of conservation. He should then describe how man has wasted or misused that kind of material or wildlife and what can be done to protect it. He may study "Conservation" in *The World Book Encyclopedia.*

ANSWER KEY

Match

1. b
2. c
3. d
4. e
5. f
6. h
7. a
8. g

Fill

9. truck farming
10. wedge
11. lever
12. pulley
13. wheel and axle
14. inclined plane
15. windmill
16. turbine
17. steward
18. raw materials

Decide

19. no
20. no
21. no
22. yes
23. no
24. yes

Lesson 5

Do You Remember What You Learned?

Match each word on the right to its meaning on the left.

1. Raising plants in fields
2. Milking cows and selling milk
3. Farm animals
4. Makes work easier
5. Catches the wind
6. Is turned by falling water
7. Using materials wisely
8. Skills and knowledge needed to do work

 a. conservation
 b. crop farming
 c. dairying
 d. livestock
 e. machine
 f. sail
 g. technology
 h. water wheel

Fill the blanks with words from the word box.

inclined plane	screw	wedge
lever	steward	wheel and axle
pulley	truck farming	windmill
raw materials	turbine	

9. A field of lettuce or strawberries is an example of ——.
10. The sharper the ——, the easier it splits wood.
11. A —— has more force when the load is moved closer to the pivot point.
12. A —— makes it easier to lift something by pulling down on a rope.
13. A long handle on a —— is easier to turn than a short handle.
14. It is easier to push a heavy load up a long —— than up a short, steep one.
15. Water can be pumped with a —— that runs by the wind's power.
16. As falling water spins a large ——, its energy is changed to electricity.
17. Each person is a —— of his belongings.
18. God made all ——, which man can use in either right or wrong ways.

Decide whether each sentence is true, and write yes or no.

19. Wool and cotton come from livestock.
20. A farmer who lets his fields become weedy should expect a good harvest.
21. A tractor is a simple machine.
22. Our bodies use muscle energy to do work.
23. Building a dam across a river causes the falling water to have less energy.
24. Falling water can supply energy to run machines.

Lesson 5

To your students, the topics covered in this unit may not seem closely related. Therefore, you may need to spend more time in viewing the unit as a whole. Express these main ideas:

1. God provided man with materials, energy, and intelligence to meet his physical needs and to glorify God.
2. Man is accountable to God for the way he uses the materials, machines, energy, and technology.

Choose the best ending for each sentence.

25. Farming provides our
    (a) food and clothing.   (b) heat and shelter.   (c) shelter and exercise.
26. To stay healthy, livestock must be
    (a) forced to work.   (b) protected from disease.   (c) kept indoors.
27. A simple machine made of a rope on a wheel is a
    (a) pulley.   (b) wedge.   (c) lever.
28. To do work, there must be
    (a) muscles.   (b) energy.   (c) electricity.
29. The energy of a waterfall comes from
    (a) the wind.   (b) electricity.   (c) gravity.
30. Soon people may use up
    (a) the coal and petroleum.
    (b) the wind's energy.   (c) the water power.
31. A good steward will
    (a) leave a burning campfire.
    (b) protect wild birds and animals.   (c) throw trash into a stream.
32. It is wrong to
    (a) build large buildings.
    (b) be proud of our skills.   (c) use much technology.

Find the word that does not belong, and write it on your paper.

33. Which one is not a lever?
    wheelbarrow   tweezers   needle   scissors
34. Which one is not a wheel and axle?
    highway ramp   telephone dial   steering wheel   doorknob
35. Which one is not an inclined plane?
    mountain   dustpan   stairway   screwdriver
36. Which one is not a wedge?
    knife   tongs   pin   saw
37. Which one is not a screw?
    pump handle   winding stairway   end of light bulb
    lid of ketchup bottle

Use good sentences to give the answers.

38-39. Write two reasons why a farm is a good place to live.
40-41. How were Noah's ark and the Tower of Babel alike? How were they different?
42-43. Give two good purposes for using the materials God made.
44-45. Give a right reason and a wrong reason for studying science.

Choose

25. a
26. b
27. a
28. b
29. c
30. a
31. b
32. b

Find

33. needle
34. highway ramp
35. screwdriver
36. tongs
37. pump handle

Use

38-39. A farm is a good place to live because the whole family can work together. They learn to trust God (or to care for plants and animals). *(3 points)*

40-41. Both Noah's ark and the Tower of Babel were large and were built by using many raw materials (or much technology). Noah's ark was built to honor God, but the Tower of Babel honored people.

(6 points)

42-43. A good purpose is to provide food, shelter, and clothing for people.
Another good purpose is to tell others about Jesus. *(3 points)*

44-45. A right reason to study science is to honor God (or to learn to care for His creation). A wrong reason is to honor ourselves.

(3 points)

(Total: 49 points)

YEAR END REVIEW

Your class could page through the book as was suggested at the beginning of the book for the first science period. They could read the unit titles orally and recall what they remember best from each unit.

One helpful method of book review is to assign the review exercises at the end of each unit. You could assign two, three, or more reviews each science period, depending on the number of school days that remain and on the students' workload otherwise.

End-of-Year Vocabulary Review

First, tell the students to study the vocabulary words and meanings for each chapter. Then divide the class into two teams. Give a definition from the textbook, and ask the first student on one team to tell the vocabulary word. (You may also want to give a choice of three vocabulary words.) If he can do so, give his team a point. If he cannot, ask the first person on the opposite team. Continue in this way. Of course, the team with the most points is the winner.

God's Protected World

Unit 1 Test   Score _____

Name _____ Date _____

Unit 1 Test Answers

Matching

Match the letters to the correct numbers.

_____ 1. It is solid water.   a. condensation

_____ 2. It is water that is a gas.   b. evaporation

_____ 3. It changes shape but not size.   c. ice

_____ 4. It means water going into the air.   d. liquid

_____ 5. It means heating solids until they   e. melting

          become liquids.   f. steam

_____ 6. It means water coming out of the air.

Matching
1. c
2. f
3. d
4. b
5. e
6. a

Match these sentences about the water cycle with their correct place in the drawing. The

first one is done for you.

__D__ Rain falls from the clouds.

_____ 7. The wind carries the evaporated water back to land.

_____ 8. Heating causes water to evaporate from the ocean.

_____ 9. Rivers carry the water to the ocean.

_____10. Cooling causes the water in the air to condense into

          liquid water.

Number in Order
7. B
8. A
9. E
10. C

Yes or No?

11. yes
12. no
13. yes
14. yes
15. yes
16. yes
17. no

Choose the Best Answer

18. b
19. c
20. a

Yes or No?

Write yes *if the sentence is true and* no *if it is not true.*

_____11. Every living thing needs water.

_____12. Water pressure is greatest at the top of the ocean.

_____13. One property of water is its good taste.

_____14. Without evaporation, we would have no rivers.

_____15. Water is pushed uphill by water pressure.

_____16. If an object weighs less than the buoyant force, it will float.

_____17. All solids melt with the same amount of heating.

Choose the Best Answer

Write the letter for the words that best finish each sentence.

_____18. Steam is made by

(a) melting water.

(b) boiling water.

(c) freezing water.

_____19. The weight of water causes

(a) condensation.

(b) cooling.

(c) pressure.

_____20. God sent the Flood because of

(a) man's sinfulness.

(b) careless farmers.

(c) wasted hillsides.

_____21. Gullies and badlands are caused by

    (a) erosion.

    (b) pressure.

    (c) buoyant force.

_____22. Soil is *not* carried away by

    (a) evaporation.

    (b) erosion.

    (c) floods.

_____23. Wood floats because of

    (a) condensation.

    (b) buoyant force.

    (c) erosion.

21. a
22. a
23. b

Answer the Questions

24-26. What are three ways we use water?

_____

_____

27-29. Where are three places God put water?

_____

_____

30-31. What are two ways farmers can take good care of the soil?

_____

_____

Answer the Questions

24-26. (Any three) drinking, washing, making things, making solutions, putting out fires

27-29. (Any three) sky or clouds, ground, streams, rivers, lakes, oceans

30-31. planting cover crops, plowing around hills (or contour plowing), strip-cropping

32-33. A penny sinks because its weight is greater than the buoyant force. A ship floats because its weight is less than the buoyant force.

(Total: 33 points)

32-33. Why does a penny sink, but a heavy ship floats? (Your answer should compare their *weight* and *buoyant force.*)

_____

_____

_____

_____

God's Protected World

Unit 2 Test

Score _____

Name _____ Date _____

Matching

Match each letter to the correct word group. There is one extra letter.

_____ 1. Makes strong bridges and buildings

_____ 2. Makes good electric wire

_____ 3. Wood used to make paper

_____ 4. Makes lightweight airplanes

_____ 5. Most important liquid

_____ 6. Heavy liquid metal

_____ 7. Cleans paintbrushes

_____ 8. Makes holes in cake

a. aluminum

b. carbon dioxide

c. copper

d. hardwood

e. iron

f. mercury

g. pulpwood

h. turpentine

i. water

Which Word Does Not Belong?

Cross out the word that does not belong.

9. Cross out the one that does not tell about working with wood.

    sawing   nailing   painting   mining

10. Cross out the one that is not a natural resource.

    cars   rocks   petroleum   trees

11. Cross out the one that is not connected with getting petroleum or making it useful.

    condensation   refinery   oil well   alcohol

12. Cross out the one that does not come from petroleum.

    asphalt   ammonia   gasoline   greases

13. Cross out the one that is not connected with the gas we breathe.

    natural gas   air   atmosphere   oxygen

Unit 2 Test Answers

Matching

1. e
2. c
3. g
4. a
5. i
6. f
7. h
8. b

Which Word Does Not Belong?

9. mining
10. cars
11. alcohol
12. ammonia
13. natural gas

Yes or No?

14. yes
15. no
16. yes
17. yes
18. yes
19. yes
20. no
21. no

Fill in the Blanks

22. nitrogen
23. wind
24. ammonia
25. helium
26. Natural gas
27. Carbon dioxide

Yes or No?

If the sentence is true, write yes. *If it is not true, write* no.

_____14. Lumber comes from the trunk and limbs of a tree.

_____15. Hardwood trees have needles and cones.

_____16. Coal, alcohol, and natural gas are burned as fuel.

_____17. Everything we have and use was once a raw material.

_____18. The properties of a material tell us how to use it.

_____19. Propane is put into bottles as a fuel for torches.

_____20. The oxygen in the air keeps fires from burning too fast.

_____21. Sandstone rock makes good gravestones.

Fill in the Blanks

Fill the blanks with words from the word box.

ammonia	helium	nitrogen
carbon dioxide	natural gas	wind

22. Air is a mixture of oxygen and _____

23. Moving air is called _____ .

24. When dissolved in water, _____ makes a good cleaner.

25. A very light gas is _____ .

26. _____ comes from deep in the earth.

27. _____ puts out fires.

Write the Answers

28-29. Give two good uses of alcohol.

_____

_____

_____

30-31. How is a liquid distilled?

_____

_____

_____

_____

32-33. Give two reasons why we need oxygen.

_____

_____

Write the Answers

28-29. (Any two) Burn it as fuel. Make solutions or medicine with it. Use it for rubbing itchy skin. Use it to keep water in car radiators from freezing.

30-31. A liquid is distilled by boiling it and catching the gas. Then the gas is cooled until it condenses into a liquid.

32-33. We need oxygen to breathe. We need oxygen so that our fires can burn.

(Total: 33 points)

God's Protected World

Unit 3 Test   Score _____

Name _____   Date _____

Matching

Match the words to their meanings. There is one extra letter.

_____ 1. Moving in a circle   a. crops

_____ 2. Half of the earth   b. germination

_____ 3. Slant of the earth's axis   c. hemisphere

_____ 4. Turning on an axis   d. revolution

_____ 5. The colors in white light   e. rotation

_____ 6. Changing from a seed to   f. spectrum

        a tiny plant   g. tilt

Classifying

Below are some things needed for a harvest. Write M before man's part. Write G before

God's part.

_____ 7. Plow the soil

_____ 8. Make the minerals

_____ 9. Send the sunshine

_____10. Provide a growing season

_____11. Harvest the crops

_____12. Plant the seeds

Unit 3 Test Answers

Matching

1. d
2. c
3. g
4. e
5. f
6. b

Classifying

7. M
8. G
9. G
10. G
11. M
12. M

226   Tests

Choose the Right One

13. summer
14. night
15. east
16. west
17. moon
18. sun

Yes or No?

19. yes
20. yes
21. no
22. yes

Fill in the Blanks

23. orbit
24. 366
25. full
26. tides

Choose the Right One

Underline the best choice for each sentence.

13. When the Northern Hemisphere is tilted toward the sun, it has (summer, winter).

14. We have (day, night) when our part of the earth turns away from the sun.

15. The sun rises in the (east, west).

16. The sun sets in the (east, west).

17. The gravity of the earth keeps the (sun, moon) in orbit.

18. The moon gets its light from the (earth, sun).

Yes or No?

If the sentence is true, write yes. If it is not true, write no.

_____19. The moon takes almost a month to revolve around the earth.

_____20. The moon's shape seems to change because we see different parts of its lighted side.

_____21. Summer is warmer than winter because the sunlight is more slanted.

_____22. A rainbow reminds us of God's faithfulness.

Fill in the Blanks

Fill each blank with the correct word.

23. The path of the earth around the sun is called its _____ .

24. A leap year has _____ days.

25. We can see a _____ moon all night.

26. The moon's gravity causes _____ in the oceans.

Label the Pictures

Use words from the word box to label each picture.

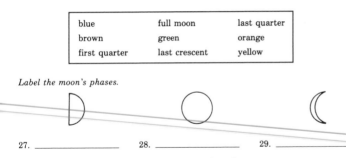

blue	full moon	last quarter
brown	green	orange
first quarter	last crescent	yellow

Label the moon's phases.

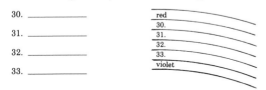

27. _____   28. _____   29. _____

Put the missing colors of the rainbow in the right order.

30. _____   red
31. _____   30.
32. _____   31.
33. _____   32.
                      33.
                      violet

Label the Pictures
27. first quarter
28. full moon
29. last crescent
30. orange
31. yellow
32. green
33. blue

(Total: 33 points)

God's Protected World

Unit 4 Test

Name _____ Date _____ Score _____

Matching

Match each word to its meaning.

_____ 1. Making things cooler

_____ 2. Changing from a liquid to a gas

_____ 3. Circling motion of heated liquids

_____ 4. The sun's light and heat

_____ 5. How hot or cold something is

_____ 6. To become smaller

_____ 7. To become moldy

_____ 8. To become larger

a. contract

b. convection

c. evaporation

d. expand

e. refrigeration

f. solar energy

g. spoil

h. temperature

Yes or No?

If the sentence is true, write yes. If it is not true, write no.

_____ 9. Sunlight changes to heat when it travels through a clear material.

_____ 10. Sunlight travels to the earth by radiation.

_____ 11. Most of the earth's heat comes from the sun.

_____ 12. Air expands and contracts.

_____ 13. Cold food will spoil faster than warm food.

_____ 14. Sweating helps warm our bodies.

_____ 15. Evaporation causes the cooling in a freezer.

Unit 4 Test Answers

Matching

1. e
2. c
3. b
4. f
5. h
6. a
7. g
8. d

Yes or No?

9. no
10. yes
11. yes
12. yes
13. no
14. no
15. yes

Choose the Right One

16. little
17. conduction
18. insulator
19. rises
20. cooled

Label the Picture

21. 100°
22. 212°
23. 37°
24. 98°
25. 20°
26. 68°
27. 0°
28. 32°

Write the Answers

29. (Any one) Solar energy heats water, heats homes, makes electricity, melts metal, and shapes plastic.

Choose the Right One

Choose and underline the best answer for each sentence.

16. When sunlight falls on a white roof, (much, little) of it is absorbed.

17. When one end of a copper wire is heated, heat travels to the other end by (conduction, convection).

18. Cloth is a good (conductor, insulator).

19. When warm and cold water are in the same bowl, the warm water (rises, sinks).

20. Mercury in a thermometer contracts when it is (heated, cooled).

Label the Picture

Use the temperatures from the box below to label the thermometer.

100°	20°	212°	98°
68°	32°	37°	0°

	Celsius		Fahrenheit
boiling point of water	21. _____		22. _____
body temperature	23. _____		24. _____
room temperature	25. _____		26. _____
freezing point of water	27. _____		28. _____

Write the Answers

29. Name one way that man has used solar energy to do work for him.

_____

_____

30-31. In what way does freezing water act differently than other liquids? Name one problem caused by freezing water.

_____

_____

_____

_____

32-33. John heated a copper wire to 90°F. He heated an aluminum wire to 150°F. Then he twisted the two wires around each other. Will heat flow from the copper wire to the aluminum wire, or from the aluminum wire to the copper wire? Explain why.

_____

_____

_____

_____

30-31. (Any one) Freezing water expands instead of contracts. Freezing water causes water pipes to burst and roads to become rutted.

32-33. Heat will flow from the aluminum wire to the copper wire because heat always flows from something warm to something cooler.

(Total: 33 points)

God's Protected World

Unit 5 Test

Name _____   Date _____

Score _____

Unit 5 Test Answers

Matching

Match each sentence beginning to the best ending.

_____ 1. The epidermis	a. can cause poor posture.
_____ 2. The dermis	b. may be caused by germs.
_____ 3. Work and exercise	c. holds blood, glands, and fat.
_____ 4. A disease	d. give us energy to work.
_____ 5. Sugar and starch	e. help us sleep well.
_____ 6. Being grumpy and unhappy	f. is tough and strong.

Yes or No?

If the sentence is true, write yes. *If it is not true, write* no.

_____ 7. Our hair and nails have many nerve endings in them.

_____ 8. A person who keeps himself clean is less likely to become sick.

_____ 9. We want to use good stewardship because our bodies belong to God.

_____ 10. Eating too much food is good stewardship.

_____ 11. A lazy person is likely to have weak muscles.

_____ 12. Adults need more sleep than children.

Matching
1. f
2. c
3. e
4. b
5. d
6. a

Yes or No?
7. no
8. yes
9. yes
10. no
11. yes
12. no

Fill in the Blanks

13. hair
14. sweat
15. nail
16. Fat
17. nerve ending
18. Oil
19. stomach
20. skin
21. blood

Choose the Best Answer

22. c

Fill in the Blanks

Finish each sentence by choosing the part of the body that does that work.

blood	nail	skin
fat	nerve ending	stomach
hair	oil	sweat

13. Our _____ keeps our heads warm and protects them from bumps.

14. When _____ evaporates, it cools our bodies.

15. A _____ protects each of our fingers and toes.

16. _____ gives our bodies energy and protects them from bumps.

17. A _____ in our skin tells us how something feels.

18. _____ keeps our skin soft and our hair strong.

19. Our _____ liquids kill many germs that we eat with our food.

20. Our _____ stops many germs from entering our bodies.

21. Our _____ keeps our skin alive and destroys many germs.

Choose the Best Answer

Choose and write the letter of the best answer for each exercise.

____ 22. Which breakfast has food from each food group?

(a) pancakes, syrup, peanut butter, grape juice

(b) oatmeal, milk, muffin, orange

(c) bacon, cheese, toast, apple juice

____ 23. Protein is

    (a) burned mostly for energy.

    (b) stored in our bodies.

    (c) used to build our bodies.

____ 24. Which uses the most energy?

    (a) singing

    (b) running

    (c) eating

____ 25. Calories are

    (a) changed to fat.

    (b) used to measure energy.

    (c) harmful to our bodies.

____ 26. Food that we do not need

    (a) helps to digest food.

    (b) is changed into energy.

    (c) is stored as fat.

23. c
24. b
25. b
26. c

Label the Pictures

Write good posture *or* poor posture *under each picture.*

27. _____   28. _____   29. _____

Label the Pictures
27. poor posture
28. good posture
29. poor posture

Write the Answers

30–32. Brush our teeth every day. Keep our nails trimmed. Take a bath often (or wash our skin with soap and water).

33. Someone with healthy emotions enjoys working to help other people.

(Total: 33 points)

Write the Answers

30-32. Tell how we should take good care of our teeth, nails, and skin.

_____

_____

_____

33. How does someone with healthy emotions feel about working?

_____

_____

God's Protected World

Unit 6 Test

Score _____

Name _____ Date _____

Choose the Right One

In each sentence, underline the right word.

1. Classification helps us study (many, few) kinds of animals.

2. Animals are classified by the characteristics that are (different, alike).

3–4. Gills take oxygen from the (air, water), but lungs take oxygen from the (air, water).

5. Amphibians have (dry, moist) skin.

6. Most snakes are (helpful, harmful) to man.

7. (Mammals, Reptiles) feed milk to their young.

Matching

Choose the best ending for each sentence. Write the correct letter beside the number.

There is one extra letter.

_____ 8. A great change in an animal's body is a

_____ 9. A snake's poison is called

_____ 10. A reptile egg has a

_____ 11. A turtle is protected by a

_____ 12. A whale's habitat is the

_____ 13. Mammals have hair or

_____ 14. The world around an animal is its

a. environment.

b. fur.

c. grassland.

d. hard shell.

e. leathery shell.

f. metamorphosis.

g. ocean.

h. venom.

Unit 6 Test Answers

Choose the Right One

1. many
2. alike
3. water
4. air
5. moist
6. helpful
7. Mammals

Matching

8. f
9. h
10. e
11. d
12. g
13. b
14. a

Yes or No?

15. yes
16. no
17. no
18. yes
19. yes
20. yes
21. yes
22. no

Number in Order

23. 3
24. 4
25. 2

Fill in the Blanks

26. rodents
27. scales
28. marine

Yes or No?

Write yes *if the sentence is true.* Write no *if it is not true.*

_____ 15. God planned that animals eat other animals to keep the balance of nature.

_____ 16. Amphibians are protected from the cold by growing extra thick fur.

_____ 17. Salamanders and lizards are reptiles.

_____ 18. Amphibians live part of their lives in the water and part of it out of the water.

_____ 19. A snake that is molting is shedding its skin.

_____ 20. A crocodile has claws on its feet.

_____ 21. Animals hibernate or migrate by instinct.

_____ 22. Both hibernation and migration protect animals in the summer.

Number in Order

Number these phrases about a toad's life cycle. Put them in the right order. The first one is done for you.

___1___ Eggs in a pond

_____ 23. Tadpole with lungs and a short tail

_____ 24. Toad with no tail

_____ 25. Tadpole with gills and a long tail

Fill in the Blanks

Fill each blank with the missing word.

26. Chipmunks, mice, and all other _____ have long front teeth for gnawing.

27. Snakes and lizards have skin that is covered with _____.

28. Whales and porpoises are called _____ mammals.

Write the Answers

29. How did God save the animals during the great Flood?

_____

_____

30–31. Explain the meanings of *hibernation* and *migration*.

_____

_____

_____

32–33. What is the difference between cold-blooded animals and warm-blooded animals?

_____

_____

_____

_____

_____

_____

Write the Answers

29. He saved each kind of animal in the ark.

30–31. Hibernation is a deep sleep during the winter. Migration is a trip to another area.

32–33. Cold-blooded animals cannot make their own heat; warm-blooded animals can (or the temperature of a cold-blooded animal changes with the temperature of things around it; a warm-blooded animal's temperature stays about the same).

(Total: 33 points)

God's Protected World

Unit 7 Test   Score _____

Name _____ Date _____

Matching

Match each sentence beginning to the best ending.

_____ 1. Farm animals

_____ 2. Truck farming

_____ 3. Pulleys

_____ 4. Trees and petroleum

_____ 5. Good stewards

_____ 6. The ends of a garden hose

a. is producing vegetables.

b. lift heavy loads.

c. are called livestock.

d. practice conservation.

e. are screws.

f. are raw materials.

Yes or No?

Write yes *or* no *for each sentence.*

_____ 7. A farm is a good place for a Christian family to live because the family can work together.

_____ 8. A rope on a wheel is a wedge.

_____ 9. Both turbines and water wheels are turned by falling water.

_____ 10. The farther water falls, the less energy it has.

_____ 11. God is the steward of all our possessions.

Unit 7 Test Answers

Matching
1. c
2. a
3. b
4. f
5. d
6. e

Yes or No?
7. yes
8. no
9. yes
10. no
11. no

242   *Tests*

Label the Pictures

12–13. lever, B
14–15. inclined plane, A
16–17. wheel and axle, A
18–19. wedge, A

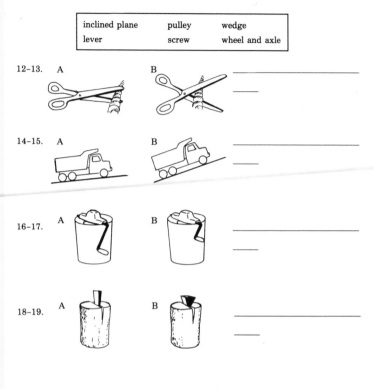

Label the Pictures

Under each pair of pictures below, write two answers. In the first blank, tell which simple machine is shown. Choose a simple machine from the word box. In the second blank, write A or B to tell which picture shows work being done in the easiest way.

inclined plane	pulley	wedge
lever	screw	wheel and axle

12–13.   A   B   _____
                                       ____

14–15.   A   B   _____
                                       ____

16–17.   A   B   _____
                                       ____

18–19.   A   B   _____
                                       ____

Choose the Best Answer

Choose the best ending for each sentence below.

_____ 20. A farmer who is a good steward

    (a) allows disease in his crops.

    (b) gives his livestock a balanced diet.

    (c) lets erosion carry away topsoil.

_____ 21. A sailboat is powered by the energy of

    (a) gravity.

    (b) the wind.

    (c) falling water.

_____ 22. Large waterfalls and dams supply energy

    (a) that is used to run windmills.

    (b) that is used by our bodies.

    (c) that is changed into electricity.

_____ 23. A wrong use of God's gifts is

    (a) telling others about God.

    (b) sharing food and clothing.

    (c) telling others how much we know.

_____ 24. Both Noah's ark and the Tower of Babel

    (a) were built to honor God.

    (b) were built by using technology.

    (c) were helpful to man.

Choose the Best Answer

20. b
21. b
22. c
23. c
24. b

Write the Answers

25–29. (Answers may vary.) We receive cotton, milk, eggs, grain, and meat from farms.

30–31. (Any two) Protect wildlife. Use fuel carefully. Put out fires. Protect the soil from erosion. Put trash into a trash can.

32–33. Energy from wind and moving water

(Total 33 points)

Write the Answers

25–29. Name one kind of cloth and four kinds of food that we receive from farms.

_____

_____

_____

_____

30–31. What are two ways in which we can practice conservation?

_____

_____

32–33. Name two kinds of energy that are clean, free, and can never be used up.

_____

_____

God's Protected World

Final Test

Score _____

Name _____ Date _____

Matching

Match the words on the right to their meanings on the left.

_____ 1. Water going into the air

_____ 2. Is made into electric wire

_____ 3. The most important liquid

_____ 4. A heavy metal that is liquid

_____ 5. Moving in a circle

_____ 6. The colors in white light

_____ 7. Can be a needle or a knife

_____ 8. How hot or cold an object is

_____ 9. A great change in an animal's body

_____ 10. Can be stairs or a highway ramp

_____ 11. The world around an animal

a. copper

b. environment

c. evaporation

d. inclined plane

e. mercury

f. metamorphosis

g. revolution

h. spectrum

i. temperature

j. water

k. wedge

Choose the Right One

Underline the correct answers.

12. When our side of the earth turns away from the sun, we have (day, night).

13. The earth's gravity keeps the (sun, moon) circling in orbit.

14. We can see a (new, full) moon all night.

15. When heated air moves in circles throughout a room, the heat moves by (conduction, convection).

16. When air becomes cooler, it (expands, contracts), or takes up less space.

Final Test Answers

Matching

1. c
2. a
3. j
4. e
5. g
6. h
7. k
8. i
9. f
10. d
11. b

Choose the Right One

12. night
13. moon
14. full
15. convection
16. contracts

17. conductor
18. proteins
19. Amphibians
20. wheel and axle

Fill in the Blanks

21. dermis
22. moon
23. ammonia
24. hair
25. pressure
26. oxygen
27. balance of nature
28. refrigeration
29. carbon dioxide

17. Iron is a good (conductor, insulator) of heat.

18. Your body needs (sugars, proteins) to build and repair your body.

19. (Amphibians, Reptiles) live part of their life in water, and part of it on land.

20. The handle of a pencil sharpener is a (wheel and axle, pulley).

Fill in the Blanks

In each blank, write the correct word from the word box. Not all the words will be used.

ammonia	dermis	moon	refrigeration
balance of nature	environment	oxygen	sun
carbon dioxide	hair	pressure	

21. The _____ holds blood, glands, and fat.

22. The shape of the _____ seems to change because we see different parts of its lighted side.

23. When dissolved in water, _____ makes a good cleaner.

24. Your _____ helps protect your head and keep it warm.

25. Water can be pushed uphill by water _____.

26. We need _____ in the air to live.

27. God planned that animals eat other animals to keep the _____ _____.

28. We use _____ to keep foods such as milk and eggs from spoiling quickly.

29. Some fire extinguishers use _____ to put out fires.

Yes or No?

If the sentence is true, write yes. *If it is not true, write* no.

_____ 30. Heating causes the water in the air to condense into liquid raindrops.

_____ 31. Hardwood trees bear green leaves and seeds or nuts.

_____ 32. Coal, gasoline, and natural gas are burned as fuel.

_____ 33. Winter is colder than summer because the sunlight is more slanted.

_____ 34. Condensation causes the cooling in a refrigerator.

_____ 35. A person with good posture is likely to have weak muscles.

_____ 36. Washing your hands with soap helps destroy germs that spread disease.

_____ 37. Most animals are classified by their color.

_____ 38. A pulley is used to lift heavy loads.

_____ 39. At many dams, the energy of falling water is changed into electricity.

Choose the Best Answer

Write the correct letter for each exercise.

_____ 40. Steam is made by

    (a) melting water.

    (b) boiling water.

    (c) freezing water.

_____ 41. Gullies and badlands are caused by

    (a) erosion.

    (b) pressure.

    (c) buoyant force.

Yes or No?

30. no
31. yes
32. yes
33. yes
34. no
35. no
36. yes
37. no
38. yes
39. yes

Choose the Best Answer

40. b
41. a

42. b
43. c
44. c
45. b
46. a

_____ 42. Wood floats because of

(a) condensation.

(b) buoyant force.

(c) erosion.

_____ 43. The freezing point of water is

(a) 98°F.

(b) 212°F.

(c) 32°F.

_____ 44. Which lunch has food from each food group?

(a) jelly sandwich, apple, candy bar, and lemonade

(b) hamburger, cheese curls, cookie, and milk

(c) chicken sandwich, orange, cake, and chocolate milk

_____ 45. Food energy is measured in

(a) pounds.

(b) Calories.

(c) degrees.

_____ 46. The animals that feed milk to their young are the

(a) mammals.

(b) reptiles.

(c) amphibians.

Answer the Questions

47. How is liquid distilled?

_____

_____

_____

_____

48. Explain how to take good care of your teeth.

_____

_____

49. Explain what migration is.

_____

_____

50. What is one way we can practice conservation?

_____

_____

Answer the Questions

47. A liquid is distilled by boiling it and catching the gas. Then the gas is cooled until it becomes a liquid.

48. Brush your teeth every day.

49. Migration is a trip that some birds and animals take to a warmer home for the winter.

50. We can practice conservation by using fuel carefully. (or by protecting the soil from erosion, protecting wildlife, putting out fires, etc.)

(Total: 50 points)

Index

Italics indicates vocabulary words and the
pages on which the definitions are found.